Embryogenesis in Mammals

The Ciba Foundation for the promotion of international cooperation in medical and chemical research is a scientific and educational charity established by CIBA Limited – now CIBA-GEIGY Limited – of Basle. The Foundation operates independently in London under English trust law.

Ciba Foundation Symposia are published in collaboration with Elsevier Scientific Publishing Company / Excerpta Medica / North-Holland Publishing Company in Amsterdam.

Elsevier / Excerpta Medica / North-Holland, P.O.Box 211, Amsterdam

Embryogenesis in Mammals, London, 1975.

Ciba Foundation Symposium 40 (new series)

1976

Elsevier · Excerpta Medica · North-Holland
Amsterdam · Oxford · New York

ISBN Excerpta Medica 90 219 4045 0
ISBN American Elsevier 0-444-15206-7

Published in May 1976 by Elsevier / Excerpta Medica / North-Holland, P.O.Box 211, Amsterdam, and
American Elsevier, 52 Vanderbilt Avenue, New York, N.Y. 10017.

Suggested series entry for library catalogues: Ciba Foundation Symposia.
Suggested publisher's entry for library catalogues: Elsevier / Excerpta Medica / North-Holland.

Ciba Foundation Symposium 40 (new series)

Library of Congress Cataloging in Publication Data

Symposium on Embryogenesis in Mammals, London, 1975.
    Embryogenesis in mammals.

    (Ciba Foundation symposium ; 40 (new ser.))
    Bibliography: p.
    Includes indexes.
    1. Embryology—Mammals—Congresses. I. Title.
II. Series: Ciba Foundation. Symposium ; new ser.,
40.
QL959.S98 1975   599'.03'3   76-7009
ISBN 0-444-15206-7

Printed in The Netherlands by Mouton & Co, The Hague

Contents

A. MCLAREN Introduction 1

R. L. GARDNER & J. ROSSANT Determination during embryogenesis 5
Discussion 18

N. ŠKREB, A. ŠVAJGER & B. LEVAK-ŠVAJGER Developmental potentialities of the
germ layers in mammals 27
Discussion 39

A. MCLAREN Growth from fertilization to birth in the mouse 47

M. H. L. SNOW Embryo growth during the immediate postimplantation period
53
Discussion 66

N. LE DOUARIN Cell migration in early vertebrate development studied in interspecific chimeras 71
Discussion 97

General Discussion I
Determination/differentiation 103
Origin of the germ cells 110

V. M. CHAPMAN, D. ADLER, C. LABARCA & L. WUDL Genetic variation of
β-glucuronidase expression during early embryogenesis 115
Discussion 124

R. A. PEDERSEN & A. I. SPINDLE Genetic effects on mammalian development
during and after implantation 133
Discussion 149

A. GROPP   Morphological consequences of trisomy in mammals   155
    Discussion   171

M. EDIDIN   The appearance of cell-surface antigens in the development of the
    mouse embryo: a study of cell-surface differentiation   177
    Discussion   194

M. SPIEGELMAN   Electron microscopy of *T*-locus mutants   199
    Discussion   220

General Discussion II
    Culture system for embryos   227
    Gene mutations in early mammalian development   230
    Development of bilateral symmetry   235

G. EGUCHI   'Transdifferentiation' of vertebrate cells in cell culture   241
    Discussion   253

W. J. RUTTER & R. L. PICTET   Hormone-like factor(s) in mesenchymal epithelial
    interactions during embryonic development   259
    Discussion   270

R. O. KELLEY & G. C. PALMER   Regulation of mesenchymal cell growth during
    human limb morphogenesis through glycosaminoglycan-adenylate cyclase
    interaction at the cell surface   275
    Discussion   288

Final Discussion   291
    Terminology for germ layers   292
    Teratocarcinoma cells: a model for differentiation   296

Index of contributors   301

Subject index   303

Participants

Symposium on Embryogenesis in Mammals held at the Ciba Foundation, London, 17–19 June 1975

ANNE MCLAREN (*Chairman*) MRC Mammalian Development Unit, University College London, Wolfson House, 4 Stephenson Way, London NW1 2HE, UK

DOROTHEA BENNETT Dept of Anatomy, Cornell University Medical College, 1300 York Avenue, New York, NY 10021, USA

V. M. CHAPMAN Roswell Park Memorial Institute, 666 Elm Street, Buffalo, NY 14263, USA

J. COOKE Division of Developmental Biology, National Institute for Medical Research, The Ridgeway, Mill Hill, London NW7 1AA, UK

M. EDIDIN Mergenthaler Laboratory, The Johns Hopkins University, Baltimore, Md. 21218, USA

G. EGUCHI Institute for Biophysics, Faculty of Science, University of Kyoto, Kyoto 606, Japan

R. L. GARDNER Dept of Zoology, Oxford University, South Parks Road, Oxford OX1 3PS, UK

SALOME GLUECKSOHN-WAELSCH Dept of Genetics, Albert Einstein College of Medicine of Yeshiva University, 1300 Morris Park Avenue, Bronx, NY 10461, USA

C. F. GRAHAM Dept of Zoology, Oxford University, South Parks Road, Oxford OX1 3PS, UK

A. GROPP Abt. für Pathologie der Medizinischen Hochschule, Ratzeburger Allee 160, Lübeck 2400, Germany

J. B. GURDON MRC Laboratory of Molecular Biology, University Postgraduate Medical School, Hills Road, Cambridge CB2 2QH, UK

H.C. HENSLEIGH   MRC Mammalian Development Unit, University College London, Wolfson House, 4 Stephenson Way, London, NW1 2HE, UK*

BRIGID L.M. HOGAN   Imperial Cancer Research Fund, Burtonhole Lane, The Ridgeway, Mill Hill, London NW7 1AD, UK

R.O. KELLEY   Dept of Anatomy, The University of New Mexico School of Medicine, Basic Medical Sciences Building, North Campus, Albuquerque, New Mexico 87131, USA

NICOLE LE DOUARIN   Laboratoire d'Embryologie de l'Université de Nantes, 38 Boulevard Michelet, B.P. 1044, 44037 Nantes-Cedex, France†

GILLIAN M. MORRISS   Dept of Anatomy, Cambridge University, Downing Street, Cambridge CB2 3DY, UK

D.R. NEWTH   Dept of Zoology, University of Glasgow, Glasgow G12 8QQ, UK

R.A. PEDERSEN   Laboratory of Radiobiology, University of California School of Medicine, San Francisco, California 94143, USA

P.E. POLANI   Paediatric Research Unit, Guy's Hospital Medical School, Cameron House, Guy's Hospital, London SE1 9RT, UK

W.J. RUTTER   Dept of Biochemistry and Biophysics, University of California School of Medicine, San Francisco, California 94143, USA

L. SAXÉN   Third Department of Pathology, University of Helsinki, SF–00290 Helsinki 29, Finland

N. ŠKREB   Dept of Biology, Faculty of Medicine, PO Box 166, 41000 Zagreb, Salata 3, Yugoslavia

M.H.L. SNOW   MRC Mammalian Development Unit, University College London, Wolfson House, 4 Stephenson Way, London NW1 2HE, UK

MARTHA SPIEGELMAN   Dept of Anatomy, Cornell University Medical College, 1300 York Avenue, New York, NY 10021, USA

A.K. TARKOWSKI   Dept of Embryology, University of Warsaw, Krakowskie Przedmieście 26–28, Warsaw 64, Poland

L. WOLPERT   Dept of Biology as Applied to Medicine, The Middlesex Hospital Medical School, London W1P 6DB, UK

Editors: Katherine Elliott (*Organizer*) and Maeve O'Connor

---

* *Present address*: Dept of Anatomy, University of Oregon Medical School, Portland, Oregon 97201, USA

† *Present address*: Institut d'Embryologie du CNRS et du Collège de France, 49 bis, Avenue de la Belle Gabrielle, 94130 Nogent-sur-Marne, France

Introduction

ANNE McLAREN

MRC Mammalian Development Unit, University College, London

It is ten years since the Ciba Foundation Symposium on *Preimplantation Stages of Pregnancy* so it seems particularly appropriate that we should be meeting here again to consider the next stage of mammalian development, the period immediately after implantation. This is a period of tremendous fascination and mystery: it opens with the embryo as a radially symmetrical blastocyst, containing as far as we know just two sorts of cells, and within a few days we see the development of a bilaterally symmetrical animal, with a front and a back and a right side and a left side, with three germ layers, with segmentation in the form of somites, and with different tissues and organs beginning to form.

The 1965 symposium was well-timed: the last ten years have seen a tremendous amount of work on preimplantation embryos and great advances in our knowledge, particularly as regards the biochemistry of these early stages. Of course an enormous amount remains to be done in the preimplantation area — we urgently need, for example, more information on a wide range of different species, so that we can make some judgement as to how far our new-found knowledge relates to mammalian development and how far merely to the development of the mouse. One can nonetheless observe a marked shift of emphasis, away from preimplantation embryos and towards the post-implantation period, and I hope that our present symposium will prove as timely as its predecessor.

Why should there be this shift of emphasis? One reason of course is simply that it is the next stage on, the next challenge, but I don't think that is the only reason. When one sees a lot of research effort and money going into a particular field, it is usually because the increased availability of relevant techniques has happened to coincide with some increase in the social relevance of the field. For the preimplantation period, the biggest technical factor was the development of really effective and simple systems of *in vitro* culture—which in turn would have been impossible without the availability of antibiotics, developed

1

under the stimulus of the 1939–1945 war. I believe it was a happy chance for mammalian embryologists that the development of culture systems coincided with the impact of the world population problem, and with the realization by national and international funding agencies that disgracefully little was known about human reproduction and that the preimplantation period offered a promising target for fertility regulation. I don't think these hopes have been realized in terms of contraceptive development, but I do think that the funds invested have earned rich dividends in increasing basic knowledge about this very early period of mammalian development.

What about the post-implantation embryo? This is altogether a tougher proposition technically, not only because the visible complexity is so much greater, but also because the embryo is so much less accessible and because culture methods are less adequate, as we shall no doubt hear, and above all because there is no test of normality, no way in which a cultured embryo can be put back into the mother's uterus to see whether it will develop normally thereafter. On the other hand techniques, mainly manipulative ones, are being developed that are opening up the post-implantation embryo and making it available to experimental analysis, and I am sure that we shall hear about these during this meeting.

There are also reasons why embryo development during this post-implantation period is of social concern. One of the most important differences between preimplantation and post-implantation embryos is that during the post-implantation period the embryo begins for the first time to be susceptible to teratogenic stimuli. Now, as perinatal mortality due to infectious diseases declines, so congenital malformations become proportionately more important. Similarly, now that women have fewer pregnancies, spontaneous abortion is seen as a more serious hazard. Obstetricians are increasingly interacting with the embryo via such techniques as amniocentesis, fetoscopy and ultrasonic irradiation. Within a decade or two, egg transfer in women may become a routine gynaecological procedure. There is even talk of gene therapy, in the sense of injecting normal cells into genetically defective embryos.

Human embryos, though hard to study for both practical and ethical reasons, pose fascinating problems. Consider chromosome abnormalities. The most recent figures that I have seen (P. A. Jacobs, personal communication) suggest that 35% of all spontaneous abortions, and 40% of those during the first trimester, show recognizable chromosome defects. Since 12% of recognized pregnancies are said to end in spontaneous abortions, this gives a minimum estimate of nearly 5%, 1 in 20 conceptuses, with an abnormal chromosome constitution. This is far higher than in any animal species studied. Only a small proportion of these chromosomally defective embryos survive until birth; on the other hand other defects appear, induced perhaps by various environmental teratogenic agents, giving an overall figure of at least 2% defective births—higher if one includes minor defects, or defects that only manifest themselves later in life. This figure of 2% is again much higher than in any animal species studied; and again we do not know why.

Mostly at this meeting we shall be talking about mice and rats. Occasionally we shall stray to the chick, and it may even be that amphibian embryos will get a mention. But perhaps even then, since we are an anthropocentric species, the human embryo and its problems may be lurking somewhere in our minds.

References

WOLSTENHOLME, G.E.W. & O'CONNOR, M. (1965) *Preimplantation Stages of Pregnancy (Ciba Found. Symp.)*, Churchill, London [now Churchill Livingstone, Edinburgh]

Determination during embryogenesis

R. L. GARDNER and J. ROSSANT

Department of Zoology, South Parks Road, Oxford

Abstract Experiments involving the isolation, transplantation and rearrangement of cells and tissues have made it possible to establish the stage during early development of the mouse embryo when several critical determinative events take place. These early determinative events share several interesting features.

(1) Determination occurs in small populations of cells.

(2) Cells can take one of only two developmental pathways at each critical period.

(3) The particular pathway that a cell takes appears to depend on its position relative to other cells in the embryo or tissue.

(4) Determination is closely followed by overt differentiation in cells contributing to extra-embryonic tissues, but not in cells destined to form the definitive embryo.

Finally, studies on chimeras produced by transplanting single cells to host blastocysts suggest that germ cells originate from the precursor cells of the definitive embryo rather than the yolk sac endoderm.

The word 'determination' has been employed in a variety of different contexts in the embryological literature (Huxley & De Beer 1937; Needham 1942). It will be understood here to mean the progressive restriction in potency of cells that is a general feature of embryogenesis (Hadorn 1965). It is perhaps worth re-emphasizing that when used in this sense, determination can be established only experimentally, by an examination of the developmental potential of cells in altered circumstances. *Drosophila* has been widely adopted as a model for analysis of this phenomenon in recent years because of the ease with which determination can be dissociated from cellular differentiation in imaginal disks (see Gehring & Nöthiger 1973 for a recent review). Most of the classical work on determination in vertebrates was carried out on amphibian embryos and often involved isolation or transplantation of relatively large groups of cells (Spemann 1938). This inevitably raises the question of whether grafts were always effectively exposed to altered conditions. One of the great virtues of studying comparable processes in the early mammalian embryo is that it is now practicable to examine the developmental potential of single transplanted cells (Gardner & Lyon 1971; Gardner & Papaioannou 1975).

Our present purpose is to identify features shared by different determinative events that occur during the early stages of mammalian development. Apart from brief reference to the germ line, we will be concerned specifically with development of the mouse embryo up to and during implantation (Fig. 1). Analysis of the developmental potentialities of tissues in the postimplantation rodent embryo has been pioneered by Škreb and his colleagues and will be discussed in another contribution to this symposium. Cell lineage relationships in the preimplantation mouse embryo have recently been established experimentally (Gardner & Papaioannou 1975), necessitating revision of the fate map derived from histological studies (Snell & Stevens 1966). The problems and strategy of analysing determination and normal cell fate in mammals are discussed in detail elsewhere (Gardner & Papaioannou 1975). Various aspects of early development discussed in this paper have been reviewed recently (Herbert & Graham 1974; Mintz 1974; Wilson & Stern 1975).

In this paper we will use the term trophectoderm to describe the outer cell layer of the blastocyst and trophoblast for its postimplantation derivatives. The abbreviation ICM will be used for the inner cell mass of the blastocyst. When referring to isolated blastomeres, we will use the notation of Tarkowski & Wróblewska (1967), i.e. 1/4 blastomere for one blastomere from the 4-cell stage, 2/8 blastomeres for two blastomeres from the 8-cell stage, and so on.

DETERMINATION OF TROPHECTODERM VERSUS ICM CELLS

The central issue is whether the primary determinative event depends on heterogeneity of the egg cytoplasm before cleavage (Dalq 1957), or on heterogeneity of cellular microenvironments set up at some stage thereafter (Mintz 1965; Tarkowski & Wróblewska 1967). On Dalcq's hypothesis all blastomeres of the rodent embryo have to be determined to form ICM or trophectoderm cells by the 8-cell stage, when segregation of cytochemically defined 'dorsal' and 'ventral' cytoplasm has taken place (Dalcq 1957; also see Mulnard 1965). However, isolated 1/8 blastomeres were later found to be able to form blastocyst-like structures in vitro (Tarkowski & Wróblewska 1967). Recent experiments have demonstrated that while such blastomeres are unable to form normal conceptuses after implantation in utero (J. Rossant, unpublished work), they can nevertheless contribute extensively to derivations of both the ICM and trophectoderm when combined with 'carrier' blastomeres of a different genotype

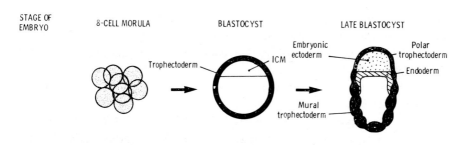

FIG. 1. Diagram illustrating the stages of early development of the mouse discussed in this paper. White background represents ICM derivatives and black background, trophectoderm derivatives.

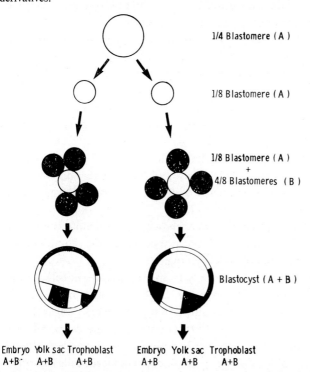

FIG. 2. Diagrammatic representation of experiments of Kelly (1975), showing the lability of pairs of 1/8 blastomeres. Chimerism was obtained in the embryo, yolk sac and trophoblast of conceptuses obtained after the two daughter 1/8 blastomeres of one isolated 1/4 blastomere of genotype A were combined with 'carrier' blastomeres of genotype B.

(Kelly 1975). The critical findings in the latter experiments were that in five cases both daughters of a single 1/4 blastomere produced this pattern of chimerism (Fig. 2; Kelly 1975). These results are clearly in direct conflict with

Dalcq's hypothesis. Furthermore, although the results do not exclude the possibility that cytoplasmic determinants or an 'organizing' centre (Seidel 1960) will segregate at some later stage, they complicate interpretations along these lines (Kelly 1975).

The importance of microenvironmental differences between blastomeres in determination was first suggested by Mintz (1965) and was formulated into the 'inside–outside' hypothesis by Tarkowski & Wróblewska (1967). Briefly, this hypothesis states that blastomeres that remain in an external position throughout cleavage are thereby determined to form trophectoderm cells, while those that become wholly enclosed are determined to form ICM cells. It leads to several predictions that are amenable to experimental investigation:

(1) All cells should remain undetermined at least until the stage of development when one or more can occupy an 'inside' position.

(2) All cells isolated before determination should be able to form trophectoderm cells. None should yield only ICM cells.

(3) The number of ICM cells formed (if any) should increase in relation to the total number of cells present when determination occurs.

(4) Before determination, cells made to occupy an inside position should become ICM cells, and those made to occupy an outside position should become trophectoderm cells.

'Inside cells' are first found between the 8-cell and 16-cell stage in serially sectioned embryos (Barlow et al. 1972). Hence, all blastomeres should still be labile at the 8-cell stage. The experiments of Kelly, described above, provide strong evidence that this is so, though conclusive proof could only be obtained if all 1/8 blastomeres of a single embryo were shown to yield chimerism in both ICM and trophectodermal derivatives of their respective 'carrier' combinations. This would clearly be a formidable undertaking.

Isolated 1/4 and 1/8 blastomeres typically form trophectoderm cells in vitro (Tarkowski & Wróblewska 1967; Sherman 1975; J. Rossant, unpublished work), and in vivo (Tarkowski 1959a, b; J. Rossant, unpublished work), regardless of whether ICM cells are present or not. Furthermore, in some cases, all sister blastomeres isolated from 4-cell and 8-cell embryos form trophectodermal vesicles (Tarkowski & Wróblewska 1967). Such trophectoderm cells can differentiate into functional trophoblast in vivo (J. Rossant, unpublished work) and in vitro (Sherman 1975), as judged by a number of morphological and physiological criteria. No convincing case of development of pure ICM tissue has been found in any of these studies. Even the non-integrated and morula-like forms exhibit the trophoblastic property of progesterone synthesis in vitro (Sherman 1975). Hence, available findings are fully consistent with the second prediction.

The third prediction cannot be tested directly at present because the time of determination is not known. Nevertheless, it is instructive to examine the number of ICM cells in relation to total cell number after blastulation of blastomeres or aggregated pairs of intact embryos. Tarkowski & Wróblewska (1967) presented such results from their *in vitro* studies on the development of 1/4, 2/8 and 1/8 blastomeres. For both 2/8 and 1/8 blastomeres the average cell number is higher in those that formed blastocysts than in those forming trophectodermal vesicles. However, the overall picture is somewhat confusing because this is not so for 1/4 blastomeres. Also, some 1/8 blastomeres formed blastocysts composed of only eight cells *in toto*, while some 1/4 and 2/8 blastomeres yielded trophectodermal vesicles consisting of nearly twice as many cells. This may be related to the very variable culture conditions evident in these experiments. Cleavage is retarded in culture as compared with *in vivo* (Bowman & McLaren 1970). Furthermore, the time of blastulation or vacuolation of cells is affected less than the rate of cleavage (Tarkowski & Wróblewska 1967), and determination could be related to the former rather than the latter.

Buehr & McLaren (1974) found that the ICMs of blastocysts derived from aggregated pairs of morulae contain more than twice the number of cells of standard blastocysts. This is entirely consistent with the third prediction of the 'inside–outside' hypothesis, since such aggregates would be expected to have a higher ratio of inside cells to outside ones than single embryos.

The last prediction has been examined in several different experiments. Mintz (1964, 1965) could find no evidence of sorting out of cells when [^{3}H]thymidine-labelled and unlabelled cleavage stages were aggregated in pairs, and when larger numbers of unlabelled embryos were arranged in a variety of different spatial configurations. She concluded that the cells differentiated according to position in such aggregates. Experiments using drops of silicone oil as markers have yielded similar results (Stern & Wilson 1972; Wilson *et al.* 1972). Stern (1973) used compression to force all blastomeres to occupy an outside position throughout cleavage and concluded that differentiation of ICM cells could be suppressed in this way. However, the validity of this conclusion depends on the assumption that only trophectodermal cells secrete blastocoelic fluid. While it is clear that maintenance of the blastocoele is a specific trophectodermal function in the mature blastocyst (Gardner 1971, 1972), observations by several authors suggest that blastulation itself may be due to secretory activity of most if not all cells of the late morula (Melissinos 1907; Mintz 1965; Calarco & Brown 1969). A general criticism applicable to all the foregoing experiments in which cell position was altered is that results have been assessed simply on the basis of morphological criteria at the blastocyst stage. It is formally possible that manipulations during cleavage could alter cell position without at the same time changing cell fate. For example, although 1/4 blastomeres *in vivo* form morphologically normal blastocysts that contain two to three inside cells, only 1/13 yielded any ICM derivatives after implantation (J. Rossant, unpublished work). This suggests either that the inside cells were not ICM cells, or that a critical number of ICM cells is necessary for further development of this tissue.

Hillman *et al.* (1972) largely avoided the above objection by constructing various arrangements of blastomeres and cleavage stage embryos in which [^{3}H]thymidine-labelled or genetically labelled cells were made to occupy either an inside or an outside position. Some movement of cells is inevitable during formation of such aggregates. Also, inside cells may divide faster than outside cells (Barlow *et al.* 1972). Nevertheless, these authors found a marked tendency for outside cells to colonize the trophectoderm and later trophoblast tissues, and for inside cells to colonize the ICM and fetus or offspring. These experiments afford the strongest support yet available for the 'inside–outside' hypothesis.

In summary, while existing data are in general consistent with the 'inside–outside' hypothesis, information essential for its critical appraisal has yet to be obtained. One major unresolved question is when determination occurs. Development of the ICM is suppressed when 2- or 8-cell embryos are cultured through to the blastocyst stage in [^{3}H]thymidine (Snow 1973*a*, *b*). Snow suggests that this agent exerts its effect at the 16-cell stage, though its mode of action is obscure. Other workers have concluded from aggregation experiments that some blastomeres are still labile at the late morula/early blastocyst stage (Mintz 1965; Stern & Wilson 1972). If the inside–outside model is correct, the fact that 1/4, 2/8 and 1/8 blastomeres can yield blastocysts argues for late determination, since they are unlikely to contain inside cells, at the equivalent of the 16-cell stage. However, one cannot at present exclude the possibility that determination may occur over a period of time rather than abruptly, so that some cells are committed earlier than others. Nevertheless, there is compelling evidence that trophectoderm and ICM determination is complete by the 64-cell stage (Gardner 1972, 1975*a*, *b*; Gardner & Johnson 1975; Rossant 1975*a*, *b*).

DETERMINATION OF PRIMITIVE ENDODERM VERSUS NON-ENDODERM CELLS

ICMs of 3.5-day post-coital (p.c.) blastocysts consist of approximately 15 cells that are alike in morphology (Enders & Schlafke 1965; Nadijcka & Hillman 1974), and probably also in developmental potential (Lin 1969; Gardner 1971, 1974, 1975*b*). Twenty-four hours later the primitive endoderm is clearly visible as a monolayer of cells on the blastocoelic surface of the ICM and adjacent mural trophectoderm (Fig. 1) (Snell & Stevens 1966; Enders 1971; Nadijcka & Hillman 1974). Endodermal cells can be distinguished from other cells of late blastocysts by their 'rough' appearance when live, and by their extensive rough endoplasmic reticulum in electron microscopic preparations (Enders 1971). They also exhibit reproducible, restricted patterns of chimerism after injection into host blastocysts that are distinct from those produced by transplanted non-endoderm cells (Gardner & Papaioannou 1975). These findings are consistent with the hypothesis that primitive endoderm cells are determined to form only the extra-embryonic endoderm of the conceptus, and that the remaining so-called embryonic ectoderm cells of the 4.5-day ICM are committed to producing the entire fetus and extra-embryonic mesoderm (Fig. 1) (Gardner & Papaioannou 1975). Evidence that embryonic ectoderm cells can produce fetal endodermal organs and tissues was first obtained by Škreb and his colleagues, by grafting germ layers isolated from postimplantation rat embryos under the kidney capsule of syngeneic adults (Levak-Švajger & Švajger 1971, 1974; see also Škreb et al., this volume).

Once the primitive endoderm layer has formed, its cells are separated from those of the embryonic ectoderm by a continuous basement membrane (Enders 1971; Nadijcka & Hillman 1974). It is therefore unlikely that further exchange of cells takes place between these tissues later in development. Is separation of the two populations of cells by such a basement membrane a prerequisite for determination or a consequence of it? Experiments are in progress to examine more closely both the fate and time of determination of ICM cells. They include investigation of the differentiation of primitive endoderm and embryonic ectodermal tissue injected into trophectodermal vesicles, and of individual rat cells of either type injected into mouse blastocysts. The advantage of the latter approach has been outlined previously (Gardner & Johnson 1975).

We have suggested that cell position may also be an important factor in determination within the ICM (Gardner & Johnson 1975; Gardner & Papaioannou 1975; Rossant 1975b). This hypothesis is based on the following observations:

(1) When transplanted rat ICMs spread out on the surface of host mouse ICMs, their cells are later found mainly in the endodermal layer of chimeric conceptuses. Occasionally, however, they remain separate and thus form complete egg-cylinders (Gardner & Johnson 1975).

(2) If aggregated pairs of 3.5-day p.c. ICMs are placed in the oviduct inside the zonae, all their outside cells show the ultrastructural features peculiar to endoderm 24 hours later. None of the inside cells show such features (Rossant 1975b).

(3) Endodermal differentiation is found in all cases in which the ICM con-

tinues to develop after cell number has been experimentally reduced at 3.5-days p.c. (Gardner 1974, 1975b). Only those in which the ICM derivatives were better developed show embryonic ectoderm as well.

(4) Endoderm cells form on the exposed surfaces of clumps of teratocarcinoma cells which undergo embryoid differentiation *in vitro* (Martin & Evans 1975).

Thus it would appear that ICM cells, part of whose surface is exposed to blastocoelic, oviducal or culture fluid, differentiate as primitive endoderm cells, while those that are surrounded by ICM and polar trophectoderm cells are determined to form embryonic ectoderm.

SUBSEQUENT DIFFERENTIATION WITHIN THE TROPHECTODERM

By 4.5 days p.c. the mural trophectoderm cells surrounding the blastocoele are conspicuously larger than the polar cells overlying the ICM (Dickson 1963, 1966). This process of transformation to giant cells is accompanied by several changes in mural cells (Dickson 1969; Gardner 1975a), including repeated endoreduplication of the genome (Barlow & Sherman 1972; Barlow et al. 1972; Sherman et al. 1972). The polar trophectoderm cells remain diploid and mitotically competent.

Gardner (1971) suggested that the ICM might be responsible for this regional differentiation. It was proposed that once trophectoderm cells have differentiated they can continue to replicate their DNA, but they lose the capacity to divide unless they remain in intimate relationship with the ICM or its derivatives (Gardner 1972, 1975a). Barlow & Sherman (1972) also suggested that the ICM might be involved in this process, by shielding polar cells from a stimulus for polyploidization provided by the blastocoele.

The basic experimental results implicating the ICM are as follows. Trophectodermal vesicles produced by microsurgery on the blastocyst (Gardner 1971, 1972), culture of cleavage stages in [^{3}H]thymidine (Snow 1973a, b), and from isolated 1/4 and 1/8 blastomeres (Sherman 1975; J. Rossant, unpublished work) behave like mural trophectoderm. They give rise only to cells whose morphology and properties are indistinguishable from trophoblastic giant cells, both *in vivo* (Gardner 1971, 1972; Snow 1973a, b; J. Rossant, unpublished work) and *in vitro* (Ansell & Snow 1975; Sherman 1975). However, if trophectodermal vesicles are recombined with ICM tissue before transformation to giant cells begins, their cells continue to proliferate and can support normal embryonic development (Gardner 1971; Gardner et al. 1973; Gardner & Johnson 1975). Experiments in progress suggest that 'determination' of mural cells may occur close to the time of morphological transformation (R. L. Gardner, unpublished work). Presumably, all such cells are committed to giant-cell formation by day 5 when endo-reduplication of DNA begins (Barlow *et al.* 1972).

Polar trophectoderm cells continue to divide, and thereby form both the ectoplacental cone and extra-embryonic ectoderm after implantation (Gardner & Papaioannou 1975). However, development of both these tissues depends on their continued proximity to the ICM and its derivatives. Transformation to giant cells is the normal fate of cells in the periphery of the ectoplacental cone (Snell & Stevens 1966). It can be induced experimentally simply by isolating ectoplacental cones or 5.5 to 6.5-day extra-embryonic ectoderm from ICM derivatives and placing them in ectopic sites or in culture (Gardner 1975*a*; Gardner & Papaioannou 1975; R. L. Gardner & L. Ofer, unpublished work). At present it is not clear how long these polar trophectoderm derivatives depend on ICM derivatives for their normal differentiation; nor do we know anything about the mechanism involved.

ORIGIN OF THE GERM-LINE IN MAMMALS

There is now considerable evidence for the existence of a specific germ cell lineage in mammals (Mintz 1960; Peters 1970) as in many other metazoa. Nevertheless, primordial germ cells can first be identified relatively late in development compared to lower vertebrates, and there is no evidence for the precociously segregating germ plasm found in amphibia (Blackler 1970) and insects (Okada *et al.* 1974). According to most authors, germ cells are first seen in the extra-embryonic endoderm of the yolk sac (e.g. Brambell 1956; Hamilton & Mossman 1972), though their origin from this tissue has been questioned (Ożdżeński 1967). So far, germ-line chimeras have only been obtained after injection of embryonic ectoderm cells into host blastocysts (R. L. Gardner & M. F. Lyon, unpublished work). Hence, it would appear that primordial germ cells originate from the embryonic ectoderm rather than from extra-embryonic endoderm, and that they secondarily migrate into the latter. Alternative explanations are that these cells have a dual origin, or that ectodermal cells continue to form primitive endoderm after 4.5 days p.c., neither of which seems likely.

It is tempting to conclude from the fact that single 4.5-day p.c. embryonic ectoderm cells yield both germ and somatic cell chimerism that segregation of the germ line has not yet taken place at this stage. However, recent work on *Xenopus* suggests that this may not be justified. Thus, Whittington & Dixon (1975) found that the total number of cells containing germ plasm increases to only about 14 between the 4-cell and late tail-bud stage, which suggests that they divide twice at most. However, the cells undergo a dramatic reduction in volume during the same period, which seems to require their participation in 10 to 11 mitoses. Whittington & Dixon (1975) conclude that the germ plasm is passively distributed, usually to only one daughter cell at each cell division, during this early period of development. Subsequently, it shifts to a perinuclear location which ensures that it is distributed to both daughter cells, thereby rapidly expanding the germ cell population. This model is reminiscent of chromatin diminution in *Ascaris* (T. Boveri, quoted in Davidson 1968). If a similar situation exists in mammals, the best that one could hope to establish by transplanting single cells would be the stage at which germ cells no longer produce somatic segregants.

CONCLUSIONS

It would be premature to generalize about determination during mammalian development on the basis of the few events analysed so far. Nevertheless, it is of interest to look for features shared by these early determinative events. They are as follows:

(1) Determination occurs in relatively small populations of cells (approximately 15–50).

(2) At each critical period cells can take one of two developmental pathways (Fig. 3).

(3) The position that a cell occupies seems to be important in deciding its eventual fate. This may be the position it holds in relation to other like cells, as in determination of trophectoderm versus ICM and endoderm versus ectoderm, or its position relative to dissimilar cells, as in regional differentiation of the trophectoderm.

(4) Initial determination in the morula and ICM results in almost immediate morphological and/or physiological differentiation of one of the two populations of cells (trophectoderm and primitive endoderm), but not in the other (ICM and embryonic ectodermal cells). Subdivision of the trophectoderm is more complicated, since it is not clear whether transforming mural cells differ initially from polar cells merely in ploidy and degree of physiological differentiation, or whether they should be regarded as a distinct class of cell. Also, although reversal of transformation to giant cells is most unlikely and has never been observed in mammals, polar cells clearly retain the capacity to form giant cells until later stages of development (Fig. 3).

The close temporal relationship between determination and overt differentiation in trophectoderm and endoderm as opposed to ICM and embryonic ectoderm cells probably reflects the fact that the physiological activities of the former are essential for supporting development of the latter during and after

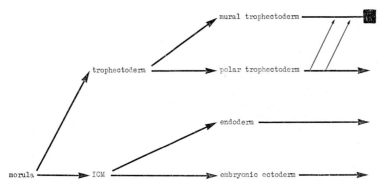

FIG. 3. Map of early determinative events in the mouse embryo. The black square represents terminal cells.

implantation. This parallels the situation in *Drosophila* where some cells of the embryo differentiate into larval structures while others are kept in abeyance as determined but undifferentiated imaginal disk cells until pupation (Hadorn 1965).

Future progress in understanding the relationship between cellular determination and differentiation during early mammalian embryogenesis would be greatly assisted if better markers of differentiation could be found. Morphological criteria can be misleading, as indicated earlier, and physiological criteria usually apply to groups of cells rather than individual cells (Gardner 1972). Development of methods of detecting molecules specific to particular types of differentiated cells at the single cell level *in situ* would avoid many of the problems inherent in present methods of analysis. Finally, we have yet to gain insight into the fundamental problem common to many developmental systems, which is how the position of cells can influence the pattern of genetic activity that they subsequently express (Ciba Foundation 1975).

ACKNOWLEDGEMENTS

We should like to thank Dr C.F. Graham and Professor A.K. Tarkowski for valuable discussion. The authors' own work discussed in this paper was supported by the Medical Research Council and the Ford Foundation. J. Rossant is in receipt of a Medical Research Council Research Studentship.

References

ANSELL, J.D. & SNOW, M.H.L. (1975) The development of trophoblast *in vitro* from blasto-cysts containing varying amounts of inner cell mass. *J. Embryol. Exp. Morphol. 33,* 177–185

BARLOW, P.W. & SHERMAN, M.I. (1972) The biochemistry of differentiation of mouse tropho-blast: studies on polyploidy. *J. Embryol. Exp. Morphol 27*, 447–465

BARLOW, P., OWEN, D.A.J. & GRAHAM, C.F. (1972) DNA synthesis in the preimplantation mouse embryo. *J. Embryol. Exp. Morphol. 27*, 431–445

BLACKLER, A.W. (1970) The integrity of the reproductive cell line in the Amphibia, in *Current Topics in Developmental Biology* (Moscona, A.A. & Monroy, A., eds.), vol. 5, pp. 71–87, Academic Press, New York

BOWMAN, P. & MCLAREN, A. (1970) Cleavage rate of mouse embryos *in vivo* and *in vitro*. *J. Embryol. Exp. Morphol. 24*, 203–207

BRAMBELL, F.W.R. (1956) Ovarian changes, in *Marshall's Physiology of Reproduction*, 3rd edn. (Parkes, A.S., ed.), vol. 1, pp. 397–542, Longmans Green, London

BUEHR, M. & MCLAREN, A. (1974) Size regulation in chimaeric mouse embryos. *J. Embryol. Exp. Morphol. 31*, 229–234

CALARCO, P.G. & BROWN, E.H. (1969) An ultrastructural and cytological study of pre-implantation development of the mouse. *J. Exp. Zool. 171*, 253–284

CIBA FOUNDATION (1975) *Cell Patterning (Ciba Found. Symp. 29)*, Associated Scientific Publishers, Amsterdam

DALCQ, A.M. (1957) *Introduction to General Embryology*, Oxford University Press, London

DAVIDSON, E.H. (1968) *Gene Activity in Early Development*, Academic Press, New York

DICKSON, A.D. (1963) Trophoblastic giant cell transformation of mouse blastocysts. *J. Reprod. Fertil. 6*, 465–466

DICKSON, A.D. (1966) The form of the mouse blastocyst. *J. Anat. 100*, 335–348

DICKSON, A.D. (1969) Cytoplasmic changes during the trophoblastic giant cell transformation of blastocysts from normal and ovariectomised mice. *J. Anat. 105*, 371–380

ENDERS, A.C. (1971) The fine structure of the blastocyst, in *Biology of the Blastocyst* (Blandau, R.J., ed.), pp. 71–94, University of Chicago Press, Chicago

ENDERS, A.C. & SCHLAFKE, S.J. (1965) The fine structure of the blastocyst: some comparative studies, in *Preimplantation Stages of Pregnancy (Ciba Found. Symp.)*, pp. 29–54, Churchill, London

GARDNER, R.L. (1971) Manipulations on the blastocyst, in *Advances in the Biosciences No. 6 (Schering Symp. Intrinsic and Extrinsic Factors in Early Mammalian Development)* (Raspé, G., ed.), pp. 279–296, Pergamon Press, Oxford

GARDNER, R.L. (1972) An investigation of inner cell mass and trophoblast tissue following their isolation from the mouse blastocyst. *J. Embryol. Exp. Morphol. 28*, 279–312

GARDNER, R.L. (1974) Microsurgical approaches to the study of early mammalian develop-ment, in *Birth Defects and Fetal Development: Endocrine and Metabolic Factors* (Moghissi, K.S., ed.), pp. 212–233, Thomas, Springfield, Ill.

GARDNER, R.L. (1975a) Origins and properties of trophoblast, in *The Immunobiology of Trophoblast* (Edwards, R.G., Howe, C.W.S. & Johnson, M.H., eds.), pp. 43–65, Cambridge University Press, London

GARDNER, R.L. (1975b) Analysis of determination and differentiation in the early mammalian embryo using intra- and inter-specific chimaeras, in *The Developmental Biology of Reproduction (33rd Symp. Soc. Dev. Biol.)* (Markert, C.L., ed.), pp. 207–238, Academic Press, New York

GARDNER, R.L. & JOHNSON, M.H. (1975) Investigation of cellular interaction and deployment in the early mammalian embryo using interspecific chimaeras between the rat and mouse, in *Cell Patterning (Ciba Found. Symp. 29)*, pp. 183–200, Associated Scientific Publishers, Amsterdam

GARDNER, R.L. & LYON, M.F. (1971) X-chromosome inactivation studied by injection of a single cell into the mouse blastocyst. *Nature (Lond.) 231*, 385–386

GARDNER, R.L. & PAPAIOANNOU, V.E. (1975) Differentiation in the trophectoderm and inner cell mass, in *The Early Development of Mammals (2nd Symp. Br. Soc. Dev. Biol.)* (Balls, M. & Wild, A.E., eds.), pp. 107–132, Cambridge University Press, London

GARDNER, R.L., PAPAIOANNOU, V.E. & BARTON, S.C. (1973) Origin of the ectoplacental cone and secondary giant cells in mouse blastocysts reconstituted from isolated trophoblast and inner cell mass. *J. Embryol. Exp. Morphol. 30*, 561–572

GEHRING, W. & NÖTHIGER, R. (1973) The imaginal discs of *Drosophila*, in *Developmental Systems: Insects* (Counce, S. & Waddington, C.H., eds.), vol. 2, pp. 212–290, Academic Press, New York

HADORN, E. (1965) Problems of determination and transdetermination. *Brookhaven Symp. Biol. 18*, 148–161

HAMILTON, W.J. & MOSSMAN, H.W. (1972) *Hamilton, Boyd and Mossman's Human Embryology*, 4th edn., Heffer, Cambridge

HERBERT, M.C. & GRAHAM, C.F. (1974) Cell determination and biochemical differentiation of the early mammalian embryo, in *Current Topics in Developmental Biology* (Moscona, A.A. & Monroy, A., eds.), vol. 8, pp. 151–178, Academic Press, New York

HILLMAN, N., SHERMAN, M.I. & GRAHAM, C.F. (1972) The effect of spatial arrangement on cell determination during mouse development. *J. Embryol. Exp. Morphol. 28*, 263–278

HUXLEY, J.S. & DE BEER, G.R. (1937) *Elements of Experimental Embryology*, Cambridge University Press, Cambridge

KELLY, S.J. (1975) Studies of the potency of early cleavage blastomeres of the mouse, in *The Early Development of Mammals (2nd Symp. Br. Soc. Dev. Biol.)* (Balls, M. & Wild, A.E., eds.), pp. 97–106, Cambridge University Press, London

LEVAK-ŠVAJGER, B. & ŠVAJGER, A. (1971) Differentiation of endodermal tissues in homografts of primitive ectoderm from two-layered rat embryonic shields. *Experientia (Basel) 27*, 683–684

LEVAK-ŠVAJGER, B. & ŠVAJGER, A. (1974) Investigation on the origin of the definitive endoderm in the rat embryo. *J. Embryol. Exp. Morphol. 32*, 445–459

LIN, T.P. (1969) Microsurgery of the inner cell mass of mouse blastocysts. *Nature (Lond.) 222*, 480–481

MARTIN, G. & EVANS, M.H. (1975) Differentiation of clonal lines of teratocarcinoma cells: formation of embryoid bodies *in vitro*. *Proc. Natl. Acad. Sci. USA 72*, 1441–1445

MELISSINOS, K. (1907) Die Entwicklung des Eis der Mäuse von dem ersten Furchungs-Phänomenon bis zur Festsetzung der Allantois an der Ectoplacentarplatte. *Arch. Mikrosk. Anat. Entwicklungsmech. 70*, 577–628

MINTZ, B. (1960) Embryological phases of mammalian gametogenesis. *J. Cell Comp. Physiol. 56, suppl. 1*, 31–44

MINTZ, B. (1964) Formation of genetically mosaic mouse embryos, and development of 'lethal (t^{12}/t^{12})-normal' mosaics. *J. Exp. Zool. 157*, 273–292

MINTZ, B. (1965) Experimental genetic mosaicism in the mouse, in *Preimplantation Stages of Pregnancy (Ciba Found. Symp.)*, pp. 194–207, Churchill, London

MINTZ, B. (1974) Gene control of mammalian differentiation. *Annu. Rev. Genet. 8*, 411–470

MULNARD, J.G. (1965) Studies of regulation of mouse ova *in vitro*, in *Preimplantation Stages of Pregnancy (Ciba Found. Symp.)*, pp. 123–138, Churchill, London

NADIJCKA, M. & HILLMAN, N. (1974) Ultrastructural studies of the mouse blastocyst substages. *J. Embryol. Exp. Morphol. 32*, 675–695

NEEDHAM, J. (1942) *Biochemistry and Morphogenesis*, Cambridge University Press, Cambridge

OKADA, M., KLEINMAN, A. & SCHNEIDERMAN, H. (1974) Restoration of fertility in sterilised *Drosophila* eggs by transplantation of polar cytoplasm. *Dev. Biol. 37*, 43–54

OŻDŻEŃSKI, W. (1967) Observations on the origin of primordial germ cells in the mouse. *Zool. Pol. 17*, 367–379

PETERS, H. (1970) Migration of gonocytes into the mammalian gonad and their differentiation. *Philos. Trans. R. Soc. Lond. B Biol. Sci. 259*, 91–101

ROSSANT, J. (1975a) Investigation of the determinative state of the mouse inner cell mass. I. Aggregation of isolated inner cell masses with morulae. *J. Embryol. Exp. Morphol. 33*, 979–990

ROSSANT, J. (1975b) Investigation of the determinative state of the mouse inner cell mass. II. The fate of isolated inner cell masses transferred to the oviduct. *J. Embryol. Exp. Morphol.* *33*, 991–1001

SEIDEL, F. (1960) Die Entwicklungs-fähigkeiten isolierter Furchungszellen aus dem Ei des Kaninchens, *Oryctolagus cuniculus*. *Wilhelm Roux' Arch. Entwicklungsmech. Org.* *152*, 43–110

SHERMAN, M.I. (1975) The role of cell-cell interaction during early mouse embryogenesis, in *The Early Development of Mammals (2nd Symp. Br. Soc. Dev. Biol.)* (Balls, M. & Wild, A.E., eds.), pp. 145–166, Cambridge University Press, London

SHERMAN, M.I., MCLAREN, A. & WALKER, P.M.B. (1972) Mechanism of accumulation of DNA in giant cells of mouse trophoblast. *Nat. New Biol.* *238*, 175–176

ŠKREB, N., ŠVAJGER, A. & LEVAK-ŠVAJGER, B. (1976) Developmental potentialities of the germ layers in mammals, in this volume, pp. 27–39

SNELL, G.D. & STEVENS, L.C. (1966) Early embryology, in *Biology of the Laboratory Mouse*, 2nd edn. (Green, E.L., ed.), pp. 205–245, McGraw-Hill, New York

SNOW, M.H.L. (1973a) The differential effect of [³H]-thymidine upon two populations of cells in pre-implantation mouse embryos, in *The Cell Cycle in Development and Differentiation (1st Symp. Br. Soc. Dev. Biol.)* (Balls, M. & Billett, F.S., eds.), pp. 311–324, Cambridge University Press, London

SNOW, M.H.L. (1973b) Abnormal development of pre-implantation mouse embryos grown *in vitro* with [³H]-thymidine. *J. Embryol. Exp. Morphol.* *29*, 601–615

SPEMANN, H. (1938) *Embryonic Development and Induction*, Yale University Press, New Haven, Conn.

STERN, M.S. (1973) Development of cleaving mouse embryos under pressure. *Differentiation 1*, 407–412

STERN, M.S. & WILSON, I.B. (1972) Experimental studies on the organisation of the pre-implantation mouse embryo. I. Fusion of asynchronously cleaving eggs. *J. Embryol. Exp. Morphol.* *28*, 247–254

TARKOWSKI, A.K. (1959a) Experiments on the development of isolated blastomeres of mouse eggs. *Nature (Lond.) 184*, 1286–1287

TARKOWSKI, A.K. (1959b) Experimental studies on regulation in the development of isolated blastomeres of mouse eggs. *Acta Theriol. 3*, 191–267

TARKOWSKI, A.K. & WRÓBLEWSKA, J. (1967) Development of blastomeres of mouse eggs isolated at the four- and eight-cell stage. *J. Embryol. Exp. Morphol. 18*, 155–180

WHITTINGTON, P.McD. & DIXON, K.E. (1975) Quantitative studies of germ plasm and germ cells during early embryogenesis of *Xenopus laevis*. *J. Embryol. Exp. Morphol. 33*, 57–74

WILSON, I.B. & STERN, M.S. (1975) Organisation in the preimplantation embryo, in *The Early Development of Mammals (2nd Symp. Br. Soc. Dev. Biol.)* (Balls, M. & Wild, A.E., eds.), pp. 81–96, Cambridge University Press, London

WILSON, I.B., BOLTON, E. & CUTTLER, R.H. (1972) Preimplantation differentiation in the mouse egg as revealed by microinjection of vital markers. *J. Embryol. Exp. Morphol. 27*, 467–479

Discussion

Tarkowski: In normal development, formation of a blastocyst is a result of two processes: first, the accumulation of a definite number of cells due to cleavage and, second, the appearance of vacuoles in the cytoplasm, followed by secretion of the fluid into the intercellular spaces, eventually leading to the formation of a blastocoele. In the mouse the second process takes place around the fifth cleavage, when the embryo consists of about 32 cells. One could argue that the embryo has to undergo four or five cleavages before fluid can start to accumulate and the blastocoele is formed. However, the picture appears to be more complicated than that. Under the conditions of culture *in vitro*—which are often if not always suboptimal—these two processes can sometimes be dissociated from each other. It happens occasionally that cleavage is affected by poor culture conditions but the timing of vacuolization is not. On several occasions I have seen 2-cell eggs which after three days in culture remained 2-cell but formed large vacuoles in the cytoplasm on a normal time schedule. It appears, therefore, that formation of vacuoles and eventually secretion of the blastocoelic fluid does not require a definite number of cell divisions but is a time-dependent process, governed perhaps by some kind of an internal clock mechanism.

I would also like to say something about the differentiation of trophectoderm and the inner cell mass, and in general about the inside-outside hypothesis. Some time ago we observed that 4-cell eggs cultured at a sublethal temperature of 40.5 °C developed into trophoblastic vesicles. Cell divisions were clearly affected, as during the two days in culture the embryos underwent only two cleavages and were composed of 16 cells. However, timing of the blastocoele formation was not affected and consequently all cells were committed to trophoblast. It appears, therefore, that irrespective of whether the embryo develops from the whole egg or from isolated single blastomeres, if the cell number remains low when the blastocoele starts to form, trophoblastic vesicles rather than blastocysts are formed (Tarkowski 1970).

Gardner: In other words, it is certainly not an artifact due to separation of cells.

Snow: I have also seen 2-cell eggs making blastocysts. It is a rare phenomenon but it occurs routinely in a very small percentage of 2-cell eggs in culture. In the process of making tetraploid mice, using cytochalasin to inhibit the second cleavage, I find that the proportion of eggs which fail to cleave any more is increased. They continue in a quite healthy fashion and at the appointed time try and make blastocysts by producing vesicles in these two cells. In these cytochalasin-treated eggs where cleavage does not re-establish it is quite clear that nuclear division still continues. One ends up with a blastocyst which is essentially 16-ploid but composed of only two cells. What has happened to the nuclear divisions in the 2-cell blastocysts in the normal diploid culture? I have never checked them but the embryo may continue with nuclear divisions but without cell division.

Tarkowski: In the 2-cell eggs I was talking about, nuclear divisions were not observed.

McLaren: Perhaps one should call such a vacuolated 2-celled object a vesicle rather than a blastocyst. It seems that both the differentiation of inner cell mass versus trophectoderm and the differentiation of primary endoderm versus ectoderm are independent of cell number. Both show this inside versus outside pattern of differentiation with either a small or a larger number of cells. This is quite different from giant cell differentiation in the ectoplacental cone, where the number of cells intervening between the inner cell mass and the periphery appears to be critical for differentiation.

For the first sort of cell-number-independent differentiation, two types of explanation seem possible. One is an inside–outside gradient combined with some threshold effect such that when the concentration of some substance is low enough (i.e. at the periphery) differentiation occurs. The other is a surface phenomenon, with differentiation taking place in any cell which has less than, say, 20% of its surface in contact with other cell surfaces. How can one distinguish between these two types of explanation?

Gardner: One might argue that a number of determined but morphologically undifferentiated endoderm cells already exist in 3.5-day inner cell masses at the time of isolation. However, given the observed variation in initial cell number due to differences in rate of development and damage during microsurgical isolation, it seems rather unlikely that they would always be appropriate in number to form the whole surface, and only the surface layer, in aggregates. Certainly, the thickness of the endodermal cell layer does not vary obviously among aggregated pairs of inner cell masses recovered from the oviduct.

I would certainly favour either an inside–outside gradient or a surface phenomenon, rather than the idea of something in a higher concentration in the medium causing differentiation, unless it is something incredibly simple—mouse embryos can of course be cultured successfully, with normal differentiation, in a very simple medium. I think it would be difficult to distinguish between the two explanations.

Snow: How do you like the idea that all blastomeres containing membrane that had been on the surface of the unfertilized egg must become trophoblast cells?

Gardner: I think that this hypothesis is in conflict with most of the experimental results obtained after rearrangement of blastomeres. For example, Wilson *et al.* (1972) found that oil drops injected into the peripheral cytoplasm of blastomeres, as opposed to centrally near the interface between cells, invariably end up in trophectoderm cells at the blastocyst stage. A proportion of the centrally injected drops are found later in inner cell mass cells. In other words there is some sort of 'cryptic preformation' in normal development which accords with your hypothesis. However, when these authors aggregated pairs of cleavage stages with peripheral oil drops, some drops ended up in inside cells at the blastocyst stage. One obvious shortcoming of this experiment is, of course, lack of evidence that these marked cells really are inner mass cells rather than misplaced trophectoderm cells.

Snow: In fact Wilson *et al.*'s (1972) experiments are not very informative in this respect. When 4- or 8-cell embryos are aggregated together it is not known how the blastomeres rearrange themselves. In those experiments where embryos carrying peripherally situated oil droplets were aggregated together, over 90% of the markers became located in the trophoblast so it could be argued that Wilson's data supported my conjecture about the egg cell surface.

Wolpert: What is the morphological basis of the inside–outside polarity? How early can any sort of physiological barrier, such as gap junctions, be detected?

Gardner: No one has looked at that. They are quite large cells and should present no problems.

McLaren: Morphologically the junctional complexes consist of tight junctions on the periphery, which hold the cells together and form an effective seal, and gap junctions internal to these (Ducibella *et al.* 1975).

Wolpert: But are they there before or after the inside–outside difference is established? Could they provide the basis for the difference in environment?

McLaren: They are there before vacuolization.

Gardner: Yes, they appear well before most people believe that determination takes place.

Snow: One can actually see regions of close apposition of membranes at the zona ends of the furrow at the 2-cell stage. The cell membranes of the two adjacent blastomeres are very closely apposed indeed.

Graham: From your remarks, Dr Gardner, it seems that the inside–outside mechanism controls the early development of mammals. One important question is whether 'outside' simply means exposure of the cell surface to the surrounding medium or whether cells can only be 'outside' with respect to other cells. The conditions which promote the development of morphologically recognizable endoderm on teratocarcinoma cells are relevant to this point (Martin & Evans 1975). It is reported that teratocarcinoma cells must be grown in suspension and in this case they aggregate into lumps with endoderm on the outside, or they must be allowed to pile up on the bottom of a Petri dish with endoderm forming on top of the piles. The important point is that endoderm is usually formed when cells are 'outside' with respect to other cells.

McLaren: This is somewhat different from trophectoderm differentiation, where even two solitary cells will undergo vacuolization.

Gardner: I am not sure that it is in conflict. This raises the question whether vacuolization is a property specific to trophectoderm cells, and since 1907 people have argued that it is a property of all cells of the morula. I think Calarco & Brown (1969), Mintz (1965) and others have suggested that at least some inside cells accumulate fluid. It may be that the initial formation of a blastocoele is a property of all the cells of the morula, then later on maintenance of the blasto-coele is a trophoblast function.

Rutter: A third possible mechanism is related to mass, especially in *in vitro* culture, where the mass of cells may contribute various elements which may be related to nutrition quite apart from specific determinants. Three kinds of ex-periments are relevant to those three postulates, namely the mass postulate which is non-specific, the cell surface postulate in which there is a specific inter-action, and the position postulate which may imply a gradient. Have experi-ments been done with heterotypic cells in such combinatorial relationships? Are heterotypic cells competent to nurse the other cells along?

Gardner: Attempts have been made to aggregate teratocarcinoma cells with cleavage stage embryos. However, this has been pursued with the aim of producing chimeras rather than of trying to alter the developmental potential of blastomeres. Janet Rossant (1975) found that the rate of implantation of inner cell mass–morula aggregates was consistently lower than that of control morula–morula aggregates. One possible explanation for these findings would be that the initially external heterotypic inner mass cells interfered with normal differentiation of underlying trophectoderm cells.

Rutter: That experiment doesn't really answer the question about mechanism because one of at least two possibilities remains to be eliminated.

Gardner: You mean the mass effect as opposed to the position effect? There are problems with studies on the development of blastomeres *in vitro* that may explain why results are not always consistent and conclusive. If conditions are suboptimal, groups of cells may do better than individual ones for trivial reasons. However, Janet Rossant (unpublished work) has repeated such ex-periments *in vivo* by putting isolated blastomeres back into the oviduct inside empty zonae—in other words in their normal environment. Her results are essentially similar to those Tarkowski & Wróblewska (1967) obtained in culture.

Rutter: One way of getting round the problem might be to devise a culture system in which the multiple cellular components are segregated; transmission of the putative components could then occur by the connecting fluid.

Cell–cell interaction may also be approached experimentally by using frag-ments of cell surfaces which might be competent to act on other cells in the medium. Alternatively, if the interactions occurred at the cell surface then cyclic nucleotide derivatives or calcium or one of the prostaglandins might replace the effect. Have either of those types of experiment been performed?

Gardner: I know Dr Graham is thinking along those lines.

Graham: In my hands, dibutyryl cyclic AMP has rather little effect on either endoderm formation by teratocarcinomas or on trophoblast differentiation by the preimplantation embryo. That does not exclude the possibility that dibutyryl cyclic AMP is important, but externally applied dibutyryl cyclic AMP doesn't have an immediately obvious effect.

Rutter: Has anyone tried the cell membrane fraction approach?

Graham: No.

Edidin: What cell membranes would you fractionate?

Rutter: One might try a mixture to start with; even though the fractions would be heterogeneous, there should be specific cell determinants that would recognize particular cells.

Edidin: But why? Are you going to try to get enough blastomeres to fractionate membranes from them?

Rutter: Yes.

Edidin: Regarding model experiments and membrane fragments, recently beads have been prepared with sugar polymers attached to them (Chipowsky *et al.* 1973). Some cultured cells adhere specifically to beads with one particular sugar, galactose, attached. To begin a series of experiments with beads one would have to prepare them with many different sugar polymers. Then one might be able to offer a cell on the outside something that had a molecular structure somewhat like the surface of another cell. Blastomeres on the outside of a morula don't seem to respond to naked plastic; presumably they would respond to the bead alone. However, a bead with a particular sugar might commit them to another pathway.

Hogan: Glutaraldehyde-fixed cells could be used.

Edidin: That might be the easiest of all.

Rutter: Naked beads coated with simple carbohydrates might be much too simple a model to rule out the possible role of cell surfaces, because the real cell surface might either have glycoprotein coats or just protein coats.

Hensleigh: Dr McLaren, does formation of the blastocyst cavity in embryos resulting from the aggregation of two 8-cell mouse embryos begin earlier than in normal embryos?

McLaren: In all these aggregation experiments the timing of blastocoele formation seems extraordinarily constant, irrespective of cell number and also of the number of cell divisions. I find this very mysterious.

Hensleigh: Is this also observed in embryos resulting from the aggregation of four 8-cell embryos?

McLaren: As far as I know, the timing of cavity formation has not yet been rigorously examined for any wide range of different cell numbers.

Gluecksohn-Waelsch: Is the formation of vacuoles in the 2-cell stage actually the same phenomenon as blastocoele formation which normally occurs later on? Maybe this is a degenerative cellular phenomenon which has nothing to do with the mechanisms normally resulting in blastocoele formation.

McLaren: I am sure that degenerative vacuoles must appear. Nevertheless, the formation of a fluid-filled vesicle implies that tight junctions must be present to contain the fluid.

Bennett: Where there are so-called blastocoeles within two cells, are the vacuoles within the cells or between two cells with tight junctions?

Tarkowski: Either alternative is possible. There may be a large vacuole inside a blastomere which pushes the nucleus to one pole of the cell, or blastomeres may form a vesicle filled with fluid. In the latter case the fluid is extracellular (Tarkowski & Wróblewska 1967).

Bennett: If this is so it implies that there is a clock that is independent of cell divisions or number of cells. I have always interpreted the inside–outside theory as applying to populations of cells, not to gradients across one or two cells. Could you comment on that?

Gardner: In terms of gradients, the most naive model would be that a meta-bolic product of the cell was building up in the inside cells to a higher level than in outside cells.

Chapman: What is the sequence of events in the different species of rodent embryos where interspecific combinations have been made? Is the number of cell divisions in the early steps of differentiation the same? Are the relative sizes of the original 1-cell eggs the same?

Gardner: The size of 1-cell eggs is similar, as also is the number of cleavage divisions before blastocyst formation. The most obvious difference is that cleavage takes about 24 hours longer in the rat. Providing that cleaving eggs are matched for stage rather than post-coital age, interspecific aggregates will form integrated blastocysts in a high proportion of cases (e.g. Stern 1973).

References

CALARCO, P.G. & BROWN, E.H. (1969) An ultrastructural and cytological study of pre-implantation development of the mouse. *J. Exp. Zool. 171*, 253–284

CHIPOWSKY, S., LEE, Y.C. & ROSEMAN, S. (1973) Adhesion of cultured fibroblasts to insoluble analogues of cell-surface carbohydrates. *Proc. Natl. Acad. Sci. USA 70*, 2309–2312

DUCIBELLA, T., ALBERTINI, D.F., ANDERSON, E. & BIGGERS, J.D. (1975) The preimplantation mammalian embryo: characterization of intercellular junctions and their appearance during development. *Dev. Biol. 45*, 231–250

MARTIN, G.R. & EVANS, M.J. (1975) Differentiation of clonal lines of teratocarcinoma cells: formation of embryoid bodies *in vitro. Proc. Natl. Acad. Sci. USA 72*, 1441–1445

MINTZ, B. (1965) Experimental genetic mosaicism in the mouse, in *Preimplantation Stages of Pregnancy (Ciba Found. Symp.)*, pp. 194–207, Churchill, London

ROSSANT, J. (1975) Investigation of the determinative state of the mouse inner cell mass. I. Aggregation of isolated inner cell masses with morulae. *J. Embryol. Exp. Morphol.* *33*, 979–990

STERN, M.S. (1973) Chimaeras obtained by aggregation of mouse eggs with rat eggs. *Nature (Lond.) 243*, 472–473

TARKOWSKI, A.K. (1970) [The nature of blastomere differentiation in early mammalian development—epigenetic or intrinsic? in *Symposium on Cellular Interactions in Differentiation and Growth* (in Russian)] pp. 117–125, Izdatelstvo 'Nauka', Moscow

TARKOWSKI, A.K. & WRÓBLEWSKA, J. (1967) Development of blastomeres of mouse eggs isolated at the four- and eight-cell stage. *J. Embryol. Exp. Morphol. 18*, 155–180

WILSON, I.B., BOLTON, E. & CUTTLER, R.H. (1972) Preimplantation differentiation in the mouse egg as revealed by microinjection of vital markers. *J. Embryol. Exp. Morphol. 27*, 467–479

Developmental potentialities of the germ layers in mammals

N. ŠKREB*, A. ŠVAJGER† and B. LEVAK-ŠVAJGER*

Department of Biology and Department of Histology and Embryology,† Faculty of Medicine,
University of Zagreb*

Abstract So that the developmental potentialities of particular constituents of
the rat embryo at the stage of gastrulation could be analysed, single germ layers
isolated from rat embryonic shields were transferred under the kidney capsule of
syngeneic adult animals and the resulting teratomas were examined histologically.
At both the pre-primitive streak and the primitive streak stage the isolated ectoderm gave rise to tissue derivatives of all three germ layers. At the head-fold stage,
however, it differentiated into ectodermal and mesodermal derivatives only.

The paramedian and lateral areas of the ectoderm, isolated and grafted at the
head-fold stage, did not differ significantly in their potentialities.

Mesoderm alone, isolated between the head-fold and the 12-somite stage, differentiated almost exclusively into brown adipose tissue.

Endoderm alone, isolated and grafted at different developmental stages, was
completely resorbed. If grafted at the head-fold stage together with the adjacent
mesoderm, the endoderm differentiated into different derivatives of the primitive
gut. The endoderm underlying the neural plate developed into derivatives of the
foregut, while the endoderm underlying the primitive streak developed mainly
into derivatives of the midgut and hindgut.

The process of germ layer formation in mammals is a period of development
which is only superficially known and which has been insufficiently analysed,
in spite of the fact that it seems to be very important in the onset of cellular
differentiation in embryogenesis. Experimental results obtained many years ago
suggested that the onset of mesoderm formation coincides with a brusque
change in the pattern of embryonic organization (Škreb 1961). We showed,
on the one hand, that the inner cell mass of the blastocyst reacts to different
doses of u.v. irradiation in accordance with the 'all-or-none' rule (Škreb *et al*.
1964). Results obtained by Seidel (1952) for the rabbit blastocyst, as well as
numerous recent findings, including those just presented by Dr Gardner
(Gardner & Rossant, this volume) seem to confirm this hypothesis. On the

other hand, the effects of different teratogens led us to conclude that during the process of mesoderm formation (the period of gastrulation) the embryo becomes progressively more sensitive to different extrinsic factors, to which it reacts by pursuing an anomalous course of development which results in the appearance of various malformations (Škreb & Bijelić 1962; Škreb & Frank 1963). The same idea was recently set forth by Austin (1973), who has reviewed numerous reports on embryo transfer and the effects of different teratogens.

If we imagine that cytoplasmic regions or gradients in the mammalian oocyte or fertilized egg are functionally analogous to the grey crescent of amphibians, this pattern of organization seems to be very unstable. The papers of Dalcq (1954) and his collaborators (e.g. Mulnard 1955) about the predetermination of bilateral symmetry in mammals have not been confirmed (Solter *et al.* 1973). Moreover, the scanty observations about epigenetic factors acting on rodent eggs need to be repeated and scrutinized (Ancel & Reyss-Brion 1956). It seems that the determination of bilateral symmetry in mammalian embryos is still a mystery compared with what has been reported for amphibians and birds. However, some recent experiments on axolotl eggs suggest that the problem of the determination of the grey crescent in amphibians is also still open to discussion (Benford & Namenwirth 1974).

EXPERIMENTS WITH WHOLE EMBRYONIC SHIELDS

In this paper, the term 'differentiation' will be used to designate a many-step process during which the previously identical embryonic cells become unlike and develop into specialized tissues. The term 'terminally differentiated tissue' will be used to designate a tissue whose appearance is similar to or the same as that in the adult animal.

If it is true that mesoderm formation is a crucial step in the development of early embryonic cells, investigations on the influence of different extrauterine sites should cast more light on some of the factors essential for the terminal differentiation of early postimplantation embryonic cells in rodents. So that these factors could be analysed, embryonic shields deprived of all extra-embryonic structures were transferred to beneath the kidney capsule (rat and mouse) (Škreb *et al.* 1971, 1972), or into the anterior chamber of the eye (Levak-Švajger & Škreb 1965) (rat only), or were explanted *in vitro* (Škreb & Švajger 1973) (rat and mouse). Most grafts and explants were studied histologically after 15 or 30 days. In both extrauterine sites transplanted rat embryonic shields developed into teratomas consisting of unordered tissue derivatives of all three germ layers. In renal homografts terminal differentiation was not influenced by the initial developmental stage of the embryonic shield (the two-layered or pre-primitive streak stage, and the three-layered or head-fold stage). In intraocular homografts, however, the embryonic shields transplanted at the pre-primitive streak stage differentiated very poorly as mesodermal derivatives (cartilage, bone, muscle). The site under the kidney capsule probably provides a much more favourable environment (with immediate incorporation and vascularization) than the anterior chamber of the eye.

In some strains of mice (Škreb et al. 1972), not all the embryonic shields transplanted under the kidney capsule differentiated into mature tissues. The cells resulting from the grafts that continued to grow in the undifferentiated form formed small clusters, morphologically indistinguishable from the nests of embryonic carcinoma cells in human or experimental teratocarcinomas. There was good evidence that these grafts had some features in common with malignant tumours. They grew rather fast, and although they did not metastasize or invade the surrounding tissues, they killed the host animals after attaining an enormous size (up to 50% of the total body weight of the adult animal).

Rat egg cylinders which had been explanted in vitro to a piece of lens paper supported by a metal grid and placed on the surface of a liquid nutritive medium containing homologous serum also gave rise to small teratomas, but they were remarkably inferior to those in renal homografts, both qualitatively and quantitatively. Often, the tissue components of the resulting teratomas did not attain the terminal degree of histological differentiation.

In summary, these experiments show that rat and mouse embryonic shields transferred to various extrauterine sites can give rise to teratomas consisting of terminally differentiated tissues derived from all three germ layers. The pattern and degree of differentiation attained depends on the species and strain of the animal and on the developmental stage of the embryonic shield at the moment of isolation, as well as on the extrauterine site, or in vitro environment, to which the shield is transferred. In experimental conditions tissue may differentiate to different degrees. The site under the kidney capsule of isologous animals has proved to provide the most favourable conditions for the expression of the histogenetic potentialities of the rat and mouse embryonic shield.

EXPERIMENTS WITH SEPARATED GERM LAYERS
OF THE RAT EMBRYONIC SHIELD

When the rodent embryo begins the process of gastrulation it consists of two germ layers: the primitive ectoderm (the inner cell layer in the rodent embryo) and the primitive endoderm (the outer cell layer). After gastrulation it consists of three definitive germ layers: the definitive ectoderm, mesoderm and endoderm. The names of the germ layers are used here only from the morphological point of view, regardless of their final developmental potentialities. On the other hand, when we speak about ectodermal, mesodermal and endodermal derivatives or tissues we are referring to the developmental potentialities of the well-established presumptive areas of all three definitive germ layers in the early embryo of amphibians and birds.

Because of technical obstacles in tracing the morphogenetic movements and developmental fate of groups of cells during gastrulation in the mammalian embryo, we could not excise presumptive ectodermal, mesodermal and endodermal areas of the embryonic shields of rodents, although this method is successful in amphibian embryos. In order to analyse in more detail the developmental potentialities of isolated parts of early rat embryonic shields, we therefore worked out a technique for separating particular germ layers. Embryonic shields are first treated for 20–30 min with proteolytic enzymes (the common method for splitting off epithelia from the underlying mesenchyme —a mixture of 0.5% [v/v] trypsin [crystallized, lyophilized, Worthington] and 2.5% [v/v] pancreatin [Difco] in calcium-free and magnesium-free Tyrode's solution at 4°C) and then microsurgically manipulated with electrolytically sharpened and polished tungsten (wolfram) needles (Levak-Švajger et al. 1969). The germ layers are separated at the level of the basement membranes which already exist at boundaries between particular germ layers in the rodent embryonic shield. Enzyme treatment decreases the mutual adhesiveness of the germ layers so much that the subsequent mechanical separation with needles is fairly easy. Details of the procedure for each of the developmental stages of the embryonic shield have been described elsewhere (Levak-Švajger & Švajger 1971, 1974). Enzyme treatment does not affect the viability of embryonic cells and their ability to differentiate into normal tissues after transplantation.

Single germ layers (or combinations of two of them) were isolated from the pre-primitive streak (8 days), the primitive streak (8.5 days) and the head-fold stage (9 days) of rat embryonic shields (deprived of extra-embryonic membranes), and were grown for 15 days under the kidney capsule of isogeneic adult animals. The resulting teratomas were examined histologically.

Endoderm

In the developmental stages tested so far (the pre-primitive streak, the early primitive streak, and the head-fold stage) the isolated endoderm did not differentiate at all when grafted alone under the kidney capsule of isogeneic adult animals. All grafts were completely resorbed. At the head-fold stage, however, the endoderm differentiated into typical endodermal epithelia when grafted together with its adjacent mesoderm (Levak-Švajger & Švajger 1974) (Fig. 1). Apparently, appropriate epithelio-mesenchymal interaction is needed for histological differentiation of endodermal organs.

At the head-fold stage the potentiality for developing into different segments of the definitive gut seems to be already roughly limited to particular areas of the endoderm, combined with its adjacent mesoderm. The endoderm from the anterior part of the embryonic shield (underlying the neural groove) gives rise to the derivatives of the foregut (tongue, oesophagus, respiratory tube, thymus, thyroid). The ectodermal derivatives of this area also belong to the head region (brain, choroid plexus, vibrissae, teeth). The endoderm from the posterior part of the embryonic shield (underlying the primitive streak) gives rise to derivatives of the midgut and hindgut (small and large intestine, urogenital sinus, prostatic complex) (Švajger & Levak-Švajger 1974).

Ectoderm

The developmental potentialities of the rat embryonic ectoderm are remarkably restricted in the course of gastrulation (Levak-Švajger & Švajger 1971,

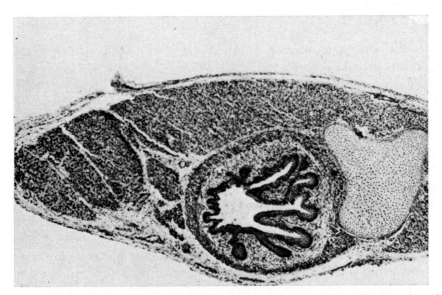

FIG. 1. Teratoma derived from the endoderm + mesoderm isolated from the rat embryonic shield at the head-fold stage. Note the well-developed oesophagus (epithelium + muscular layer), cartilage and brown adipose tissue (× 60).

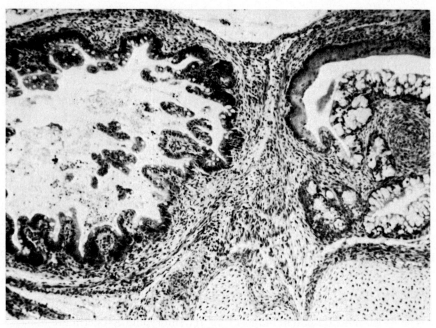

Fig. 2. Detail of a teratoma derived from the primitive ectoderm isolated from the rat embryonic shield at the early primitive streak stage. Note the well-developed derivatives of the primitive gut: intestine (left) and pharynx (right) (× 100). Reproduced with permission, from Levak-Švajger & Švajger 1974.

1974). When the isolated ectoderm of the embryo at the pre-primitive streak stage (two-layered embryonic shield, 8-day embryo) or the ectoderm, together with the incipient mesodermal 'wings' of the embryo at the primitive streak stage (beginning formation of mesoderm, 8.5-day embryo), were transplanted under the kidney capsule, the resulting teratomas consisted of mature tissue derivatives of all three germ layers. Various derivatives of the primitive gut were regularly present in these teratomas (Fig. 2). On the other hand, the embryonic ectoderm isolated at the head-fold stage (three-layered embryonic shield, head-folds, head process, 9-day embryo) differentiated into ectodermal and mesodermal tissues only (Table 1).

These results have been interpreted as suggesting an analogy with the course of events during gastrulation in the chick blastoderm (Nicolet 1971). Before gastrulation the primitive ectoderm seems to contain prospective cells of all three definitive germ layers. During gastrulation first the endodermal and then the mesodermal cells probably migrate through the primitive streak and Hensen's node and finally occupy the positions of the definitive endoderm and mesoderm. After gastrulation the primitive ectoderm becomes the definitive

TABLE 1

Incidence of mature tissues in renal homografts of rat embryonic ectoderm

Stage of embryo (Nicholas 1962):	12 (pre-primitive streak)	13 (primitive streak)	15 (head-fold)
Age of embryo (days):	8	8.5	9
Type of graft:	Ecto	Ecto + Meso	Ecto
No. differentiated	15	15	11
Ectodermal tissues			
Skin	—	—	11
Neural tissue	12	15	11
Endodermal tissues			
Pharynx, oesophagus	8	13	—
Respiratory tube	13	15	1
Glands	7	14	1
Thymus	1	2	—
Thyroid	—	3	—
Intestine	11	8	2
Total	14	15	2
Mesodermal tissues			
White adipose tissue	1	3	10
Brown adipose tissue	2	3	6
Cartilage	11	15	11
Bone	3	6	9
Smooth muscle	13	15	3
Skeletal muscle	2	5	10
Heart muscle	12	11	—

ectoderm, with developmental potentialities restricted to the characteristic 'ectodermal tissues' (nervous tissue, epidermis).

It is interesting that before gastrulation and during early gastrulation the isolated ectoderm does not differentiate into epidermis. Neural tissue is the only ectodermal tissue present in these grafts. Both neural tissue and the epidermis (with hairs and skin glands) regularly develop in homografts of the ectoderm isolated at the head-fold stage. This observation will be subjected to detailed experimental analysis.

These experiments tell us nothing about the fate of the primitive endoderm (i.e. endoderm before gastrulation). It is not clear whether it is completely or only partly replaced by cells which have migrated from the primitive ectoderm. There is some experimental evidence suggesting that after gastrulation the cells of the primitive endoderm become part of the extra-embryonic membranes (Gardner & Johnson 1975).

Finally, we shall briefly mention some as yet incompletely analysed results of experiments designed to test the regional developmental potentialities of the embryonic ectoderm before and after gastrulation. Unfortunately, due to several peculiarities of its entypic development, the rodent embryo cannot be subjected to those precise 'mapping' experiments which have contributed substantially to the knowledge of early avian embryogenesis. Therefore only a rough orientation can be expected from the experiments to be described now.

In the first series of experiments, embryonic shields from the pre-primitive streak and early primitive streak stages were used. After the primitive endoderm and all extra-embryonic parts had been removed, the remaining cylinder-shaped primitive embryonic ectoderm (alone or bearing the incipient mesodermal 'wings') was cut transversely into two parts (Fig. 3). One part (the tip of the egg cylinder) contained the anterior half of the primitive streak, Hensen's node and the posterior half of the future neural plate. The second part (close to the amniotic fold) contained the posterior half of the primitive streak and the anterior part of the future neural plate. Both parts were separately transferred to sites beneath the kidney capsule. The resulting teratomas did not significantly differ in their histological composition. Ectodermal, mesodermal and endodermal tissues were regularly present in both series. This result may

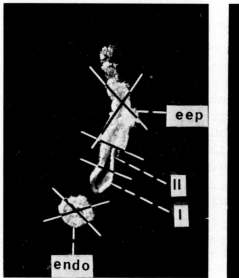 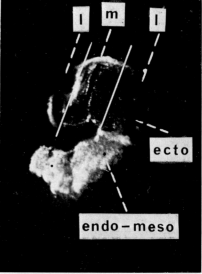

FIG. 3. *(left)* Pre-primitive streak stage rat embryo dissected to divide the primitive ectoderm into two parts (I and II). The primitive endoderm (endo) and the extra-embryonic part (eep) are discarded ($\times$ 50).

FIG. 4. *(right)* Head-fold stage rat embryonic shield dissected to isolate the median (m) and the lateral parts (l) of the ectoderm (ecto). The endoderm and the mesoderm (endo-meso) are discarded ($\times$ 50).

be interpreted as suggesting that (*a*) the prospective endodermal and mesodermal cells are not strictly localized within small areas of the primitive ectoderm, and (*b*) at least in the present experimental conditions, the migration of
prospective endodermal and mesodermal cells is not restricted to particular
parts of the primitive streak.

In the second series of experiments, the isolated ectoderm of the head-fold-
stage embryonic shield was cut longitudinally into three parts (Fig. 4). The
median part (occupying approximately the area of the neural groove) was
grafted alone, and both lateral parts were grafted together. The teratomas
resulting from the two series of grafts all contained both neural tissue and skin.
The preliminary conclusion is that at this stage these two major developmental
potentialities of the definitive ectoderm are not yet strictly confined to any
particular region.

Mesoderm

The mesoderm develops into typical mesodermal derivatives (connective and
adipose tissue, cartilage, bone, muscle) if it is transferred together with the
ectoderm or endoderm (Fig. 1). The histodifferentiation of the mesoderm seems
to be governed by organ-typical epithelio-mesenchymal inductive interactions,
for the ciliated columnar epithelium of the respiratory tube is most often associated with the non-ossifying hyaline cartilage, while the epithelium of the
gut is regularly surrounded by characteristic layers of smooth muscle cells
(Levak-Švajger & Švajger 1974).

In order to test the developmental potentialities of the mesoderm alone
('autodifferentiation'), we isolated the mesoderm from embryos ranging in age
from the head-fold to the 12-somite stage (unpublished results). Whole unsegmented mesodermal 'wings' or excised areas of the mesodermal layer were
transplanted under the kidney capsule (paraxial unsegmented mesoderm, anterior and posterior five to six somites, lateral plate, mesoderm of the tail region,
and the mesenchyme of the head and neck, including the branchial region).
In most of these grafts (the total number being more than 150) the early embryonic mesenchyme differentiated predominantly into brown adipose tissue
(Fig. 5). Small nodules of cartilage were a rare finding. Cartilage developed
regularly only in grafts of the ensemble of six posterior somites at the 12-somite
stage. As an exception, the mesenchyme isolated from the head and neck
(probably of neural crest rather than of mesodermal origin: Mulnard 1955)
differentiated almost exclusively into membrane bone.

For the time being, the regular differentiation of the isolated early embryonic mesoderm into brown adipose tissue cannot be explained. The problem

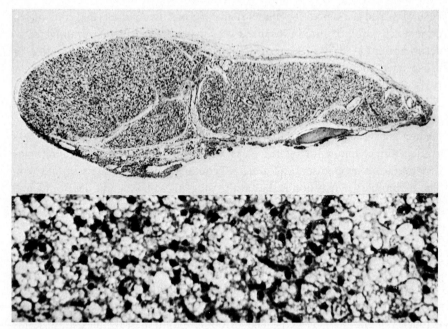

FIG. 5. Brown adipose tissue developed in the renal homograft of the mesoderm isolated from the head-fold stage rat embryonic shield. Above: general appearance of the tumour ($\times 35$). Below: histological structure ($\times 400$).

is an interesting one, but more scrupulous analysis is needed before any reasonable interpretation can be made.

DISCUSSION AND CONCLUDING REMARKS

The above experimental results on rats can usefully be compared with those obtained in relevant experiments on amphibian and avian embryos. Thanks to a recent review of the amphibian organization centre (Nieuwkoop 1973), forgotten data have been recalled and many errors in memory revealed. If we compare our findings with those obtained by Holtfreter in amphibians many years ago (1938a, b) we realize that the approaches are different. Holtfreter worked with early amphibian gastrula cut into pieces corresponding to the presumptive areas of Vogt. The development of these isolated parts was followed *in vitro* in a simple sterile medium. In our experiments germ layers, defined by their position, were isolated from rat embryonic shields at different developmental stages and their developmental potentialities were tested in renal homografts.

The rat embryonic endoderm and mesoderm can develop into typical endodermal and mesodermal tissues only if they are grafted together. If grafted separately, the mesoderm gives rise only to brown adipose tissue, whereas the endoderm fails to develop at all. Holtfreter, on the other hand, obtained various tissues in cultures of separated pieces of the presumptive endodermal and mesodermal regions. Nevertheless, the results differ only slightly if we take into consideration many details found in Holtfreter's papers. Thus he pointed out that isolated pieces of the marginal zone (presumptive mesoderm) of the early amphibian gastrula were almost never completely devoid of underlying cells rich in yolk (probably endodermal cells). Consequently, these isolated parts apparently contained both endodermal and mesodermal cells. It is evident from the tables in Holtfreter's papers (1938a, b) that there were many gut derivatives in cultures of the isolated marginal zone. A detailed analysis of his results with the isolated presumptive amphibian endoderm seems to support our view. The ventral part of the presumptive amphibian endoderm soon underwent cytolysis in Holtfreter's cultures. He states explicitly: 'Differenzierung erhalten wir erst dann wenn wir uns der Randzone nähern' (We obtain differentiation only when we approach the marginal zone). On the other hand, in explants of the parts of the presumptive endoderm which are very close to the marginal zone, the mesodermal derivatives are present too. Again it seems that the explanted endoderm was 'contaminated' with some cells of the adjacent presumptive mesoderm.

As far as the origin of the definitive endoderm is concerned, our results indirectly support the idea of a general analogy between the mammalian and the avian embryo. The definitive avian and mammalian endoderm seems to arise by morphogenetic movements during gastrulation rather than by delamination before gastrulation. Therefore, contrary to the classical view, the endoderm does not differ essentially in its origin from the endoderm of the amphibian embryo.

Finally, a marked difference seems to exist between the developmental potentialities of the amphibian and the mammalian ectoderm. The amphibian presumptive ectoderm has only a weak tendency to differentiate into epidermis, while the early rat ectoderm, depending on the developmental stage, gives rise to derivatives of all three, or at least of two, germ layers. These manifold developmental potentialities are gradually restricted during gastrulation. Apparently, these two different sets of results could also be reconciled. It has recently been shown that the isolated amphibian ectoderm can give rise to mesodermal as well as to endodermal structure if a highly purified factor is present in the culture medium (Kocher-Becker & Tiedemann 1971). Barth & Barth (1972, 1974) have shown that the isolated early amphibian ectoderm can give rise to neural and pigment cell differentiation without induction only when the concentration of certain inorganic ions is changed. It seems that different extrinsic permissive factors are necessary for the phenotypic expression of the bulk of information contained in the amphibian ectodermal cells. If this is true, there seem to be few differences, if any, between the amphibian and the rat embryonic ectoderm. In the rat, the environment under the kidney capsule probably provides many extrinsic factors indispensable for the expression of developmental potentialities.

In order to create a controlled environment in which to analyse the influence of extrinsic factors on differentiation of rat germ layers, we worked out a technique for cultivating early postimplantation rodent embryos *in vitro* (Škreb & Švajger 1973). The first experiments with explanted isolated rat ectoderm failed, in spite of the fact that entire rat embryonic shields, or endoderm–mesoderm combinations, can be cultivated for more than two weeks and various recognizable tissues obtained.

McMahon's recent hypothesis (1974) that the differentiation of embryonic cells may be determined by their content of inorganic ions and cyclic nucleotides is an additional incentive to us to study the differentiation of isolated rat germ layers in the controlled conditions of an *in vitro* system.

ACKNOWLEDGEMENTS

The work reviewed in this paper was supported by grant IV/3 from the Research Foundation of S.R. Croatia, and in part by NIH PL 480 Agreement No. 02-038-1.

References

ANCEL, P. & REYSS-BRION, M. (1956) Sur les relations entre le grand axe de l'utérus et le plan de symétrie bilatérale chez l'embryon de souris. *C. R. Hebd. Séances Acad. Sci. Sér. D. Sci. Nat. 243*, 932–935

AUSTIN, C.R. (1973) Embryo transfer and sensitivity to teratogens. *Nature (Lond.) 244*, 333–334

BARTH, L.G. & BARTH, L.J. (1972) ^{22}Na and ^{45}Ca uptake during embryonic induction in Rana pipiens. *Dev. Biol. 28*, 18–34

BARTH, L.G. & BARTH, L.J. (1974) Ionic regulation of embryonic induction and cell differentiation in Rana pipiens. *Dev. Biol. 39*, 1–27

BENFORD, H.H. & NAMENWIRTH, M. (1974) Precocious appearance of the gray crescent in heat-shocked axolotl eggs. *Dev. Biol. 39*, 172–176

DALCQ, A.M. (1954) Nouvelles données structurales et cytochimiques sur l'œuf des mammifères. *Rev. Gén. Sci. Pures Appl. 61*, 19–41

GARDNER, R.L. & JOHNSON, M.H. (1975) Investigation of cellular interaction and deployment in the early mammalian embryo using interspecific chimaeras between the rat and mouse, in *Cell Patterning (Ciba Found. Symp. 29)*, pp. 183–196, Associated Scientific Publishers, Amsterdam

HOLTFRETER, J. (1938a) Differenzierungspotenzen isolierter Teile der Urodelengastrula. *Wilhelm Roux' Arch. Entwicklungsmech. Org. 138*, 522–656

HOLTFRETER, J. (1938b) Differenzierungspotenzen isolierter Teile der Anurengastrula. *Wilhelm Roux' Arch. Entwicklungsmech. Org. 138*, 657–738

KOCHER-BECKER, U. & TIEDEMANN, H. (1971) Induction of mesodermal and endodermal structures and primordial germ cells in Triturus ectoderm by a vegetalizing factor from chick embryos. *Nature (Lond.) 233*, 65–66

LEVAK-ŠVAJGER, B. & ŠKREB, N. (1965) Intraocular differentiation of rat egg cylinders. *J. Embryol. Exp. Morphol. 13*, 243–253

LEVAK-ŠVAJGER, B. & ŠVAJGER, A. (1971) Differentiation of endodermal tissue in homografts of primitive ectoderm from two-layered rat embryonic shields. *Experientia (Basel) 27*, 683–684

LEVAK-ŠVAJGER, B. & ŠVAJGER, A. (1974) Investigation on the origin of the definitive endoderm in the rat embryo. *J. Embryol. Exp. Morphol. 32*, 445–459

LEVAK-ŠVAJGER, B., ŠVAJGER, A. & ŠKREB, N. (1969) Separation of germ layers in presomite rat embryos. *Experientia (Basel) 25*, 1311–1312

MCMAHON, D. (1974) Chemical messengers in development: a hypothesis. *Science (Wash.) D.C.) 185*, 1012–1021

MULNARD, J. (1955) Contribution à la connaissance des enzymes dans l'ontogénèse. *Arch. Biol. (Liège) 66*, 525–685

NICHOLAS, J.S. (1962) Experimental methods and rat embryos, in *The Rat in Laboratory Investigation* (Parris, E.J. & Griffith, J.A., eds.), pp. 51–67, Hafner, New York

NICOLET, G. (1971) Avian gastrulation. *Adv. Morphog. 9*, 231–262

NIEUWKOOP, P.D. (1973) The 'Organization Center' of the amphibian embryo: its origin, spatial organization, and morphogenetic action. *Adv. Morphog. 10*, 1–39

SEIDEL, F. (1952) Regulationsbefähigung der embryonalen Säugetierkeimscheibe nach Ausschaltung von Blastemteilen mit einem U.V.-Strahlenstichapparat. *Naturwissenschaften 39*, 553–554

SOLTER, D., DAMJANOV, I. & ŠKREB, N. (1973) Distribution of hydrolytic enzymes in early rat and mouse embryos—a reappraisal. *Z. Anat. Entwicklungsgesch. 139*, 119–126

ŠKREB, N. (1961) Experimental analysis of maturation of the organization pattern in rat egg, in *Symposium on the Germ Cells and Earliest Stages of Development* (Ranzi, S., ed.) pp. 691–703, Inst. Int. Embryol. & Fondazione A. Baselli, Milan

ŠKREB, N. & BIJELIĆ, N. (1962) Effects of X-rays on the rat embryos during mesoderm formation. *Nature (Lond.) 193*, 292–293

ŠKREB, N. & FRANK, Z. (1963) Developmental abnormalities in the rat induced by heat shock. *J. Embryol. Exp. Morphol. 11*, 445–457

ŠKREB, N. & ŠVAJGER, A. (1973) Histogenetic capacity of rat and mouse embryonic shields cultivated in vitro. *Wilhelm Roux' Arch. Entwicklungsmech. Org. 173*, 228–234

ŠKREB, N., MÜLLER, M. & HOFMAN, LJ. (1964) Effect of UV rays on rat blastocyst. *Rad. Jugosl. Akad. Znan. Umjet. 335*, 89–100

ŠKREB, N., ŠVAJGER, A. & LEVAK-ŠVAJGER, B. (1971) Growth and differentiation of rat egg-cylinders under the kidney capsule. *J. Embryol. Exp. Morphol. 25*, 47–56

ŠKREB, N., DAMJANOV, I. & SOLTER, D. (1972) Teratomas and teratocarcinomas derived from rodent egg-shields, in *Cell Differentiation* (Harris, R., Allin, P. & Viza, D., eds.), pp. 151–155, Munksgaard, Copenhagen

ŠVAJGER, A. & LEVAK-ŠVAJGER, B. (1974) Regional developmental capacities of the rat embryonic endoderm at the head-fold stage. *J. Embryol. Exp. Morphol. 32*, 461–467

Discussion

McLaren: The results of Dr Škreb and those of Dr Gardner seem entirely consistent in suggesting that the so-called primary or primitive endoderm does not give rise to embryonic endoderm. Is there now general agreement on this?

Škreb: Recently I discussed this problem with Dr L.C. Stevens at the Jackson Laboratory, Bar Harbor. His collaborator, Mrs Diwan (S. Diwan, personal communication, 1975), using almost the same technique in separating the germ layers in mice as we did in rats, has found cells very similar to endodermal cells 30 days after endoderm alone was grafted to the mouse testis. We obtained negative results, that is resorption only, after grafting endoderm under the rat kidney capsule, from which no clear-cut conclusion can be drawn. But from all these results together I think we can say that the primitive endoderm at the two-layer stage does not give rise to embryonic endodermal derivatives.

Wolpert: I think the current story with the chick is exactly the same.

Saxén: When you transplant the ectoderm under the kidney capsule does its differentiation represent the normal developmental potentialities of the ectoderm or could its development be affected by the new surroundings? In other words, you may be doing classical induction experiments.

Škreb: This could possibly be inferred from the results with ectoderm. At the same time the kidney capsule does not seem to induce the isolated mesoderm.

Saxén: The ectoderm might be much more flexible.

Škreb: To avoid the possible inductive action of the microenvironment under the kidney capsule, we worked out an *in vitro* technique for the whole rat embryonic shield. We have been trying to cultivate *in vitro* the separated rat germ layers, but so far we have failed with explanted isolated rat ectoderm. The endoderm and mesoderm together, separated from the ectoderm, can be cultivated easily for more than two weeks. We obtained the same results as in the whole rat embryonic explants, except that no ectodermal derivatives were present. With regard to the ectoderm alone, there were probably not enough cells, because our explants did not survive the period of two weeks necessary for the differentiation.

Saxén: When you transplanted mesoderm and endoderm together, you got good differentiation of endodermal structures. Wouldn't that mean that endoderm does differentiate, but requires an induction from the mesoderm?

Škreb: I cannot say which structures are really from the endoderm and which are from the mesoderm. A new technique may be needed for marking mesoderm and endoderm when they are put together. Then we could be sure which tissues are really derived from the endoderm.

Tarkowski: I find it very odd that when the middle layer is transferred alone, the graft is composed only of adipose tissue and does not contain any other mesodermal derivatives. Dr Saxén's remark is very important: when the two layers are transplanted together and the grafts inspected for mesodermal and endodermal derivatives, one cannot be sure which layer they originate from, and one cannot exclude the possibility of there being some kind of inductive interaction between the two layers. The two following experiments might help in clarifying the problem you are concerned with. One would be to combine the mesoderm of the mouse embryo with the endoderm of the rat, for example, and examine the resulting tissues with the help of the fluorescent antibody technique. The other experiment would be to separate the two layers with a thin Millipore filter, culture them for a short time *in vitro* so that they attach to the filter, and then transfer the whole 'packet' under the kidney capsule. Under these conditions the tissues resulting from these two layers would remain separated, at least in the original part of the graft, but the inductive interactions, if there are any between these two layers at this early stage, should not be prevented.

Škreb: That is a very good idea. It has not been done.

Edidin: We should remember that the host is not passive in these experiments. The adult rat may well develop immunity to a graft under the kidney capsule. I would be particularly worried about a mouse–rat chimera grafted to the mature rat. Even the Millipore filter I fear would attract inflammatory cells to the graft.

Škreb: As I said, we have worked out an *in vitro* technique for cultivating rat embryonic shields. In other words the combination experiment suggested by Dr Tarkowski can be done *in vitro* without any immunological obstacle.

Kelley: Can you use any other substrate—one that is not so potentially active?

Škreb: S. Diwan (personal communication, 1975) did grafting into the mouse testis. She got results in mice very similar to those we obtained in rats for ectoderm and endoderm. To my knowledge she has not obtained any positive results with isolated mouse mesoderm.

Snow: Can one grow these tissues in a developing chick embryo?

Škreb: Many years ago we tried to cultivate the rat embryonic shield on the chick chorioallantoic membrane. The whole shield or parts of it can grow there for only six days. During this time, very few if any terminally differentiated tissues were observed. That was why we abandoned the chorioallantoic membrane.

Cooke: If I have understood correctly, then by the last stage you were considering, the head-fold stage, cells that are going to form skeletal structures, muscle systems *and* the nervous system are still all situated in one layer, the ectoderm. If so, the morphogenetic movements after that must be very different from those in other vertebrate groups.

Škreb: I am referring only to these particular results of ours. For the time being I would not like to interpret them. We obtained mesodermal derivatives such as cartilage, bone, etc., from endoderm and mesoderm together, and from ectoderm alone. In other words, when these parts are separated from the same rat embryonic shield and grafted separately one can obtain mesodermal structures from them (see Levak-Švajger & Švajger 1974).

Cooke: Has anyone looked at the way the cells move?

Škreb: As far as I know the answer is no.

Gardner: When exactly can the ectoderm form skin? You said that at some stage it couldn't and then later it could, in your system.

Škreb: At the two-layer stage just neural tissue is obtained from isolated ectoderm, but at the head-fold stage skin can be formed. In preliminary experiments in Dr Stevens' laboratory the results seem to be slightly different in mice (S. Diwan, personal communication, 1975).

Gardner: Is any haemopoietic tissue formed in the host by the teratoma—that is, is there blood cell chimerism?

Škreb: I have no information on that.

Morriss: Fig. 5 (p. 36) shows a blood vessel with blood cells in the brown adipose tissue.

McLaren: But is that host blood or donor blood?

Škreb: We need markers of some kind before we can say exactly where a tissue comes from.

Gardner: Looking for nucleated red cells might be informative.

Škreb: Most capillaries are necessarily from the host. Without them the graft could not grow and differentiate. Naturally this does not mean there are no graft-derived blood cells. The red blood cells in fat tissue are without nuclei.

Glucksohn-Waelsch: You could use haemoglobins or enzymes as markers to determine chimerism of red blood cells.

Gardner: Enzymes like glucosephosphate isomerase (EC 5.3.1.9) that exhibit genetically determined polymorphisms could be used.

Rutter: It wouldn't take very much contamination, perhaps even a single cell, to complicate the results. How do you control for contamination?

Škreb: In our laboratory the same expert, Dr Švajger, always does the separation because, in my opinion, for this kind of experiment long experience in avoiding contamination is an important factor. When we isolate the germ layers we examine histological sections often and make sure that no other tissue sticks to the ectoderm or mesoderm. After long experience one can see, even *in vivo*, whether other cells are present. The different cell types are very distinctive, although we cannot be 100% sure about contamination. After enzyme treatment one can easily separate ectoderm from the mesoderm. Sometimes ectoderm even detaches spontaneously without any mechanical intervention.

Bennett: The question of contamination is almost a moot one. The cell layers that are being separated are in the process of giving rise to the primitive streak. So even if the ectoderm is cleanly separated from mesoderm on morphological criteria, there will be cells in the ectoderm which are 99.99% in the state of primitive streak cells and ready to become mesoderm. Thus some occult contamination is probably experimentally unavoidable, but I don't think it reflects unfavourably on these data.

Cooke: You mentioned a discrepancy between results from your own and from another laboratory on the differentiation capacities, in culture, of particular presumptive regions. A parallel from amphibian work may help here. When undetermined cells whose normal fate would be to form either skin or nervous system are explanted from early amphibian gastrulae into saline media, various subsequent types of differentiation are obtained under what seem to be similar conditions. Some laboratories will get nervous system derivatives all the time, while others obtain only epidermis. This has been found to relate to various differences in concentration balance for simple ions in the salt solutions (Barth & Barth 1969). So the environment you chose in your work, hoping that it was 'neutral', for testing the determination of your tissues might nevertheless not accurately replicate certain crucial conditions *in vivo*. In another laboratory where a different strain or a different rodent is being used, chemically trivial differences might give a different picture.

Gropp: To what extent do the results of your transplantation experiments depend on the complete integrity of the ectoderm–mesoderm layers? In other words did you consider completely disintegrating the ectoderm layer by trypsinization procedures?

Škreb: So far we have not done the complete cell disaggregation from an isolated germ layer. We only separate the germ layers from the rat embryonic shield at the two-layer and three-layer stages.

Saxén: Concerning the effect of the trypsin treatment, did you first separate mesoderm and endoderm and then recombine them when you implanted them?

Škreb: We haven't done that.

Gluecksohn-Waelsch: To come back to possible contamination, it must be noted that the mesoderm at the stages used is not present as a distinct layer but in clumps of individual cells which could easily stick to the ectoderm. As to the effect of trypsin, Zwilling (1954) in studies of limb bud differentiation tried to separate ectoderm and mesoderm and found that treatment with trypsin changed not only the condition of the cells but also their potential for further differentiation and development. So if mesoderm formed only brown adipose tissue in the present experiments, could this perhaps be due to extensive damage to the cell membranes as a result of treatment with trypsin? If this were the case, it would be difficult to draw conclusions from these results as to the state of determination of the cells at the time of explantation.

Škreb: I agree and I would like to confirm our results with another technique without any enzyme. If you know another feasible technique please give me the reference.

Gardner: From our experiments in which cells are transplanted between blastocysts it appears that the very first lot of endoderm cells to differentiate are committed to extra-embryonic endoderm formation. On the basis of your results, Dr Škreb, there is a later generation of endoderm from the embryonic ectoderm. The reason why this later endoderm does not give rise to any differentiated tissues when isolated and transplanted could be because it needs to interact with mesoderm in order to realize its developmental potential.

Škreb: That is possible. So that we can compare the endoderm at the two-layer and at the three-layer stage, we would like to isolate the early endoderm, when the mesoderm is not yet formed, and put it together with the mesoderm, but we haven't done that. If endoderm is isolated at any stage, in our case with enzymes, nothing at all is obtained. It is the same even at the later stage when endoderm together with mesoderm can give rise to many endodermal derivatives.

Gardner: We are trying to overcome this problem of contamination by taking individual cells from the various tissues of progressively later stages and injecting them into blastocysts. No evidence of colonization was obtained in initial studies when the cells were injected into the blastocoele. However, we have more recently been injecting the cells directly into the inner cell mass and the preliminary results are encouraging (R. L. Gardner & H. Alexandre, unpublished work). Obviously, the problem of contamination does not arise if one is dealing with just one cell.

Škreb: If you put one cell under the kidney capsule, in my opinion no tissue will be differentiated, because the cell will be resorbed.

Morriss: Some questions arise from the difference between these two situations. It seems that the term 'ectoderm' is being used in two different ways. In the very early stages that Richard Gardner described, his results suggest that the ectoderm constitutes the whole of the future embryo; in this case the earliest differentiated 'endoderm' represents only potential extra-embryonic endodermal structures. In your experiments, Dr Škreb, ectoderm at the primitive streak stage was also able to differentiate into tissues characteristic of all three layers. But in embryos of that age the embryonic endoderm is a very distinctive cell layer: ultrastructurally the cells are different from both mesoderm and ectoderm (Morriss 1973). So where is the endoderm in your ectoderm grafts actually coming from? I have the impression, looking at the ultrastructure of the embryo at that age, that neither the mesoderm nor the ectoderm contribute to the intra-embryonic endoderm, although the potential to do so may exist.

Škreb: For the time being I cannot answer that. It is possible that the definitive endoderm is formed after invagination through the primitive streak.

Kelley: Organogenesis requires interaction between adjacent epithelia and mesenchyme. In human embryos there is a cell population, the extra-embryonal mesenchyme or mesoderm, the origin of which is partially trophoblastic. In the rat is there an extra-embryonic mesenchyme at the stage when the transplantation is done?

Škreb: We do not call it mesenchyme but it is extra-embryonic mesoderm from embryonic sources formed by invagination through the primitive streak.

Kelley: So there are no cells of any other origin attached to the germ layers?

Škreb: There is extra-embryonic mesoderm from the primitive streak, but not of trophoblastic origin.

Hogan: In electron microscope sections of embryoid bodies of 6050 mouse teratoma cells that had been growing *in vivo* in ascites fluid, we found one case where the outer endoderm layer had invaginated (R. Tilley & B. Hogan, unpublished observations). The invaginated endoderm cells looked very different from the external ones although they formed part of a continuous sheet; the microvilli were of uniform size and were densely and uniformly packed, each with a central core of microfilaments and projections from the tips, exactly as found in sections of the small intestine of adult animals.

References

BARTH, L.G. & BARTH, L.J. (1969) The sodium dependence of embryonic induction. *Dev. Biol. 20*, 236–262

LEVAK-ŠVAJGER, B. & ŠVAJGER, A. (1974) Investigation on the origin of the definitive endoderm in the rat embryo. *J. Embryol. Exp. Morphol. 32*, 445–459

MORRISS, G.M. (1973) The ultrastructural effects of excess maternal vitamin A on the primitive streak stage rat embryo. *J. Embryol. Exp. Morphol. 30*, 219–242

ZWILLING, E. (1954) Dissociation of chick embryo cells by means of a chelating compound, *Science (Wash. D.C.) 120*, 219

Growth from fertilization to birth in the mouse

ANNE McLAREN

MRC Mammalian Development Unit, University College London

Sufficient information has now been accumulated to provide an overall picture of prenatal growth in the mouse. For the first week of gestation, cell counts are also available. Most of the findings to be presented here relate to a single strain, the randomly bred Q strain.

From cleavage onwards, the conceptus becomes progressively compartmentalized. For example, the trophectoderm separates off from the inner cell mass and gives rise to primary trophoblast that invades the uterine stroma and secondary trophoblast that forms part of the placenta. Therefore, no single growth curve can be drawn for the whole of gestation. Fig. 1 gives in diagrammatic form the relevant compartments during the first week of gestation. The evidence that extra-embryonic ectoderm is derived from trophectoderm and not from the inner cell mass is given by Gardner & Papaioannou (1975). Because Fig. 1 is drawn on a supposedly linear scale, the compartments are additive.

Real growth curves, unless relating to a very restricted period of time, need to be drawn on a logarithmic scale, so additivity no longer holds. Fig. 2 shows the changes in dry mass between conception and birth. Estimates of tissue volume, determined from serial sections, are included. The two scales are aligned on the assumptions that the density of embryonic tissue is 1 (hence volume in cm^3 is equal to wet weight in g), and that dry weight is 11% of wet weight for embryos in the age range used (H.C. Hensleigh, personal communication).

For the preimplantation period, we have used dry weights of the entire conceptus as measured by Hensleigh & Weitlauf (1974) on a quartz-fibre balance. These measurements relate to randomly bred Swiss mice. During cleavage, weight decreases slightly but significantly, so that at $3\frac{1}{2}$ days *post coitum* (p.c.) the embryos are lighter than at earlier stages, but thereafter weight increases markedly. For the egg cylinder between 5.7 and 7.7 days p.c., tissue volume estimations are available (Buehr & McLaren 1974); these agree well with weights of individual egg cylinders measured at 6½ and 7½ days p.c. by Hensleigh and McLaren (unpublished). The volume of the embryonic part of the egg cylinder (Snow 1976) increases much more rapidly between 6½ and 7½ days p.c. than during the preceding day. Since the fetus develops from the embryonic part of the egg cylinder, these values have been connected on Fig. 2 to the fetal weights, taken from 9½ to 18½ days p.c. by Hensleigh and McLaren (unpublished).

Cell numbers (Fig. 3) during the preimplantation period have been determined by Bowman & McLaren (1970) and Allen & McLaren (1971). The 12 blastocysts serially sectioned by Horner & McLaren (1974) averaged 55.3± 4.4 cells in total, of which 16.3 ± 1.1 were in the inner cell mass. A day later, M. Buehr (personal communication) recorded an average of 44.7 ± 5.4 cells in

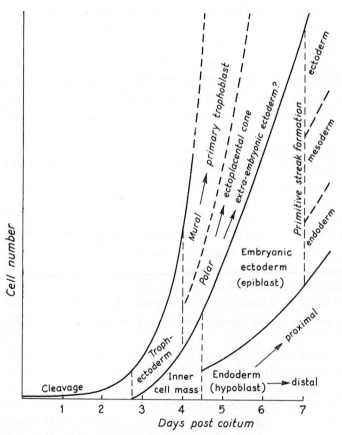

FIG. 1. Compartmentalization in the early mouse embryo.

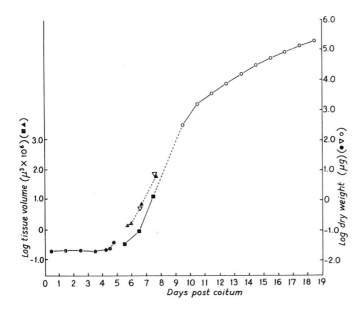

Fig. 2. Dry weight and tissue volume of mouse embryos from fertilization to birth.
●   Entire preimplantation embryos (Hensleigh & Weitlauf 1974)
▲▽ Entire egg cylinder (tissue volumes from Buehr & McLaren 1974; dry weights from Hensleigh and McLaren, unpublished)
■   Embryonic part of egg cylinder (Snow 1976)
○   Fetus (Hensleigh and McLaren, unpublished)

the inner cell mass, of which just over half (22.7 ± 3.5) had differentiated into primitive endoderm. Additional information on the proportion of cells in the inner cell mass of preimplantation embryos of various ages is taken from Barlow *et al.* (1972) and refers to Swiss-strain animals.

No findings are available on numbers of trophoblast cells at subsequent stages of development. Probably the mural trophectoderm undergoes little further cell division after $4\frac{1}{2}$ days p.c., as it then undergoes transformation to giant cells and differentiates into primary trophoblast.

The inner cell mass gives rise to the embryonic part of the egg cylinder, comprising the primary endoderm or hypoblast and the embryonic ectoderm. The number of cells in the embryonic part of the egg cylinder, and their division into endoderm and ectoderm (at $7\frac{1}{2}$ days p.c., mesoderm also), has been determined at $5\frac{1}{2}$–$7\frac{1}{2}$ days p.c. by Snow (1976). The entire egg cylinder has been examined at 4.7 days p.c. by Buehr & McLaren (1974); for subsequent days, the number of cells in the entire egg cylinder was derived from the number present in the embryonic part, since the embryonic and extra-embryonic cells are approximately equal in number.

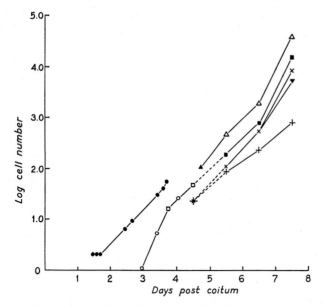

FIG. 3. Cell counts from 1½ to 7½ days *post coitum.*
● Entire preimplantation embryos (Bowman & McLaren 1970; Allen & McLaren 1971)
□ Inner cell mass, direct counts (Horner & McLaren 1974; Buehr, personal communication)
○ Inner cell mass, as a proportion of total cell counts at different stages (Barlow *et al.* 1972)
■ Embryonic part of egg cylinder (total) (Snow 1976)
× Embryonic part of egg cylinder (ectoderm) (Snow 1976)
▼ Embryonic part of egg cylinder (mesoderm) (Snow 1976)
+ Embryonic part of egg cylinder (endoderm) (Snow 1976)
▲ Total egg cylinder (Buehr & McLaren 1974)
△ Total egg cylinder (derived from ■)

In terms of both mass and cell number, the embryo proper enters its most rapid growth period at 6½ days p.c. This period is considered in more detail in the next paper (Snow 1976).

References

ALLEN, J. & McLAREN, A. (1971) Cleavage rate of mouse eggs from induced and spontaneous ovulation. *J. Reprod. Fertil. 27,* 137–140

BARLOW, P., OWEN, D.A.J. & GRAHAM, C. (1972) DNA synthesis in the preimplantation mouse embryo. *J. Embryol. Exp. Morphol. 2,* 431–445

BOWMAN, P. & McLAREN, A. (1970) Cleavage rate of mouse embryos *in vivo* and *in vitro. J. Embryol. Exp. Morphol. 24,* 203–207

BUEHR, M. & McLAREN, A. (1974) Size regulation in chimaeric mouse embryos. *J. Embryol. Exp. Morphol. 31,* 229–234

GARDNER, R.L. & PAPAIOANNOU, V.E. (1975) Differentiation in the trophectoderm and inner cell mass, in *The Early Development of Mammals (2nd Symp. Br. Soc. Dev. Biol.)* (Balls, M. & Wild, A.E., eds.), pp. 107–132, Cambridge University Press, London

HENSLEIGH, H.C. & WEITLAUF, H.M. (1974) Effect of delayed implantation on dry weight and lipid content of mouse blastocysts. *Biol. Reprod. 10*, 315–320

HORNER, D. & McLAREN, A. (1974) The effect of low concentrations of [^{3}H]thymidine on pre- and postimplantation mouse embryos. *Biol. Reprod. 11*, 553–557

SNOW, M.H.L. (1976) Embryo growth during the immediate post-implantation period, in this volume, pp. 53–66

*This paper and the next one, by M.H.L. Snow,
are discussed jointly on pp. 66–70.*

Embryo growth during the immediate postimplantation period

M. H. L. SNOW

MRC Mammalian Development Unit, University College London

Abstract   In the three days after the onset of implantation, development in the mouse is extensive and rapid. The formation of the $7\frac{1}{2}$-day egg cylinder requires an increase in tissue volume from the $4\frac{1}{2}$-day blastocyst of about 500-fold. It was not clear how much of this increase was due to increases in cell volume and how much due to a high rate of cell proliferation. Very short cell doubling times, of 5 h or less, were suggested by several indirect investigations but one direct evaluation of 7-day embryos showed a cell cycle time of 6.5 h in the embryonic ectoderm. Interest in egg–cylinder growth, in particular in the different germ layers, was renewed after the demonstration that before implantation cleavage rate in mammals is slow. Furthermore, experiments in which isolated germ layers were grafted into ectopic sites had suggested that embryonic ectoderm was developmentally labile and capable of producing both mesodermal and endodermal derivatives. An alternative hypothesis, namely that a population of undifferentiated cells is present in the embryo before gastrulation, was indicated by recent observations on teratocarcinomas.

Growth rate and cell proliferation rate have been studied by determining changes in cell and tissue volumes, and in cell numbers, during this period of development.

The results show that growth is achieved by a high rate of cell proliferation and that cell volume actually decreases. Estimates of cell numbers suggest that cell cycle times in the region of 5 h are necessary if the growth rate found between $6\frac{1}{2}$ and $7\frac{1}{2}$-days of age is to be achieved. Furthermore the production of mesoderm in this time requires a contribution of cells from some other tissue and cannot be explained on the basis of proliferation from a small number of stem cells. The simplest model is that of cell migration from the ectoderm through the primitive streak with subsequent development as mesoderm.

FOCUS

In the three days after implantation in the mouse, embryo development is considerable. The morphological changes at this time were first correctly de-

53

scribed nearly 100 years ago (Fraser 1882), and there followed in the early
1900s a series of detailed microscopical analyses of the anatomy of the developing egg cylinder in the rat and mouse (Jenkinson 1900; Sobotta 1903,
1911; Huber 1915).

Although it must have been apparent, no comment was made about the
extreme rapidity with which the embryo grows during this 3-day period. Fig. 1
illustrates the change in size between $4\frac{1}{2}$ and $7\frac{1}{2}$ days *post coitum* (p.c.) in the
Q strain of mouse. The formation of the $7\frac{1}{2}$-day egg cylinder from the blastocyst
inner cell mass apparently requires more than a 500-fold increase in tissue
volume. Possibly the presence of the amniotic cavity, the exocoelom and the
ectoplacental cavity served to obscure the extent of cellular development, or
perhaps, by comparison with early stages in other species, especially amphibians, such rapid growth was not a noteworthy event. Whatever the reason,
this interesting aspect of this period in mouse development has largely been
ignored. Only two direct investigations into duration of the cell cycle have been
made. Solter & Škreb (1968) and Solter *et al.* (1971) studied the differences in

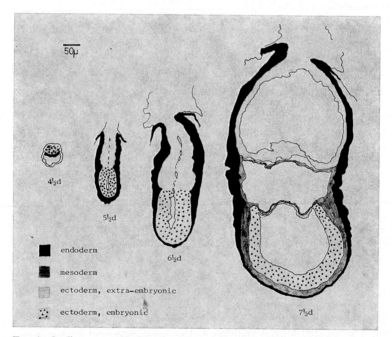

FIG. 1. Outline camera lucida drawings of Q strain mouse embryos. Note the progressive
regional variation in endoderm thickness, and the variation in mesoderm distribution at
$7\frac{1}{2}$ days. See also Figs. 3–5.

cycle time between mesoderm and ectoderm in 7-day-old C3H mouse embryos, finding that ectoderm with a cycle time of 6.5 h proliferated faster than mesoderm. Two further reports provide indirect evidence of growth rates at this time. Kohler et al. (1972), using a combination of histological analysis and biochemical estimates of DNA content, postulated a period of rapid cell proliferation involving cell cycle times of 5 h or less. Unfortunately it is unclear whether their DNA determinations were applied solely to the derivatives of the tissues measured histologically at the earlier stage. If additional tissue was included then the actual proliferation rate could be much slower. In the other study, Goedbloed (1972) estimated tissue volumes and weights from reconstructions of serially sectioned embryos. The results were subjected to the most rigorous statistical tests and the volume changes recorded are undoubtedly accurate, but in the absence of knowledge about changes in cell volumes during the same period nothing can be concluded about proliferation rates. Nevertheless between $5\frac{1}{2}$ and $7\frac{1}{2}$ days of gestation a 70-fold increase in volume of the embryonic portion of the egg cylinder is recorded.

PERSPECTIVE

Recent publications in several fields of research have revived interest in growth and gastrulation in the rodent egg cylinder. First, it has been established that unlike other embryonic systems the cell cycle during cleavage in the mouse is initially long (about 20 h) but progressively shortens to about 10 h by the blastocyst stage. In the 7-day embryo a cycle time of 6.5 h has been demonstrated in the embryonic ectoderm (review by Graham 1973). Thereafter cell cycle times progressively lengthen to reach essentially adult values shortly before parturition. Information about the period between the onset of implantation (4 days p.c.) and 7 days is not available. It has been shown that in mouse aggregation chimeras a downward regulation in size takes place during this period (Buehr & McLaren 1974), but how this is achieved is not known.

Secondly, the outcome of experiments with teratocarcinomas and with transplants to ectopic sites of the separated germ layers of the rat egg cylinder raises a number of questions about ectoderm and mesoderm formation and the process of gastrulation in the rodent. The elegant work of Škreb, Švajger and Levak-Švajger (see Škreb et al., this volume, pp. 27–39), following an initial observation by Grobstein (1952), has shown that in isolation, when transplanted to an ectopic site such as the kidney, the embryonic ectoderm before mesoderm formation is capable of giving rise to derivatives of all three germ layers. One possible explanation for these observations is that pre-primitive streak ectoderm is multipotential and essentially undifferentiated. In view of the distinctive morphology and increased basophilia of the ectoderm by this stage such a hypothesis seems unlikely. However, the observation that ectodermal regions other than the primitive streak region also differentiate into mesoderm and endoderm in ectopic sites does not allow us to disregard such a theory entirely, although it is possible that the developmental capabilities of the tissues in these experiments are modified by surgical trauma.

Recent work with teratocarcinomas permits another interpretation of the findings on ectopic transfer. It is now well established that teratomas can be produced by transplanting pieces of early embryos to ectopic sites (reviewed Damjanov & Solter 1974). Some of the teratomas are transplantable from mouse to mouse within the strain and can be maintained in this way. These are teratocarcinomas and they owe their transplantability to the presence of groups of undifferentiated cells called pluripotent or embryonal stem cells. In some mouse strains the stem cells, which are unlike the cells in the embryonic germ layers, can be cloned *in vitro* and shown to give rise to all the differentiated tissues characteristic of the teratoma, including derivatives of ectoderm, mesoderm and endoderm (Martin 1975). It must be concluded either that some cells of the original embryonic graft give rise to these stem cells by a process of dedifferentiation, or that some pluripotent cells were included in the original graft and are present in the normal embryo. This latter possibility allows the surmise that such stem cells are located in the ectoderm and offers a ready explanation for the results of the germ layer graft experiment without bringing into question the differentiated state of most of the ectoderm. It also would permit the formation of mesoderm without the involvement of morphogenetic cell movement such as is seen in other vertebrates during gastrulation.

EVIDENCE

Attempts have been made to detect morphogenetic movements in mammalian embryos. Daniel & Olson (1966) followed the movement of neutral red-stained cells across the embryonic shield of the rabbit and concluded that movement over short distances did occur but rather slowly. Movements were in the right direction for gastrulation but analysis of the mitotic index over the same areas revealed no regions of high proliferation rate such as have been associated with gastrulation in other vertebrates (Chen 1932; Spratt 1966). Corliss (1953), in a very extensive study of rat gastrulation, also failed to find consistent regional or indeed tissue differences in mitotic activity in the germ layers and concluded that morphogenetic cell movement was unimportant in rat gastrulation. Bellairs (1971) in discussing these two reports states '... it would perhaps be advisable to accept the findings of Corliss, since they are based on a more extensive study'. But unknown to Bellairs the experiments of Corliss were based on a fundamental misconception. To facilitate the study of mitotic activity he administered colchicine to the pregnant rats so that divisions in the embryos would accumulate. He assumed that colchicine was not toxic, and cited Van Dyke & Ritchey (1947) as showing that similar doses of colchicine did not disturb development of rat embryos at the stage under study (8 to $8\frac{3}{4}$ days). In fact what Van Dyke & Ritchey had found was that injections of colchicine into 6- or 8-day pregnant rats resulted in 100% embryonic death three days later; they did not look at embryos earlier than three days after injection of colchicine but they commented that the dead embryos were only partially re-sorbed, implying recent death. Further doubt has been thrown on the influence of colchicine and other antimitotic agents on embryos by recent work with rats showing that as well as inhibiting spindle formation and accumulating mitoses agents can also inhibit cells in the DNA synthesis phase (Williams & Carpentieri 1967; Williams 1968, 1970). The assumption made by Corliss there-fore seems unjustified and an accurate interpretation of his results impossible.

Earlier work had shown a significant difference in mitotic index between ectoderm and mesoderm in the rat (Preto 1938) and mouse embryo (Pasteels 1943), a difference sufficient for Pasteels (1943) to form the opinion that gastrulation in the rat and mouse (with implied cell movement) could be as-sociated with differences in mitotic index and the presence of centres of high proliferation rate; in these instances the embryonic ectoderm showed the highest mitotic index. The findings of Solter et al. (1971) add more direct evidence for this view. Nevertheless, for such differences in rate of cell proliferation to be positively associated with morphogenetic movements other information, such as demonstrable cell movement, or knowledge of changes in cell number in the various tissues, is essential.

INVESTIGATION

I have been concerned with estimating changes in cell number during egg cylinder development. Until the work of Gardner & Johnson (1973, 1975) and Gardner & Papaioannou (1975) the derivation of the various regions in the rodent egg cylinder was a matter of some speculation. Their experiments with chimeras, however, indicate that the blastocyst inner cell mass contributes only the endoderm and the embryonic ectodermal portion of the egg cylinder. The extra-embryonic ectoderm apparently is derived from the trophectoderm. It has thus become possible to measure the rate of proliferation of the inner cell mass as it grows and differentiates into the ectoderm and mesodermal com-ponents of the post-primitive-streak embryo.

The randomly bred Q strain of mouse was used throughout this study. Gestation is usually 19 days, occasionally 18. The mice were housed under natural diurnal lighting, and ovulation and mating generally occurred between midnight and 0300 h. Autopsies were performed between 1200 and 1500 h on the appropriate day to yield embryos $4\frac{1}{2}$, $5\frac{1}{2}$, $6\frac{1}{2}$ or $7\frac{1}{2}$ days p.c. The small variation between females in conception time was compensated for by using several litters for each stage. The entire uterus was dissected out and fixed. Uteruses of $4\frac{1}{2}$ days were wax-embedded and sectioned sagittally; $5\frac{1}{2}$-, $6\frac{1}{2}$- and $7\frac{1}{2}$-day decidual swellings were excised and most were wax-embedded and serially sectioned either transversely, frontally or sagittally to the embryo. Some $6\frac{1}{2}$- and $7\frac{1}{2}$-day embryos were dissected out of their decidua, embedded in Epon and sectioned at 1 μm for detailed examination. Initially reconstructions were made from camera lucida drawings of each stage and tissue volumes were computed from measurements of the tissue areas made with a planimeter. Since section thickness is known, volume estimates are simply calculated. It quickly became apparent that $5\frac{1}{2}$-, $6\frac{1}{2}$- and $7\frac{1}{2}$-day Q strain embryos conform closely to regular geometrical shapes and that tissue volume could be accurately calculated from measurements of length and cross-sectional dimensions of the embryo. Embryos of $5\frac{1}{2}$ and $6\frac{1}{2}$ days are circular or slightly elliptical in cross-section and conform well to a model of a cylinder with a cap on the end. The cap is either hemispherical or half a spheroid (oblate or prolate depending upon the length of its various axes, which reflect how elliptical the egg cylinder is in cross-section). The distinction between embryonic and extra-embryonic regions of the egg cylinder is clearly marked and recognizable in both longitudinal and transverse sections. Measurements of tissue volume were always made on transverse sections, while determinations of cell volume (see below) were made on both longitudinal and transverse sections. In $5\frac{1}{2}$-day embryos the pro-amniotic cavity is usually closed but in some, and in $6\frac{1}{2}$-day embryos, it is opened to varying degrees. Appropriate correction is made for this space.

The model best fitting $7\frac{1}{2}$-day embryonic regions is that of a cylinder with a plug in one end. The embryonic region of these egg cylinders is almost invariably circular in cross-section. Since mesoderm migration had completely covered the ectoderm in all embryos studied, it was possible to determine tissue volume from both transverse and longitudinal sections. Because of variation in the thickness of the mesoderm layer at different levels in the embryo, transverse dimensions were measured in three places in $7\frac{1}{2}$-day embryos. Similar precautions were taken in $6\frac{1}{2}$-day egg cylinders where significant variations in endoderm dimensions exist as a result of regional differences in the extent of vacuolation in this tissue. Fig. 2 shows in diagrammatic form the embryonic models used and the dimensions measured, and Figs. 3–5 show median long-

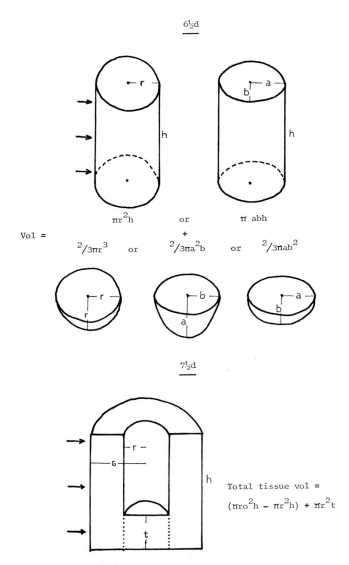

FIG. 2. The geometric models most closely resembling the embryonic regions of mouse egg cylinders. The arrows indicate the places where cylinder dimensions were measured.

itudinal sections of $5\frac{1}{2}$–$7\frac{1}{2}$-day embryos, illustrating the changes in tissue morphology.

Cell volumes were calculated from camera lucida drawings of various regions of the egg cylinder. For each drawing tissue volume was calculated from planimeter measurements, and the number of nuclei apparent in that tissue

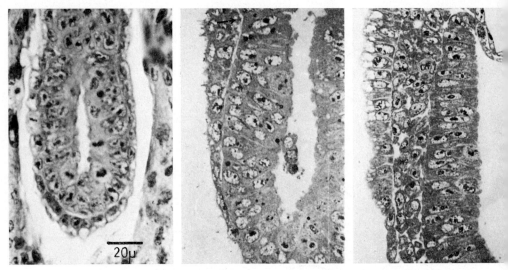

FIG. 3. *(left)* The embryonic region of a 5½-day embryo. All endoderm cells are vacuolated.
FIG. 4. *(centre)* Part of the embryonic region of a 6½-day embryo. Endoderm vacuolation is reduced. The arrow marks the transition from embryonic to extra-embryonic region.
Fig. 5. *(right)* Part of the embryonic region of a 7½-day embryo. Towards the junction with the extra-embryonic region the endoderm is still vacuolated and the mesoderm layer varies in thickness.

was counted. The number of such nuclear points present in any one section depends on section thickness and the size and orientation of the nucleus. Abercrombie (1946) devised a formula for estimating the number of nuclear mid-points in a section from such crude findings. Provided that the axes of nuclei can be measured and their orientation and shape conforms to that of the cell, i.e. that the long axis of a nucleus is parallel to the long axis of the cell, and elongated nuclei are present in elongated cells, then the estimate of nuclear mid-points is a good estimate of the number of cells present in that tissue.

Comparison of longitudinal and transverse sections of the embryo shows that these conditions pertain, at least for ectoderm and mesoderm of all embryos, and for endoderm, at 5½ and 6½ days. In 7½-day embryos the endoderm is stretched over the surface of the embryonic region and as a result the cell shape is no longer similar to that of its nucleus. However, the endoderm at this stage represents a very small proportion of the tissue and is difficult to detect over the end of the egg cylinder in many wax-embedded embryos.

Abercrombie's formula states that $N = AM/(L + M)$ where A = number of nuclei observed, M = section thickness, L = nuclear length and N = number of nuclear mid-points. To avoid overestimating cell numbers, I calculated the mean nuclear 'length' in each tissue section from the 10 largest values measured in each region (a minimum of 10 nuclei per section for $5\frac{1}{2}$- and $6\frac{1}{2}$-day embryos, and 30 nuclei per section for $7\frac{1}{2}$-day embryos). I therefore avoided the possibility of measuring incomplete nuclei, i.e. those cut by the knife, but probably slightly overestimated cell volume and consequently underestimated cell numbers.

One further aspect of $7\frac{1}{2}$-day embryos leads to cell numbers being underestimated. Although allantois formation has not yet begun, the exocoelomic cavity is lined with mesoderm. I made no attempt to measure this tissue but it is a thin layer only one to two cells thick and it would not be expected to represent more than 10% of the total mesoderm in the $7\frac{1}{2}$-day egg cylinder.

Mitotic index (the number of divisions per 100 cells) was calculated from total counts of divisions in each tissue. Care was taken to avoid recording twice those dividing nuclei which were transected during sectioning and which therefore appear in two sections. With anaphases in which the spindle is perpendicular to the section surface it is possible for the two chromosome sets to be separated by one 6-μm section.

DISCOVERY

Table 1 summarizes the results for tissue and cell volume and cell number for $5\frac{1}{2}$- to $7\frac{1}{2}$-day embryos. The mesoderm and endodermal values are pooled for the $7\frac{1}{2}$-day stage because of the difficulty in most embryos of accurately distinguishing these cell layers. In only three embryos was a clear distinction possible and in these the endodermal component represented 10, 11.8 and 9.6%

TABLE 1

Tissue volume, cell volume and cell number in mouse embryos ($\pm$ standard error %)

		$5\frac{1}{2}$ days (9 embryos, 3 litters)	$6\frac{1}{2}$ days (10 embryos, 5 litters)	$7\frac{1}{2}$ days (12 embryos, 4 litters)
Tissue volume (μm^3)	Endoderm	$224\,233 \pm 11.5$	$296\,340 \pm 16.2$	$\}6\,487\,404 \pm 11.0$
	Mesoderm	—	—	
	Ectoderm	$117\,111 \pm 9.5$	$603\,570 \pm 17.5$	$6\,413\,633 \pm 15.8$
Cell volume (μm^3)	Endoderm	$2\,505 \pm 1.7$	$1\,316 \pm 7.7$	$\}\,875 \pm 4.7$
	Mesoderm	—	—	
	Ectoderm	$1\,120 \pm 3.2$	$1\,091 \pm 3.5$	930 ± 2.8
Cell number	Endoderm	89 ± 11.2	238 ± 19.3	$\}\,7\,387 \pm 9.5$
	Mesoderm	—	—	
	Ectoderm	105 ± 9.5	552 ± 15.2	$8\,740 \pm 11.3$

of the cells. If these values are representative then an average of 770 endoderm cells and 6600 mesoderm cells are present at $7\frac{1}{2}$ days.

It proved extremely difficult to obtain measurements of the inner cell mass (ICM) at $4\frac{1}{2}$ days because of variation in orientation within the uterus and confusion between the ICM and its overlying trophectoderm. Only three such embryos yielded ICM cell counts (19, 31 and 41 respectively) but it was not possible to determine tissue volume accurately.

TABLE 2

Mitotic index in mouse embryos

	$5\frac{1}{2}$ days	$6\frac{1}{2}$ days	$7\frac{1}{2}$ days
Endoderm	0.029 ± 0.008	0.038 ± 0.007	$\left.\begin{array}{c}\\\\\end{array}\right\}0.023 \pm 0.002$
Mesoderm	—	—	
Ectoderm	0.079 ± 0.018	0.042 ± 0.006	0.056 ± 0.008

Table 2 shows the mitotic indices in $5\frac{1}{2}$- to $7\frac{1}{2}$-day embryos. These figures confirm the findings of Preto (1938) and Pasteels (1943) that ectoderm shows a higher proliferation rate than other tissues in the rodent egg cylinder.

The calculated increase in embryo total cell number between $5\frac{1}{2}$ and $7\frac{1}{2}$ days requires 6.3 cell divisions, i.e. an average cell cycle duration of 7.7 h. However, the growth rate is not uniform and 4.3 divisions are required in the second 24 h, suggesting a mean cell cycle time in this period of 5.6 h. Clearly the endoderm divides slowly (cycle time about 16 h) and according to the mitotic index ectoderm divides more rapidly than mesoderm. If all ectoderm and mesoderm at $7\frac{1}{2}$ days is derived from the ectoderm at $6\frac{1}{2}$ days the overall time required for the cell cycle is 5.1 h, indicating doubling times of less than 5 h in ectoderm and more than 5 h in mesoderm.

ENLIGHTENMENT

This study was prompted by my cynical disbelief in the published data on rodent embryos and a firm refusal to accept that very short cell doubling times were to be found in mammals. The demonstration that cleavage in mammals is a slow process, coupled with the extensive evidence on mammalian cell cycle times in various tissues of both adults and embryos (see Cleaver 1967, pp. 126–129, for data and references), suggested that cell cycle times of 5 h or so were intrinsically extremely unlikely. I have already outlined the problems of interpreting the reports by Kohler et al. (1972) and Goedbloed (1972). The work of

Solter *et al.* (1971) based on tested and accepted procedures seems much more reliable, but it should nevertheless be considered with some caution. In following the passage of a cohort of cells labelled with [³H]thymidine through the cell cycle Solter *et al.* reported 100% labelled divisions in both the first and second division of the labelled cells. Furthermore they reported achieving a 100% labelling index for all cells, which they concluded indicates the absence of non-proliferating cells. The analysis was carried out on 6-μm sections of wax-embedded material and on theoretical grounds alone a 100% labelling index should be impossible to achieve. The β emission from tritium is a low energy particle and more than 90% of such emissions would be incapable of penetrating 1 μm of tissue (Hill 1962; Thrasher 1966; Cleaver 1967; Modak *et al.* 1973), although β particles with the maximum energy would penetrate some 5 μm of tissue. It was shown subsequently that these limitations in the auto-radiographic technique can be corrected for statistically (Modak *et al.* 1973; England *et al.* 1973) but there is no indication that Solter *et al.* (1971) were aware of this particular technical artifact.

The procedures I have used for estimating cell numbers cannot escape criticism either. One assumption that is made, for instance, is that there is no variation in shrinkage with fixation, either between stages or between tissues. Although differences between tissues cannot be assessed, the effect of fixation on whole embryos has been measured on 10 embryos at $6\frac{1}{2}$ and $7\frac{1}{2}$ days which were dissected from their decidua in physiological saline, measured with a Vernier microscope, then fixed and remeasured. Shrinkage was less than 10% in both groups, which did not differ significantly from one another.

The limitations of Abercrombie's (1946) formula for determining cell number (and hence volume) have been mentioned. Provided the overall trend in cell volume changes is correctly determined then the actual value is somewhat irrelevant to the general assessment of proliferation rate. Only if actual cell volumes diverge significantly from the estimates in different directions in consecutive stages could the measured tissue growth reflect longer (or maybe shorter) cell cycle times than those estimated. My measurements have throughout guarded against overestimates in cell number, so the calculated increases could be regarded as minimum estimates.

If the above cell volume measurements are accurate then estimates for changes in cell number in the embryos studied by Goedbloed (1972) can be made. Accordingly his $5\frac{1}{2}$-day embryos would contain about 130 cells, the $6\frac{1}{2}$-day embryos 1500 and $7\frac{1}{2}$-day about 19 000. The difference between these findings and those in Table 1, small at $7\frac{1}{2}$ days but large at $6\frac{1}{2}$ days, is almost certainly a reflection of the difference in autopsy time in the two studies, as Goedbloed collected his embryos in late afternoon or early evening. Such proliferation rates would require a 7.1 h cycle time between $5\frac{1}{2}$ and $6\frac{1}{2}$ days and 6.7 h in the second 24 h period. Again, differences in proliferation rate between tissues argues for a shorter doubling time in ectoderm.

CONCLUSIONS

The rapid growth of the mouse embryo shortly after implantation is not brought about by increases in cell size but is achieved by extremely rapid cell proliferation. Despite the potential errors involved in the determination of volume and cell number, cell cycle times of 5–6 h, and maybe shorter, must be considered to account for such growth. The close similarity between the results presented here and those of Goedbloed (1972), Kohler et al. (1972) and Solter et al. (1971) constitute strong evidence for this conjecture, despite the criticism levelled at the last two papers.

In addition, the appearance of over 6000 mesoderm cells in the 24 hours between $6\frac{1}{2}$ and $7\frac{1}{2}$ days cannot be explained by the postulate that a small number of pluripotent stem cells is present at $6\frac{1}{2}$ days. If a cycle time of between 6 and 7 h is assumed for mesoderm then at $6\frac{1}{2}$ days an initial population of between 400 and 700 cells would be needed to produce 6600 mesoderm cells in 24 h. Such a population of 'stem' cells does not exist and these mesoderm cells must therefore originate progressively from some other tissue. The most acceptable source is of course from the embryonic ectoderm by a process involving cell movement through the primitive streak.

References

ABERCROMBIE, M. (1946) Estimation of nuclear population from microtome sections. *Anat. Rec. 94*, 239–247

BELLAIRS, R. (1971) *Developmental Processes in Higher Vertebrates*, Logos Press, London

BUEHR, M. & McLAREN, A. (1974) Size regulation in chimaeric mouse embryos. *J. Embryol. Exp. Morphol. 31*, 229–234

CHEN, B.K. (1932) The early development of the duck's egg, with special reference to the origin of the primitive streak. *J. Morphol. 53*, 133–188

CLEAVER, J.E. (1967) *Thymidine Metabolism and Cell Kinetics*, North-Holland, Amsterdam

CORLISS, C.E. (1953) A study of mitotic activity in the early rat embryo. *J. Exp. Zool. 122*, 193–227

DAMJANOV, I. & SOLTER, D. (1974) Experimental teratoma, in *Current Topics in Pathology*, vol. 59, pp. 69–130, Springer, New York & Heidelberg

DANIEL, J.C. & OLSON, J.D. (1966) Cell movement, proliferation and death in the formation of the embryonic axis of the rabbit. *Anat. Rec. 156*, 123–128

ENGLAND, J.M., ROGERS, A.W. & MILLER, R.G. (1973) The identification of labelled structures on autoradiographs. *Nature (Lond.) 242*, 612–613

FRASER, A. (1882) On the inversion of the blastodermic layers in the rat and mouse. *Proc. R. Soc. Lond. 34*, 430–437

GARDNER, R.L. & JOHNSON, M.H. (1973) Investigation of early mammalian development using interspecific chimaeras between rat and mouse. *Nature New Biol.* 246, 86–89

GARDNER, R.L. & JOHNSON, M.H. (1975) Investigation of cellular interaction and deployment in the early mammalian embryo using interspecific chimaeras between the rat and mouse, in *Cell Patterning (Ciba Found. Symp. 29)*, pp. 183–196, Associated Scientific Publishers, Amsterdam

GARDNER, R.L. & PAPAIOANNOU, V.E. (1975) Differentiation in the trophectoderm and inner cell mass, in *The Early Development of Mammals (2nd Symp. Br. Soc. Dev. Biol.)* (Balls, M. & Wild, A.E., eds.), pp. 107–132, Cambridge University Press, London

GOEDBLOED, J.F. (1972) The embryonic and post natal growth of rat and mouse. *Acta Anat.* 82, 305–336

GRAHAM, C.F. (1973) The cell cycle during mammalian development, in *The Cell Cycle in Development and Differentiation (1st Symp. Br. Soc. Dev. Biol.)* (Balls, M. & Billet, F.S., eds.), pp. 293–310, Cambridge University Press, London

GROBSTEIN, C. (1952) Intra-ocular growth and differentiation of clusters of mouse embryonic shields cultured with and without primitive endoderm and in the presence of possible inductors. *J. Exp. Zool. 119*, 355–380

HILL, D.K. (1962) Resolving power with tritium autoradiography. *Nature (Lond.) 194*, 831–832

HUBER, G.C. (1915) The development of the albino rat, *Mus norvegicus albicus. J. Morphol. 26*, 247–358

JENKINSON, J.W. (1900) A reinvestigation of the early stages of the development of the mouse. *Q. J. Microsc. Sci. 43*, 61–82

KOHLER, E., MERKER, H.J., EHMKE, W. & WOJNOROWICZ, F. (1972) Growth kinetics of mammalian embryos during the stage of differentiation. *Naunyn-Schmiedeberg's Arch. Pharmakol. 272*, 169–181

MARTIN, G. (1975) Teratocarcinomas as a model system for the study of embryogenesis and neoplasia: A review. *Cell 5*, 229–243

MODAK, S.P., LEVER, W.E., THERWATH, A.M. & UPPULURI, V.R.R. (1973) Estimation of the proportion of cell nuclei in tissue sections falling within tritium-autoradiographic range. *Exp. Cell Res. 76*, 73–78

PASTEELS, J. (1943) Proliferation et croissance dans la gastrulation et la formation de la queue des Vertèbres. *Arch. Biol. 54*, 1–51

PRETO, V. (1938) Analisi della distribuzione dell'attivata mitotica in giovani embrioni di ratto. *Arch. Ital. Anat. Embriol. 41*, 165–206

ŠKREB, N., ŠVAJGER, A. & LEVAK-ŠVAJGER, B. (1976) Developmental potentialities of the germ layers in mammals, in this volume, pp. 27–39

SOBOTTA, J. (1903) Die Entwicklung des Eies der Maus vom Schluss der Furchungsperiode bis zum Auftreten der Amniosfalten. *Arch. Mikrosc. Anat. Entwicklungsmech. 61*, 274–330

SOBOTTA, J. (1911) Die Entwicklung des Eies der Maus vom ersten Auftreten des Mesoderms an bis zur Ausbildung der Embryonalanlage und dem Auftreten der Allantois. *Arch. Mikrosc. Anat. Entwicklungsmech. 78*, 271–352

SOLTER, D. & ŠKREB, N. (1968) La durée du cylindre-œuf de la souris. *C. R. Hebd. Séances Acad. Sci. Sér. D Sci. Nat. 267*, 659–661

SOLTER, D., ŠKREB, N. & DAMJANOV, I. (1971) Cell cycle analysis in the mouse egg-cylinder. *Exp. Cell Res. 64*, 331–334

SPRATT, N.T. (1966) Some problems and principles of development. *Am. Zool. 6*, 9–19

THRASHER, J.D. (1966) Analysis of renewing epithelial cell populations, in *Methods in Cell Physiology* (Prescott, D.M., ed.), vol. 3, pp. 323–357, Academic Press, New York

VAN DYKE, J.H. & RITCHEY, R.G. (1947) Colchicine influence during embryonic development of the rat. *Anat. Rec. 97*, 375 (abstr.)

WILLIAMS, J.P.G. (1968) Inhibition of embryonic deoxyribonucleic acid synthesis by Colcemid. *Eur. J. Pharmacol. 3*, 337–340
WILLIAMS, J.P.G. (1970) Selective inhibition of embryonic deoxyribonucleic acid synthesis by
vinblastine. *Cell Tissue Kinet. 3*, 155–159
WILLIAMS, J.P.G. & CARPENTIERI, U. (1967) The different response of embryonic and adult
rats to demecolcin. *Life Sci. 6*, 2613–2620

Discussion

Gurdon: During mammalian development there are steps when the cells become limited in their eventual developmental capacity; that is, they undergo what I would call increasing degrees of determination. I suggest that these events can take place only between one cell cycle and the next. Are cell divisions in fact fast enough for that proposition to be true? If cell divisions are rather slow at these relatively early stages, so that steps of determination must occur more frequently than there are cell divisions, it would eliminate that particular proposition.

Snow: I feel that during these stages of development the number of determinative events is probably few, in relation to the number of divisions. A suggestion of an answer to your question may emerge from the work in progress on size regulation in aggregation chimeras (A. McLaren & M. Buehr, personal communication). It has already been shown that there is a downward regulation in size at between $5\frac{1}{2}$ and 6 days of development (Buehr & McLaren 1974). It is not yet known how this is achieved but it is possible that a reduction in division rate could be involved, in which case the same number of determinative events as in normal development would be taking place with fewer divisions. This I think would indicate that determinative events and cell division can occur separately.

Gluecksohn-Waelsch: In amphibians morphogenetic cell movements during gastrulation associated with progressive changes in the state of determination are independent of cell divisions. An extensive study by Holtfreter (1943) led to the conclusion that 'the principle of cell division can be dismissed as a causative or guiding factor in early amphibian morphogenesis'.

Gurdon: As far as I know, the increasing degrees of determination have not been well enough defined to say whether they occur more frequently than the rate of cell division. Cell division rate is rather slow, I agree, during determination.

Gluecksohn-Waelsch: In amphibian gastrulation the notochord–mesoderm comes to underlie the overlying ectoderm and determines it to form nervous tissue in the absence of cell division.

Newth: But cell division does continue through gastrulation, though its rate may fall.

Gurdon: The fact is that some cells are dividing, and since people normally do determination tests on many cells it is not easy to say that determination is (or is not) occurring in just those cells that are passing into the next cell cycle.

Cooke: I reported recently that morphogenetic movements can continue normally, as can determination and histodifferentiation, for a period equivalent to some three normal rounds of cell division after a mitotic block has been imposed, by two different means, in the amphibian early gastrula (Cooke 1973). But we must be careful here, because it was not shown whether the duplication of chromosomes had also stopped. Later biochemical work (B.C.Goodwin, personal communication) seems to show that, in those embryos, the same amount of precursor has been incorporated into DNA as would have been incorporated in a normal embryo over the same period. What Dr Gurdon is saying about the possible relationship between determinative events and replication processes in cells may still be true for chromosome replication but not for cell division as such. The same proviso would apply to any of these ideas in relation to mammals.

McLaren: At this stage of mammalian development the cell cycle time is very short. Until we have a much more detailed schedule of determinative events, it would be difficult to test Dr Gurdon's proposition.

Gurdon: I suppose that at this stage, cell cycles are about 12 hours in length. Is that still too short to discuss the transition from one determined state to the next?

McLaren: I would think so.

Gardner: At $3\frac{1}{2}$ days in the mouse blastocyst there do not seem to be any committed endoderm cells, while at $4\frac{1}{2}$ days there apparently are. We have to work backwards between those two times if we want to define the stage when two different populations of cells first appear in the inner cell mass.

Rutter: But isn't that just the time when there is a very limited proliferation? What is the population of cells at $3\frac{1}{2}$ and $4\frac{1}{2}$ days?

McLaren: It depends which compartment one is considering.

Gardner: The inner cell mass as a whole would have increased from 15 to between 40 and 50 cells. At least two cell divisions have happened.

Cooke: When the mesoderm is first distinguishable anatomically, do the cells seem to divide at a different rate from those in the cell population that has given rise to it, Dr Snow?

Snow: That would be extremely interesting and useful information but it is incredibly difficult to get. We can't get it with our method. Autoradiography is the obvious choice. One can in fact derive all the components of the cell cycle within half a cell cycle by a continuous labelling system, and that should give an indication. If studies were done on enough embryos with only very few mesoderm cells present one might be able to get information of that sort. I tried to back these observations up with autoradiographic evidence but unfortunately the $6\frac{1}{2}$-day mouse embryo is a very peculiar beast. Of two mice from the same cage, treated in exactly the same way, one may contain labelled embryos and the other unlabelled embryos. Until there is an explanation for this sort of variation any autoradiographic findings one might get from $6\frac{1}{2}$-day embryos need very careful interpretation.

Kelley: What is happening to the G_1 phase? Early mouse embryos (cleavage stages) do not seem to have a G_1 phase and only gradually develop one. Is this phase affected in the $6\frac{1}{2}$-day embryo?

Snow: I don't really know. The G_1 is established in cleavage stages in the mouse and is a well-recognized part of the cell cycle at the blastocyst stage. In my continuous labelling experiments, if the labelling information from the $6\frac{1}{2}$-day embryos is to be believed, then all I can say at present is that the period from the end of the S phase, through G_2, division and to the next S, is about 3 hours. There is an identifiable G_2, probably of about an hour. It is generally assumed that division takes between 30 and 45 minutes—the actual process probably can't be got through any quicker than that. That leaves a short period of time for G_1, but the observations are not very reliable.

Kelley: Are you suggesting that it is the S phase that fluctuates?

Snow: The S phase obviously has to be very short. Solter *et al.* (1971) showed that it was short at $7\frac{1}{2}$ days.

Gardner: In the 1940s Kerr, who was looking at the mechanism of resorption of early embryos, used colchicine and got extensive resorption within about 6 hours (Kerr 1947). The postimplantation embryo is clearly very susceptible to disturbance of that sort.

Is there any indication of synchrony of mitotic activity? And are there regional differences in mitotic activity?

Snow: I looked to see whether I could plot regional differences in the mitotic index. In the $7\frac{1}{2}$-day embryos, where there is extensive mesoderm formation, there is no obvious regional variation in the mitotic index around the inside of the ectoderm. None of my $6\frac{1}{2}$-day Q embryos had any mesoderm formation. The problem there is knowing where to make the sectors. If one could divide the egg cylinder up accurately, so that the primitive streak region was definitely in one quarter, and so on, one could perhaps accumulate figures from several embryos and find a difference. I haven't done that. I should do that analysis at the $6\frac{3}{4}$-day stage, when there is an identifiable mesoderm.

Gardner: In relation to the formation of the primitive streak in Dr Bennett's

t^9 mutant, where in the homozygote there is an accumulation of cells that seem to fail to form proper mesoderm, is that due to the activity of a local proliferative zone in the so-called embryonic ectoderm, or is equal cell division going on everywhere, giving an escalator effect?

Bennett: We think that normally mesoderm cells continue to proliferate quite actively as they migrate away from their source of origin, whereas in t^9 this is not the case.

Gardner: So it is an anomaly of distribution rather than of proliferation?

Bennett: We interpret the failure of t^9 mesoderm cells to populate the embryo as indicating that the ability to divide and the ability to migrate are coupled, and that both these qualities of emerging mesoderm cells fail. Which one is truly dependent on the other is not clear.

Spiegelman: There are certainly fewer mesoderm cells in the t^9. Even though the primitive streak is arrested and looks larger at $8\frac{1}{2}$ days, the derivatives from the primitive streak are reduced in number compared with those of normal littermates. We haven't analysed this yet but just from the dramatic difference in size between mutant and normal mesoderm, cell division must be depressed in the t^9 embryo.

Snow: Throughout the ectoderm, groups of cells remain in fairly close synchrony. Under an oil immersion objective, regions of ectoderm with 60 nuclei visible can be seen in sections 6 μm thick. About 30 of those can be in either prophase or in division. That represents a fairly high degree of synchrony and might be an indication of waves of mitosis.

Bennett: Regional differences would be very interesting to find. From the results you have on serial sections of embryos, do you think that a simple computer program could be written that would survey the embryo around the cylinder or from top to bottom? Perhaps that would give information on regional differences in proliferation that might serve to identify the site of the future primitive streak before it could be identified on morphological grounds.

Snow: That certainly should be possible. I also tried to plot planes of cleavage for the various divisions that one finds around the inside of the egg cylinder, in the hope that I would be able to say that the orientation of 70% of these divisions would lead to movements of cells in such and such a direction. The problem is that at $6\frac{1}{2}$ days one is really looking for a hole inside a sphere. As we don't know where that hole is until the primitive streak has formed, doing the analysis simply by looking at pictures is extremely difficult.

Gluecksohn-Waelsch: It would appear unlikely that cell divisions would be synchronized throughout the entire embryo. Differential rates of cell division and differential growth may be expected to be associated particularly with those developmental changes that cannot be ascribed to morphogenetic movements or changes in shape of cells. I would expect specific differences to exist between the division rates of different cell groups.

Snow: I don't think that there is a particularly great change in form during this period. The embryonic portion of the $7\frac{1}{2}$-day egg cylinder is really only a blown-up $6\frac{1}{2}$-day portion: the cavity in the middle happens to have got bigger.

Gluecksohn-Waelsch: Yes, but there is the beginning of some anterior-posterior differentiation at $7\frac{1}{2}$ days, and the increase in size is not evenly distributed.

Snow: The pockets of division may simply be artifacts caused by the short cell cycles. Presumably it is fairly difficult to make the prophase–metaphase–anaphase any shorter than it is in most other cells. The mechanics of it must put a limit on the speed of the process. The mitotic process therefore probably occupies a greater proportion of the cell cycle than it does in other less rapidly dividing cells.

Rutter: Is it known whether the ploidy of these cells remains constant during this period?

Snow: One can assume that it does. For other reasons I have made a lot of chromosome preparations from embryos at this stage and I have never found tetraploidy or higher numbers of chromosomes. If a tetraploid DNA content is ever exceeded, then to account for the diploid number of chromosomes found during these stages, one would have to assume that the cells divide into four instead of two.

References

BUEHR, M. & MCLAREN, A. (1974) Size regulation in chimaeric mouse embryos. *J. Embryol. Exp. Morphol. 31*, 229–234

COOKE, J. (1973) Morphogenesis and regulation in spite of continued mitotic inhibition in *Xenopus* embryos. *Nature (Lond.) 242*, 55–57

HOLTFRETER, J. (1943) A study of the mechanics of gastrulation, I. *J. Exp. Zool. 94*, 261–318

KERR, T. (1947) On the effect of colchicine treatment on mouse embryos. *Proc. Zool. Soc. Lond. 116*, 551–564

SOLTER, D., ŠKREB, N. & DAMJANOV, I. (1971) Cell cycle analysis in the mouse egg-cylinder. *Exp. Cell Res. 64*, 331–334

Cell migration in early vertebrate development studied in interspecific chimeras

NICOLE LE DOUARIN

*Laboratoire d'Embryologie, Université de Nantes**

Abstract A biological cell-labelling technique based on structural differences between the interphase nucleus of two closely related species of birds, the Japanese quail (*Coturnix coturnix japonica*) and the chick (*Gallus gallus*), was used in this investigation. Cell migration was studied in the neural crest and during histogenesis of haemopoietic organs. Early transplantation of quail neural crest into chick embryos showed the importance of the ectomesenchyme in the morphogenesis of the head and pharynx and enabled new derivatives of the neural crest (calcitonin-producing cells and type I cells of the carotid body) to be identified. The pattern and chronology of migration of the neuroblasts of the autonomic nervous system were investigated. The phenotypic expression of the neuroblasts as cholinergic or adrenergic neurons probably depends on the site the cells have reached when they finish migrating.

With the quail-chick marker system it can be shown that haemopoietic cells do not differentiate by the transformation *in situ* of cells from the rudiments of the thymus and bursa but derive from blood-borne stem cells which invade the haemopoietic primordia at a precise stage of their development.

Embryonic development implies extensive movements of either isolated cells or groups of cells. The best known of these movements leads to the formation of the germ layers. It has also been recognized for a long time that, after the primary embryonic organization has been set up, further cell movements and cell migrations play an important role in many morphogenetic and histogenetic processes. Pioneer studies, based on careful histological examination of the developing embryo, demonstrated the migrations of the neural crest and primordial germ cells. However, early intraembryonic cell movements are difficult to analyse since the cells are not differentiated and cannot be distinguished from the tissues through which they move. Experimental techniques for study-

---

* *Present address*: Institut d'Embryologie du CNRS et du Collège de France, Nogent-sur-Marne

ing the fate and the pathways of migration of undifferentiated moving cells therefore had to be devised.

When the presumed migratory cells are initially grouped in a defined embryonic area, the whole area can be removed. Deficiencies after the operation give information about the presumptive fate of the excised territory. This experimental approach has often been used for studying the migration of primordial germ cells in birds and that of neural crest cells in lower and higher vertebrates (Hörstadius 1950; Weston 1970). However, the extirpation of large embryonic areas usually disturbs developing processes; moreover this technique is seriously hampered by the regulating capacities of early embryonic tissues which make difficult the interpretation of the experimental findings.

A second method uses cell markers, either intrinsic or artificial. The latter include vital dyes or minor marking particles such as carbon, chalk or carmine. However, tritiated thymidine (Taylor et al. 1957) is better than these because it is non-deleterious and more cell-specific. But although it is accurate and precise this provides information only about events occurring over a short period of time, because the nuclear marker is unstable and becomes diluted through the rapid proliferation of embryonic cells.

Natural markers have been used mainly in amphibians. They are based on morphological differences between various types of cells in the embryo or cells from different species or genera. Cell size, presence of yolk or pigment granules, and staining properties (Raven 1937; Triplett 1958) have been used to study the migration of neural crest cells but they allow only groups of cells to be identified, not single cells. Nuclear markers generally show up more clearly and are more stable than others. The mutation 'anucleolate', discovered by Elsdale et al. (1958), was at the origin of a cell tracing technique used for studying primordial germ cell migration (Blackler & Fischberg 1961), and several workers took advantage of the possibility of inducing polyploidy in amphibians to follow the movements of haemopoietic stem cells (Hollyfield 1966; De Paris 1967; Turpen & Volpe 1975).

In higher vertebrates, no natural cell markers have so far been available except chromosome markers; these have proved especially useful in experimental haematology since they allow cells to be identified regardless of the extent of proliferation and differentiation. They have been successfully used for analysing haemopoietic stem cell traffic in the chick embryo (Moore & Owen 1965, 1967; Owen & Ritter 1969; Metcalf & Moore 1971). An inherent drawback of the technique is that it is limited to the dividing cell population.

This paper deals with the use for the study of cell migration of a natural cell-labelling technique (Le Douarin 1969, 1973a) which has the advantage of being stable and applicable to the embryo of higher vertebrates. We have used it to investigate cell migration in the neural crest and during histogenesis of haemopoietic organs.

A NUCLEAR CELL-MARKING TECHNIQUE

The cell-marking technique used throughout this investigation is based on a special feature of the interphase nucleus of the Japanese quail (*Coturnix coturnix japonica*). In all embryonic and adult cell types of this species a large amount of heterochromatic DNA is associated with the nucleolus and can be shown up easily with the Feulgen-Rossenbeck stain or in the electron microscope after the routine uranyl acetate–lead citrate staining procedure. This disposition of the chromatin material does not usually exist in vertebrate cells where the amount of nucleolus-associated chromatin is small and most often undetectable by Feulgen-Rossenbeck staining (Bernhard & Granboulan 1968). In chick or mouse cells, for instance, the chromatin is evenly distributed in the nucleoplasm during the interphase and forms a fine network with only small dispersed chromocentres. The presence of heterochromatin condensations in the nucleus means that quail cells can be used as natural markers when combined *in vitro* or *in vivo* with chick or mouse cells (Fig. 1).

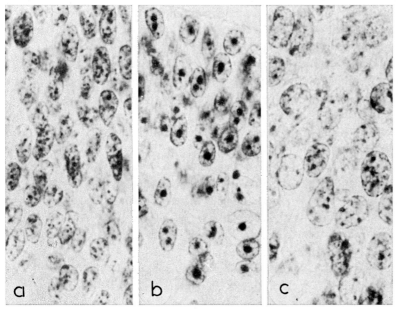

FIG. 1. Neuroblasts of the spinal cord, Feulgen-Rossenbeck stained in (*a*) 7-day chick, (*b*) 7-day quail and (*c*) 11-day mouse embryos. Note the large mass of heterochromatic DNA in quail cells, × 1300.

The structure of the quail nucleolus varies somewhat according to the cell type considered and the state of differentiation reached. In undifferentiated cells characterized by a high proliferation rate, such as young blastomeres during gastrulation and early organogenesis, or haemopoietic stem cells, the nucleus has a large nucleolus made up of Feulgen-positive material with irregular outlines and a reticulated structure. When the Unna-Pappenheim technique (Unna 1913) is used in addition to electron microscope observations, the RNA-containing structures of the nucleolus are seen to be mixed with the DNA. With the EDTA technique (Bernhard 1968), which stains RNA preferentially while DNA and most of the proteins remain uncontrasted, it appears that the nucleolar RNA is located inside the centronuclear DNA mass as dispersed strands. It is interesting to note that this type of nucleolus substructure is always associated with a highly basophilic ribosome-rich cytoplasm, and it may be assumed to be a functional state of the nucleolus characterized by a high level of ribosomal RNA synthesis (type III nucleolus: Le Douarin 1973b). Besides young blastomeres and blood stem cells, the type III nucleolus is observed in various kinds of differentiated cells such as secretory kidney tubules and duodenal epithelium. While organogenesis and differentiation are in progress the relationships between the RNA and DNA nucleolar components are modified in most cell types.

The nucleolus type most often encountered in differentiated cells contains a large centronuclear mass of heterochromatin which is seen to be strongly Feulgen-positive and compact under the light microscope; in the electron microscope it appears to be made up of a densely coiled fibrillar material, unstained after application of EDTA. The ribonucleoprotein-containing structures of the nucleolus are in two or three patches, lateral to the heterochromatic mass (Fig. 2) (type I nucleolus according to Le Douarin 1973b).

In certain cells the heterochromatin is divided into several fragments associated with a variable amount of RNA, each of these complex structures representing a nucleolus. Such a nuclear pattern is encountered in muscle and fibrous connective tissues, the cells of which show an elongated nucleus. In the hepatocytes and exocrine pancreatic cells, heterochromatin also appears separated into fragments, which in this case are assembled by the nucleolar RNA component, so that the nucleolus is large and often irregular in shape (type III nucleolus according to Le Douarin 1973b). Comparison of the nucleolar structure of homologous cell types in quail and chick has shown that the nucleolus is bigger in quail than in chick, due to the presence of heterochromatin among the fundamental nucleolar components.

It therefore appears that quail and chick cells can be readily identified in chimeric tissues under light microscopy when the Feulgen-Rossenbeck stain is

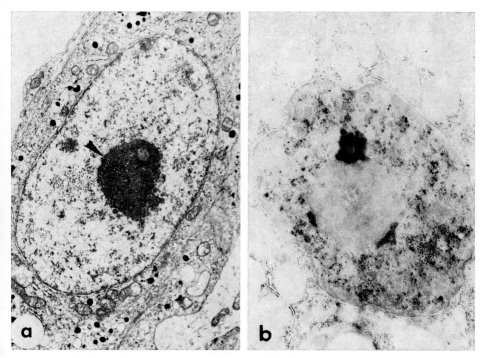

Fig. 2. (a) Adrenomedullary cell of a 12-day quail embryo, with characteristic large nucleolus, showing the heterochromatic DNA (arrow) and a lateral structure containing ribonucleoprotein (RNP). Uranyl acetate–lead citrate staining, × 8700.

(b) Metanephritic anlage of a 13-day quail. EDTA treatment: the heterochromatin is unstained while the lateral RNP-containing structures of the nucleolus are contrasted, × 8700.

used. In electron microscopy the uranyl acetate–lead citrate staining makes it possible to identify quail cells in most cell types. If necessary, the preferential regressive staining procedure for RNA, using EDTA (Bernhard 1968), allows quail nuclei to be recognized by the large amount of nucleolus-associated heterochromatic DNA, which does not occur in any chick cell type.

THE EVOLUTION OF THE NEURAL CREST AS STUDIED IN QUAIL–CHICK CHIMERAS

Although they have provided much important information, the experimental techniques used for investigating the differentiating capabilities of the neural crest (excision and electrocauterization of the neural anlage, and various cell-labelling techniques: see Hörstadius 1950; Weston 1970; and Le Douarin 1974 for references) have not provided a complete and precise picture of the migra-

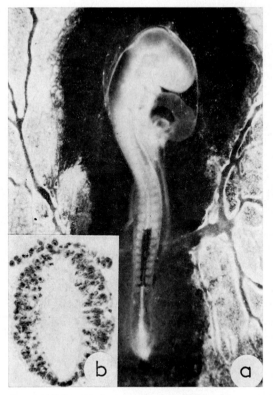

FIG. 3. (*a*) Dorsal view of a chick embryo after removal of the neural anlage at the level of somites 20 to 26. The notochord can be seen in the groove left after excision.

(*b*) Quail neural tube and associated neural crest isolated by trypsin treatment. Feulgen-Rossenbeck staining, $\times 350$.

tion pathways and developmental fate of the whole population of cells deriving from this structure. Many of its characteristics make the neural crest a provocative system with which to study various problems in developmental biology. From this transitory structure diverse cell types arise which differentiate in defined locations which they reach after extensive and precise migrations through the developing embryo. The factors which control their distribution and phenotypic expression are still poorly understood.

The normal fate of the neural crest cells was first investigated by isotopic and isochronic grafting of fragments of the quail neural primordium into the chick at all levels of the neural axis. Some series of grafts were done in the reverse sense (chick into quail) as controls. Once their normal fate had been established, we studied the determination of the crest cells at various times during embryogenesis, focusing our attention on the cell interactions responsible for their differentiation.

Identification of the neural crest derivatives by interspecific grafts of the neural primordium

Experimental procedure. Grafts of fragments of quail neural tube and associated neural folds were implanted orthotopically in chick embryos of the same developmental stages. The chick neural primordium was excised by microsurgery *in ovo*, the endoderm, notochord and somites being left *in situ* (Fig. 3a). The quail neural tube and associated neural folds were isolated by incubating transverse sections of the quail embryo in Mg^{2+}-, Ca^{2+}-free Tyrode solution with 0.1 % (v/v) trypsin added. Thus, the grafted neural anlage was completely uncontaminated with mesenchymal cells (Fig. 3b). In a second step, the quail neural primordium was grafted into the chick host in the groove resulting from the excision.

To ensure that crest cells had not migrated at the time of the graft, we varied the level of the operation according to the developmental stage of the embryo. The more cranial the level of the neural crest investigated, the younger the embryo. Operations involving the prosencephalon were done at the 2- to 5-somite stage, for the mesencephalon at the 5- to 7-somite stage, and for the rhombencephalon at the 6- to 10-somite stage. The experiments on the spinal cord were done at the level of the last somites formed.

Whatever the level of the graft, the grafted tissue was rapidly covered by healing host ectoderm and underwent normal histogenesis. In the head region where the operations were done at early developmental stages, malformations of the encephalon were sometimes seen, especially in the forebrain. The graft was often done unilaterally at this level, a procedure which in most cases ensured normal development of the head.

We were able to follow the migration of the implanted neural crest cells of the quail until they were fully differentiated. The stability of the labelling provided by the nuclear marker meant that quail cells could be recognized on sections of the host embryo after Feulgen-Rossenbeck staining or in the electron microscope.

In the trunk region, the sensory and orthosympathetic ganglia and the aortic adrenergic plexus were entirely made up of quail cells at the level of the graft (Fig. 4). In rachidian nerves and communicating ramus, the Schwann's cells also showed the nuclear marker (Le Douarin & Teillet 1970; Teillet 1971b). On the other hand, when a quail neural tube was grafted into a White Leghorn chick, quail melanoblasts migrated into the host skin, the feathers of which exhibited

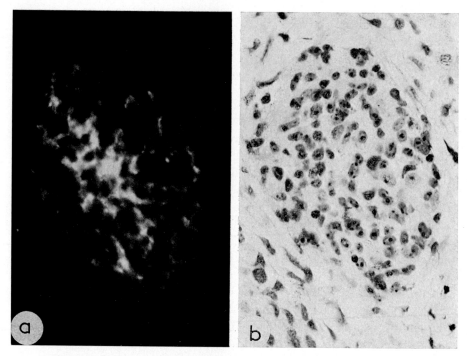

Fig. 4. Cervical superior ganglion of a 6½-day chick embryo which has received at 12-somite stage the graft of a quail neural tube at the level of somites 6 to 10.

(a) Falck's reaction for detection of fluorogenic monoamines shows a greenish fluorescence in ganglion cells.

(b) The same section as (a), post-stained with Feulgen-Rossenbeck, shows that the ganglion originates from the graft of quail neural primordium, × 650.

the characteristic pigmentation of the donor (Fig. 5). The chronology and pattern of migration of the presumptive pigment cells could be followed at various stages after grafting (Teillet & Le Douarin 1970; Teillet 1971a).

The melanoblasts migrated essentially through the mesoderm and penetrated massively into the ectoderm during the 5th and 6th days of incubation. Soon after their homing in the ectoderm, they actively divided and the number of quail cells in the host ectoderm increased sharply during the 7th day of development. During the 8th and 9th days pigment synthesis began in differentiating melanocytes. From the 9th day, quail cells were abundant in the epidermis and completely absent in the feather bud mesenchyme. The pigmented skin stripes of the host overlapped those of the graft broadly, indicating that the migration of the melanoblasts was not strictly metameric.

In fact the cells radiated around each point of the neural crest in the entire plane of the skin area. A significant proof of this view is that a complete trans-

FIG. 5. Transverse pigmented stripe resulting when a fragment of a quail neural tube was grafted into a White Leghorn chick embryo.

verse pigmented stripe was observed after grafts of either the right or the left half, alone, of the quail neural tube. Observations of well-known derivatives of the neural crest, such as sensory ganglia, orthosympathetic chains and melanocytes, indicated that in our experimental conditions the patterns of differentiation and migration of the grafted crest cells did not differ in the host and in normal developmental conditions. When this had been established, the normal fate of the crest was investigated at the cephalic and trunk levels, successively, of the neural axis.

Developmental fate of the cephalic crest cells. Experiments, mainly on amphibians, have shown that the cephalic neural crest gives rise to mesenchymal cells which participate in the formation of the facial and visceral skeleton (see Hörstadius 1950 for references). In higher vertebrates, extirpation experiments (Hammond & Yntema 1953, 1964) suggested that various visceral and cranial cartilages originate from mesectodermal cells. Johnston (1966) has confirmed and extended these findings in the chick embryo by using cells labelled with tritiated thymidine. However, those studies did not provide precise information

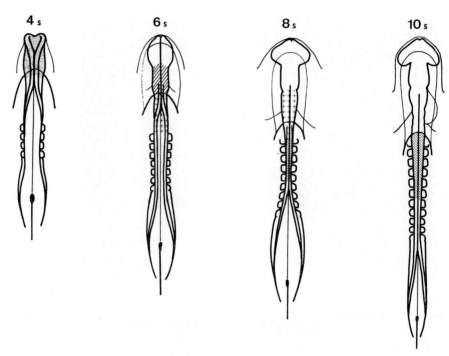

FIG. 6. Participation of neural crest cells in morphogenesis of head and pharynx. Levels of the graft and stages of the operated embryos (4- to 10-somite stages) in the various experimental series: grafts of the prosencephalon (finely stippled), the mesencephalon (diagonal lines) and the anterior (crosses) and posterior rhombencephalon (coarsely stippled), in that order.

on the extent of migration of neural crest cells in the head and pharynx, nor did they reveal the developmental capabilities of the crest cells, since the label is diluted out before histodifferentiation occurs.

The various kinds of grafts in this experimental series are shown in Fig. 6 and the distribution of the neural crest cells in the head and pharynx of the host is shown in a $3\frac{1}{2}$-day embryo in Fig. 7. The frontal and ventrolateral areas of the head mesenchyme derive essentially from the prosencephalic and mesencephalic neural crest, with contributions also from the placodal ectoderm and the mesoderm (C. Le Lièvre & N. Le Douarin, unpublished).

The grafted neural crest cells migrated into the facial regions and at the 20- to 25-somite stage of the host they appeared to be distributed in two sheets, one beneath the superficial ectoderm and the other around the forebrain wall. Between these two mesectodermal layers, the mesenchyme was made up of both quail and host cells. The eye cup was surrounded by mesenchymal cells which were almost completely of neural crest origin and which participated in the formation of the sclera. In contrast, the muscles associated with the inner part

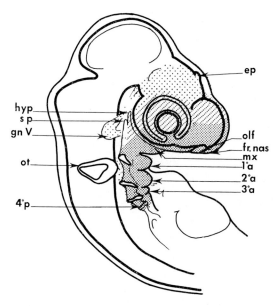

FIG. 7. Position of the neural crest cells in a 3½-day embryo.
ep: epiphysis; fr. nas.: fronto-nasal process; hyp: hypophysis; mx: maxillary process;
olf: olfactory pit; ot: auditory pit; s.p.: Seessel's pouch; 1°a, 2°a, 3°a: 1st, 2nd, and 3rd branchial arches; 4°p: 4th branchial pouch.

of the eye came from the host mesoderm. In the experimental embryos the
mesenchyme of the nasal bud was made up of cells with the quail nuclear
marker. The neural crest cells which migrated medioventrally along the prosencephalic rudiment became localized in the ventrolateral side of the forebrain
and accumulated in the vicinity of the hypophysial anlage, where they were
mixed with mesodermal cells.

   The grafts carried out at the midbrain and hindbrain levels revealed the contribution of the neural crest to the lower facial and the pharyngeal regions (Le
Lièvre 1974; Le Lièvre & Le Douarin 1975). In 4-day-old chick embryos which
received a graft of quail mesencephalon, the maxillary buds and the 1st branchial
arches were entirely made up of quail mesectodermal cells, except in a central
core derived from the mesoderm and corresponding to the muscle plate. Some
cells originating from the midbrain also contributed to the 2nd branchial arch.
In the latter, however, as well as in the 3rd and 4th arches, the mesenchyme
derived predominantly from the rhombencephalon (Fig. 8). The muscle plate
was made up essentially of host cells, with a small but noticeable contribution
(10%) of mesectodermal cells, and the endothelium of the aortic arches was
of host origin at all the pharyngeal levels.

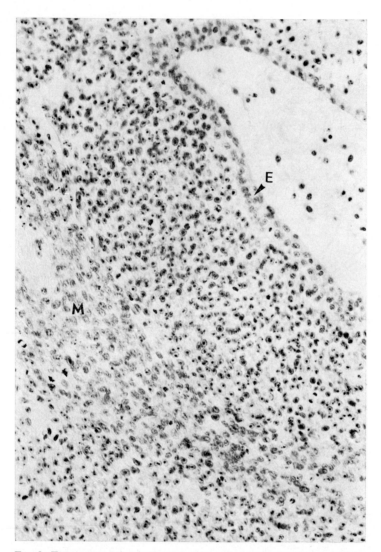

FIG. 8. Transverse section in the second branchial arch of a 4½-day chick host embryo with a quail rhombencephalon grafted at the 7-somite stage. The pharyngeal endoderm (E) is of chick host origin while the mesenchymal cells are derived from the grafted neural rudiment of the quail. The muscle plate (M) is essentially made up of host mesodermal cells together with some quail mesectodermal cells. Feulgen-Rossenbeck staining, × 320.

Mesectodermal cells colonizing the branchial arches and the facial regions gave rise to the entire visceral skeleton. In addition, neural crest cells gave rise to many other kinds of cells. Their distribution in the various pharyngeal derivatives of a 9-day host is indicated in Fig. 9. They gave rise to the dermis of the face and the lateroventral sides of the neck, the smooth erector muscles associated with feathers, and the subcutaneous adipose layer. The connective tissue of the face, the lower jaw, the tongue and the ventral part of the neck were derived from the mesectoderm. So was the mesenchymal component of the salivary glands, the thymus, the thyroid and the parathyroid. The wall of the oesophagus and the trachea, on the other hand, was of mesodermal origin.

Due to the elongation of the neck and the anteroposterior movement of the heart during the first half of embryogenesis, the blood vessels deriving from aortic arches moved caudally and became incorporated into the thoracic cavity. Except for the endothelium, the wall of the large arteries deriving from the aortic arches originated entirely from mesectoderm.

We paid special attention to the contribution of the neural crest to the histogenesis of ultimobranchial and carotid bodies. The ultimobranchial body derives from a caudal diverticulum of the 4th pharyngeal pouches and contains the cells responsible for the secretion of calcitonin (C-cells). On the other hand, the carotid body, the main function of which is chemoreception (Biscoe 1971), appears in the 3rd branchial arch and is essentially made up of cells characterized from an early developmental stage by a high content of fluorogenic monoamines (Fontaine 1973). A possible origin of these cells from neural crest has been suggested (Pearse 1969) and we submitted this hypothesis to an experimental test, using the quail nuclear marker.

When quail rhombencephalic neural primordium was grafted into a chick at the 6- to 10-somite stage, quail cells extensively colonized the endodermal ultimobranchial epithelial rudiment of the host. After they had invaded the ultimobranchial endoderm, the quail cells divided actively and differentiated into calcitonin-producing cells (Le Douarin 1974), as demonstrated by ultrastructural (Le Douarin & Le Lièvre 1970, 1971), cytochemical (Le Douarin et al. 1974) and immunocytochemical techniques (Polak et al. 1974). The endodermal cells deriving from the 4th pharyngeal pouch gave rise to the lining cells of the glandular cords of the ultimobranchial body.

After a quail rhombencephalon had been grafted into a chick, the carotid body of the host was almost entirely made up of quail cells. When the cytochemical technique for the detection of fluorogenic monoamines through fixation with formaldehyde vapour (Falck 1962) was used, the quail cells which constituted the carotid body of the chick host fluoresced bright green like the glomic cells of the normal quail (Le Douarin et al. 1972). In addition, by microspectrofluorometry of formaldehyde-induced fluorescence, the biogenic amine present in the carotid body type I cells was identified as dopamine in the quail and 5-hydroxytryptamine (5HT) in the chick. In the experimental embryos which received the graft of a quail rhombencephalic primordium, the carotid

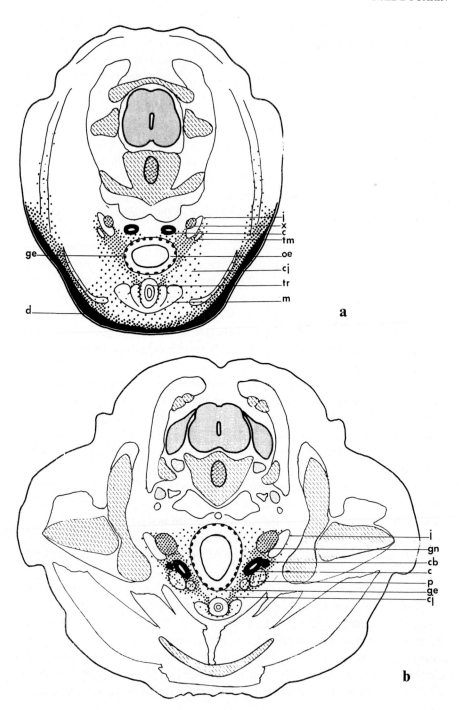

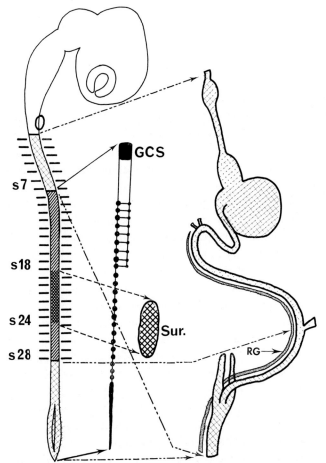

GCS

s7

s18

s24

Sur.

s28

RG→

Fig. 10. Diagram showing the levels of origin on the neural axis of the autonomic neurons and adrenomedullary cells. The vagal level of the neural crest (from somites 1 to 7) provides all the enteric ganglia of the preumbilical gut and contributes to the innervation of the post-umbilical gut. The lumbosacral level of the neural crest gives rise to the ganglion of Remak (RG) and to most of the ganglia of the post-umbilical gut. The orthosympathetic chain derives from the level of the neural crest posterior to the 6th somite and the adrenomedullary cells originate from the level of somites 18 to 24. Sur.: suprarenal gland; GCS: superior cervical ganglion.

←

Fig. 9. Distribution of neural crest derivatives in the pharyngeal derivatives of a 9-day host embryo after an interspecific graft of the mesencephalon and rhombencephalon primordia.

(a) Transverse section in the neck.

(b) Transverse section at the level of the carotid bodies.

Solid areas: Tissues entirely made up of quail cells: dermis (d); wall of carotid arteries (c); enteric ganglia (ge); carotid body (cb).

Stippled areas: Tissues made up of a mixture of neural crest and mesodermal cells: loose connective tissues (cj); Schwann cells of the vagus nerve (x); glial cells of the ganglion nodosum (gn); connective tissue of thyroid, parathyroid (p) and thymus (tm). j: jugular vein; m: tracheohyoideus and tracheolateralis muscles; tr: trachea.

body cells were recognized by the presence of dopamine and the absence of 5HT, like cells from the quail neural crest (Pearse *et al.* 1973).

Origin of the autonomic neurons and adrenomedullary cells. Although the origin of the adrenal medulla (Van Campenhout 1930; Hammond & Yntema 1947; Strudel 1953) and the autonomic neurons (see Le Douarin 1974 for references) from the neural crest is now fully accepted, the level of the neural axis from which each is derived has not been precisely established and remains controversial, especially for cells of the enteric ganglion.

Isotopic and isochronic grafts of pieces of quail neural primordium into chick (or vice versa) were systematically made from the mesencephalon down to the posterior side of the neural axis. From observations on the intestine, the orthosympathetic chains and the suprarenal glands of the host, the following picture of the developmental capabilities of the trunk neural crest emerged (Fig. 10). The enteric ganglia appeared to have a double origin from the vagal (level of somites 1 to 7) and the lumbosacral (behind the level of the 28th somite) neural crest (Le Douarin & Teillet 1973). The most important contribution to these ganglia is from the anterior level; when an isotopic graft was derived from this region, quail cells made up the whole of the host pre-umbilical gut ganglia and part of the post-umbilical section of the digestive tract. When the posterior region was grafted, on the other hand, quail cells were encountered only in the post-umbilical gut and in the ganglion of Remak. When the cervico-dorsal region (from somites 8 to 28) was grafted, no parasympathetic ganglion cells of the host embryo arose from the quail tissue, but the quail cells were then found in the orthosympathetic chain and the aortic plexus. Thus, they migrated to the vicinity of the intestine but never penetrated into the dorsal mesenchyme.

The presence of quail cells in the *adrenal medulla* was observed only when an isotopic graft was from the level corresponding to somites 18 to 24. When this whole area was grafted, all the adrenomedullary cells of the host suprarenal gland showed the quail nuclear marker (Le Douarin & Teillet 1971; Teillet & Le Douarin 1974).

These observations indicate that neuroblasts originating from the cervico-dorsal region of the neural crest (somites 8 to 28) give rise only to orthosympathetic adrenergic neurons and do not participate in parasympathetic intestinal innervation. It was then of interest to investigate whether the neuroblasts

---

→

FIG. 11. (A) Schema of the heterotopic transplantation of the 'adrenomedullary' level of a quail neural tube into the 'vagal' level of a chick embryo.

(B) Result of the experiment indicated in A: the digestive tract of the host is innervated by quail cells (*a*), which differentiate into neurons as revealed by the silver impregnation technique (*b*). A, Auerbach's, and M, Meissner's, plexuses.

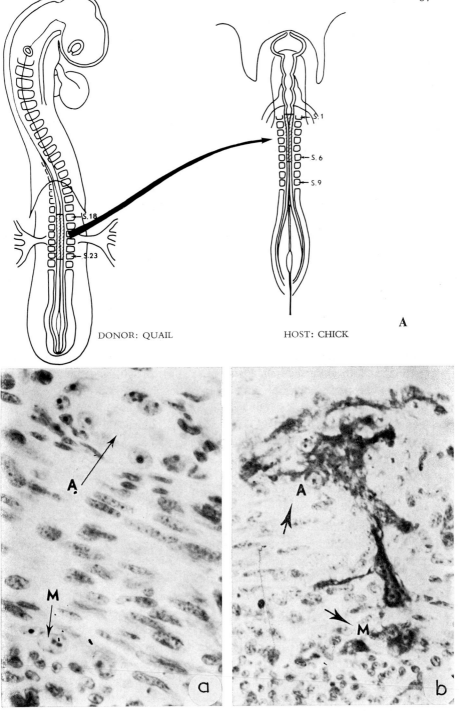

DONOR: QUAIL   HOST: CHICK

A

B

originating from the cervicodorsal region and from the vagal level are already programmed, when they leave the neural crest, to differentiate into adrenergic and cholinergic neurons respectively.

Factors controlling the migration and differentiation of the autonomic neuroblasts

Adrenomedullary segments of the quail neural tube (from the level of somites 18 to 24) were transplanted heterotopically to the 'vagal' level (somites 1 to 7) of chick embryos (Fig. 11A). The intestine of the host was observed histologically so that we could see whether, in these conditions, dorsal neural crest cells are able to colonize the gut and give rise to enteric ganglia. No fluorogenic amine was found in the enteric ganglia made up of quail cells. This indicates that quail neuroblasts which colonize the gut under these experimental conditions do not differentiate into catecholaminergic neurons, which was their presumptive fate.

The cholinergic innervation of smooth intestinal muscles was characterized by physiological assays done as previously described (Le Douarin et al. 1975). The gizzard and duodenal loop associated with the right branch of the vagus nerve were dissected from 15- to 17-day-old embryos. The preparation was transferred into a Perspex chamber with a device that makes it possible to stimulate the nerve while the gizzard and duodenal loop are bathed in oxygenated Tyrode solution. The contractions of the ascending limb of the duodenal loop were recorded by an RCA 5734 electromechanical transducer valve connected to a Tektronix 502 A oscilloscope. The nerves were stimulated by rectangular current pulses (50/min, 15 V, 20 ms) for 1 min between two platinum electrodes fixed in the lateral frame of the chamber. Acetylcholine was added to the medium in final concentrations of 10^{-8}–10^{-4}M. Pretreatment by atropine (10^{-4}M) lasted 45 min. Between assays the preparation was perfused at a flow rate of 2.5 ml/min.

The physiological properties of duodenal innervation were tested first in control embryos. The experimental conditions made it possible to record the mechanical activity of the duodenal loop for several hours. Fig. 12 shows a typical response consisting of an increase in tension. A positive inotropic effect was also frequently observed. The response was qualitatively the same whatever the stage of development of the embryos (15–18 days of incubation) but its amplitude increased with age. In most cases the positive tonotropic effect slowed down several minutes after stimulation stopped. When several series of stimuli were separated by 15-min resting periods, the inotropic effect decreased but the positive tonotropic effect persisted. Sensitivity to acetylcholine was seen at final

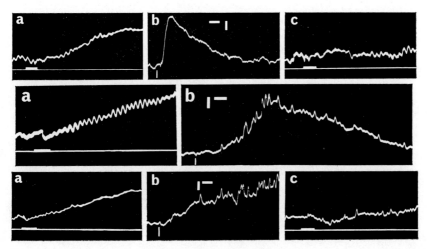

FIG. 12. Top row: Mechanical activity of the ascending limb of the duodenal loop in normal 17-day-old chick embryo. Calibration (indicated in (*b*)): vertical scale, 5 mg; horizontal scale, 1 min. (*a*) Vagus stimulation (large part of the baseline); a progressive positive tonotropic effect develops. (*b*) Acetylcholine administration (10^{-5} g/ml) at the time marked by a vertical line; note the rapid appearance of the tonotropic effect. (*c*) Lack of effect of nerve stimulation (large part of the baseline) in atropine-treated preparation.

Middle row: Mechanical activity of the ascending limb of the duodenal loop in 17-day-old grafted embryo (isotopic and isochronic graft). (*a*) Nerve stimulation (large part of the baseline); positive inotropic and tonotropic effects are observed. (*b*) Acetylcholine administration (10^{-5} g/ml) at the time marked by a vertical line.

Bottom row: Mechanical activity of the ascending limb of the duodenal loop in 17-day-old grafted embryo (heterotopic graft). (*a*) Nerve stimulation (large part of the baseline). (*b*) Acetylcholine administration (10^{-5} g/ml) at the time marked by a vertical line. (*c*) Lack of effect of nerve stimulation (large part of the baseline) in atropine-treated preparation. Note that these results are similar to those obtained in normal or isotopically grafted embryos.

concentrations of 10^{-6}M–10^{-4}M (Fig. 12). Normal mechanical activity returned after 30–90 min. Pretreatment with atropine inhibited the effects of nerve stimulation (Fig. 12) and acetylcholine.

The same physiological assays were applied to 17-day-old experimental embryos. After isotopic and isochronic grafts of the vagal region of the neural crest, nerve stimulation and acetylcholine administration both produced results in good agreement with those obtained in controls and the graft did not disturb the development of the duodenal loop innervation (Fig. 12).

The same result was observed after heterotopic grafts of quail adrenomedullary neural primordium to the vagal level of the chick. Nerve stimulation resulted in positive inotropic and tonotropic effects (Fig. 12) and in both cases sensitivity to acetylcholine was similar to that in controls. This response was observed several times, and after stimulation the effect decreased very slowly. Pretreatment of the preparations with atropine suppressed the response to both acetyl-

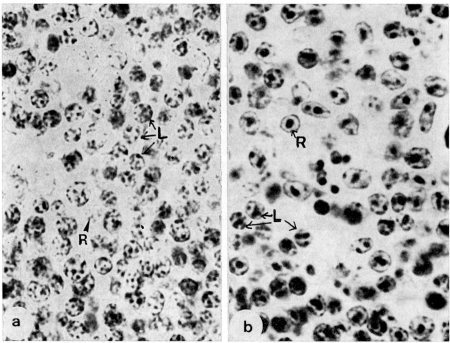

FIG. 13. Thymic tissue, Feulgen-Rossenbeck stained, × 1200. (*a*): 16-day chick thymus. Reticular cells (R) are characterized by a clear nucleus. Lymphocytes (L) show a nucleus with several small chromocentres. (*b*): 16-day quail thymus. R: reticular cells with a large central condensation of chromatin. L: lymphocytes with a large, irregularly shaped mass of heterochromatin and small Feulgen-positive dense patches attached to the nuclear membrane.

choline and stimulation, as in the two series previously studied (control and isotopically grafted embryos).

The results reported above show that the neuroblasts of the dorsal neural crest, which in normal development do not participate in the innervation of the gut wall, can migrate into the splanchnic mesoderm and differentiate into normally organized ganglia of Auerbach's and Meissner's plexuses, when transplanted at the vagal level at an early stage.

As already demonstrated (Le Lièvre & Le Douarin 1973, 1975; Le Lièvre 1974), the developmental conditions of pharyngeal morphogenesis produce a massive lateroventral migration of crest cells. The crest cells are then in contact with the gut endoderm and become incorporated into the splanchnic mesodermal layer. Thereafter they migrate caudally in the gut wall and become organized in Auerbach's and Meissner's plexuses on the internal and external sides, respectively, of the circular muscle layer.

It has been established that catecholamine synthesis is induced in the orthosympathoblasts through a tissue interaction with the somitic mesenchyme (Cohen 1972; Norr 1973). Since the cells forming the anterior somites spread at early developmental stages, the ganglioblasts from the dorsal crest transplanted at the vagal level are in contact with the somitic mesenchyme for only a short time. They do not stay in the dorsal mesenchyme as they do at the trunk level, but proceed on their migration, become ventrally localized, and colonize the gut. In contact with the splanchnic mesoderm, they differentiate into normal cholinergic parasympathetic neurons and do not synthesize catecholamines, which was their presumptive fate.

Thus it can be concluded that the autonomic neuroblasts have a choice between two programmes of differentiation when they begin to migrate, and that the nature of the neurotransmitter they synthesize depends on the microenvironment in which they are localized.

THE ORIGIN OF THE HAEMOPOIETIC STEM CELLS IN THE THYMUS AND THE BURSA OF FABRICIUS

Much descriptive information based on histological observations exists on the development of lymphoid components in the haemopoietic organs. This has led to controversial views about the embryonic origin of the lymphocytes in the thymus and the bursa of Fabricius (see Metcalf & Moore 1971 for references).

Moore & Owen (1965, 1966, 1967), using chromosomal markers, showed that blood-borne lymphocytic precursor cells enter the primordia of the thymus and bursa during the early stages of development, and they suggested an extrinsic origin for the lymphoid population of these organs. Since the technique allows the origin of only dividing cells to be analysed, a contribution to lymphopoiesis of cells belonging to the rudiments of the thymus and bursa could not be excluded. Thus it seemed interesting to apply the quail–chick marker system to this problem. It is indeed possible to distinguish easily the various cell types of the developing lymphoid organs (reticular, connective and lymphoid cells) in the two species by either light or electron microscopy (Fig. 13) (Le Douarin & Jotereau 1973a, b, 1975; Jotereau 1975; Le Douarin et al. 1975).

Thymus rudiments from quail embryos ranging from the 15-somite stage to 8 days of incubation were grafted into the somatopleure of 3-day chick embryos. The same experiment was done with bursa rudiments from 7- to 11-day embryonic quails. When the total age (age at the time of the graft plus duration of the graft) was 14 days for the thymus and 18–19 days for the bursa, the explants were fixed and examined histologically. When grafted into a chick embryo before the end of the 5th day of incubation the quail thymus developed as a chimeric tissue in which reticular and connective cells belonged to the graft while the

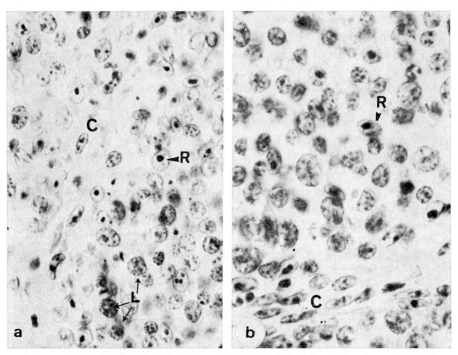

FIG. 14. (a) Thymus rudiment of a 4-day quail embryo grafted for 10 days into a chick. The reticular (R) and connective cells of the interlobular spaces (C) are of quail origin while the lymphocytes (L) belong to the host, × 1000.

   (b) Graft of a 6-day quail bursa into a chick embryo for 13 days. Same result as in (a). Feulgen-Rossenbeck staining, × 1000.

whole lymphoid cell population was derived from the chick host (Fig. 14a). If the thymic rudiment was taken from the quail donor during the 6th day of incubation, the lymphocytes were of mixed host and donor origin. In contrast, thymuses which developed in the host after being grafted from the 7th day onwards were populated by quail lymphocytes. The results indicate that the lymphocytes which differentiate in the thymus are entirely derived from extrinsic blood-borne stem cells which colonize the thymic primordium at a precise developmental stage. Neither the endoderm nor the mesoderm of the thymus have the capacity to give rise to lymphocytes.

   In another experimental series, thymuses taken from quail embryos after colonization by lymphocytoblasts (at 7 to 10 days of incubation) were grafted into 3-day chicks. The duration of the graft was prolonged so that the total age of the organ at the time the animal was killed was 17 to 25 days. In this case, the donor lymphocytes which initially developed in these organs were progressively replaced by host cells which invaded the thymic cortex from the periphery to the medulla. The latter was the last thymic area to be colonized by host lymphoid cells. This observation shows that the first inflow of stem cells which takes place during thymic organogenesis is followed later by a second colonization of new lymphocytic precursors which completely renews the lymphoid cell population at around hatching time (Le Douarin & Jotereau 1973b).

In similar experiments, chick thymic rudiments of various ages were grafted into quail embryos. In the chick, the first inflow of lymphoid stem cell lasts about 36 hours, between $6\frac{1}{2}$ and 8 days of incubation. As with the quail-into-chick grafts described above, the lymphoid cells were renewed when the graft time in the quail was prolonged (Le Douarin & Jotereau 1975).

The assumption that the lymphoid precursor (Moore & Owen 1967; Owen & Ritter 1969) is the large basophilic cell described by several authors (Maximow 1909) in the thymic rudiment was shown beyond doubt to be correct when we used the quail–chick marker system. By grafting into quail embryos thymic rudiments taken from 6-day chicks we were able to identify the basophilic cells as being of quail origin and, later, to follow their differentiation into lymphocytes (Le Douarin et al. 1975).

The results of the experiment carried out on the bursa of Fabricius are summarized in Table 1. As for the thymus, it appears that the haemopoietic differentiation of the bursa depends entirely on an immigration process of stem cells (Fig. 14b), which lasts longer than for the thymus; for the quail, the stem cell inflow is continuous from the end of the 6th day of incubation and becomes significantly lower only after the 11th day. As already shown (Le Douarin 1967), heterotopic transplantation into the somatopleure of the undifferentiated thymic endoderm isolated from the pharynx at the 15- to 30-somite stage leads to the formation of normal thymic tissue, indicating that the attraction for precursor cells lies in the endodermal component of the thymus. Stem cells circulating in the blood cross the vessel wall near the thymus and actively colonize the thymic endoderm. It can be assumed that the invasion of the haemopoietic rudiments results from a chemotactic mechanism whose intensity varies during embryonic life. After a period of strong attraction which is responsible for the first inflow of lymphoid precursor cells, the endodermal thymic component becomes much less attractive for a while. Then, while the primary stem cells differentiate into lymphocytes, the attraction reappears in the haemopoietic rudiment and the lymphoid population is then renewed.

SUMMARY AND CONCLUSIONS

The stability of labelling provided by the quail nuclear marker allows problems related to cell migration during embryogenesis to be investigated. Using

TABLE 1   Origin of cells after quail bursa rudiments from 5- to 11-day old embryos had been grafted into 3-day chick hosts.

Stage of development of donor (days) \ Duration of the graft (days)	7	8	9	10	11	12	13	14
5							Host	Host
6						Host	Host	
7					Host/Donor	Host/Donor		
8				Host/Donor	Host/Donor			
9			Host/Donor	Host/Donor				
10		Donor	Donor					
11	Donor	Donor						

Donor   Host/Donor   Host

Total age of the bursa at the time of fixation was 18 to 19 days. Lymphoid cells were exclusively of host type when the bursa was grafted at 5 and 6 days of incubation. Lymphocytes were a mixture of host and donor cells when the graft was done at 7 to 9 days, and solely of donor type when the bursa was transplanted from 10 days onwards.

the 'quail–chick' marking technique we have been able to identify new derivatives of the neural crest and to learn more about the contribution that this structure makes to cephalo-cervical morphogenesis. We have also paid special attention to the mechanisms controlling the migration and differentiation of autonomic neuroblasts. Predetermined migration pathways characteristic of various levels of the embryo have been demonstrated (Le Douarin & Teillet 1974), especially concerning the colonization of the gut by enteric ganglion cells. The autonomic neuroblasts appear competent to synthesize either catecholamines or acetylcholine when they leave the neural crest. Their phenotypic expression as either cholinergic or adrenergic neurons depends on the particular microenvironment they are in when they stop migrating. If the cells differentiate in the perichordal area they synthesize catecholamines, whereas when they are in contact with the splanchnic gut mesoderm they elaborate acetylcholine.

The use of the quail nuclear marker for studying the development of the haemopoietic organs demonstrated that cells of the primordia of thymus and bursa could not differentiate into lymphocytes. Lymphocytes are derived from extrinsic stem cells which are specifically attracted by the endodermal component of these organs; in addition this component induces the stem cells to differentiate into lymphocytes.

References

BERNHARD, W. (1968) Une méthode de coloration régressive à l'usage de la microscopie électronique. *C. R. Hebd. Séances Acad. Sci. Sér. D Sci. Nat. 267*, 2170–2173

BERNHARD, W. & GRANBOULAN, N. (1968) Electron microscopy of the nucleolus in vertebrate cells, in *The Nucleus* (Dalton, A.J. & Haguenau, F., eds.), (*Ultrastructure in Biological Systems*, vol. 3), pp. 81–149, Academic Press, New York

BISCOE, T.J. (1971) Carotid body: structure and function. *Physiol. Rev. 51*, 437–495

BLACKLER, A.W. & FISCHBERG, M. (1961) Transfer of primordial germ cells in *Xenopus laevis. J. Embryol. Exp. Morphol. 9*, 634–641

COHEN, A.M. (1972) Factors directing the expression of sympathetic nerve tracts in cells of neural crest origin. *J. Exp. Zool. 179*, 167–182

DE PARIS, P. (1967) Sur la destinée des cellules de l'îlot sanguin après échange de greffons entre embryons diploïdes et triploïdes chez l'amphibien urodèle *Pleurodeles waltlii. C. R. Séances Soc. Biol. Fil. 161*, 2275–2278

ELSDALE, T.R., FISCHBERG, M. & SMITH, S. (1958) A mutation that reduces nucleolar number in *Xenopus laevis. Exp. Cell Res. 14*, 642

FALCK, B. (1962) Observations on the possibility of the cellular localization of monoamines by a fluorescence method. *Acta Physiol. Scand. Suppl. 56*, 197

FONTAINE, J. (1973) Contribution à l'étude du développement du corps carotidien et du corps ultimobranchial des oiseaux: Le contenu en monoamines et la capacité de capter la L-dopa des cellules glomiques et des cellules à calcitonine au cours de la vie embryonnaire. *Arch. Anat. Microsc. Morphol. Exp. 62*, 89–100

HAMMOND, W.S. & YNTEMA, C.L. (1947) Depletions of the thoraco-lumbar sympathetic system following removal of neural crest in the chick. *J. Comp. Neurol. 86*, 237–266

HAMMOND, W.S. & YNTEMA, C.L. (1953) Deficiencies in the visceral skeleton of the chick after removal of the cranial neural crest. *Anat. Rec. 115*, 393

HAMMOND, W.S. & YNTEMA, C.L. (1964) Depletions of pharyngeal arch cartilages following extirpation of cranial neural crest in chick embryo. *Acta Anat. 56*, 21–34

HOLLYFIELD, J.G. (1966) The origin of erythroblasts in *Rana pipiens* tadpoles. *Dev. Biol. 14*, 461–480

HÖRSTADIUS, S. (1950) *The Neural Crest: Its Properties and Derivatives in the Light of Experimental Research*, Oxford University Press, London

JOHNSTON, M.C. (1966) A radioautographic study of the migration and fate of cranial neural crest in the chick embryos. *Anat. Rec. 156*, 130–143

JOTEREAU, F. (1975) Etude comparative du développement du thymus chez la caille et le poulet. Réalisation d'ébauches thymiques chimères de ces deux espèces. *Arch. Biol. 86*, 139–161

LE DOUARIN, N. (1967) Détermination précoce des ébauches de la thyroïde et du thymus chez l'embryon de poulet. *C. R. Hebd. Séances Acad. Sci. Sér. D Sci. Nat. 264*, 940–942

LE DOUARIN, N. (1969) Particularités du noyau interphasique chez la caille japonaise (*Coturnix coturnix japonica*). Utilisation de ces particularités comme 'marquage biologique' dans les recherches sur les interactions tissulaires et les migrations cellulaires au cours de l'ontogenèse. *Bull. Biol. Fr. Belg. 103*, 435–452

LE DOUARIN, N. (1973a) A biological cell labelling technique and its use in experimental embryology. *Dev. Biol. 30*, 217–222

LE DOUARIN, N. (1973*b*) A Feulgen-positive nucleolus. *Exp. Cell Res.* 77, 459–468

LE DOUARIN, N. (1974) Cell recognition based on natural morphological nuclear markers. *Med. Biol. (Helsinki)* 52, 281–319

LE DOUARIN, N. & JOTEREAU, F. (1973*a*) Recherches sur l'origine embryologique des lymphocytes du thymus chez l'embryon d'oiseau. *C. R. Hebd. Séances Acad. Sci. Sér. D Sci. Nat.* 276, 629–632

LE DOUARIN, N. & JOTEREAU, F. (1973*b*) Origin and renewal of lymphocytes in avian embryo thymuses. *Nat. New Biol.* 246, 25–27

LE DOUARIN, N. & JOTEREAU, F. (1975) Tracing of cells of the avian thymus through embryonic life in interspecific chimaeras. *J. Exp. Med.* 142, 17–40

LE DOUARIN, N. & LE LIÈVRE, C. (1970) Démonstration de l'origine neurale des cellules à calcitonine du corps ultimobranchial chez l'embryon de poulet. *C. R. Hebd. Séances Acad. Sci. Sér. D Sci. Nat.* 270, 2857–2860

LE DOUARIN, N. & LE LIÈVRE, C. (1971) Sur l'origine des cellules à calcitonine du corps ultimobranchial de l'embryon d'oiseau. *C. R. Assoc. Anat.* 152, 558–568

LE DOUARIN, N. & TEILLET, M.A. (1970) Sur quelques aspects de la migration des cellules neurales chez l'embryon de poulet étudiés par la méthode des greffes hétérospécifiques de tube nerveux. *C. R. Séances Soc. Biol. Fil.* 164, 390–397

LE DOUARIN, N. & TEILLET, M.A. (1971) Localisation, par la méthode des greffes interspécifiques, du territoire neural dont dérivent les cellules adrénales surrénaliennes chez l'embryon d'oiseau. *C. R. Hebd. Séances Acad. Sci. Sér. D Sci. Nat.* 272, 481–484

LE DOUARIN, N. & TEILLET, M.A. (1973) The migration of neural crest cells to the wall of the digestive tract in avian embryo. *J. Embryol. Exp. Morphol.* 30, 31–48

LE DOUARIN, N. & TEILLET, M.A. (1974) Experimental analysis of the migration and differentiation of neuroblasts of the autonomic nervous system and of neurectodermal mesenchymal derivatives, using a biological cell marking technique. *Dev. Biol.* 41, 162–184

LE DOUARIN, N., LE LIÈVRE, C. & FONTAINE, J. (1972) Recherches expérimentales sur l'origine embryologique du corps carotidien chez les oiseaux. *C. R. Hebd. Séances Acad. Sci. Sér. D Sci. Nat.* 275, 583–586

LE DOUARIN, N., FONTAINE, J. & LE LIEVRE, C. (1974) New studies on the neural crest origin of the avian ultimobranchial glandular cells—interspecific combinations and cytochemical characterization of C cells based on the uptake of biogenic amine precursors. *Histochemistry* 38, 297–305

LE DOUARIN, N., RENAUD, D., TEILLET, M.A. & LE DOUARIN, G. (1975) Cholinergic differentiation of presumptive adrenergic neuroblasts in interspecific chimaeras after heterotopic transplantations. *Proc. Natl. Acad. Sci. USA* 72, 728–732

LE LIÈVRE, C. (1974) Rôle des cellules mésectodermiques issues des crêtes neurales céphaliques dans la formation des arcs branchiaux et du squelette viscéral. *J. Embryol. Exp. Morphol.* 31, 453–477

LE LIÈVRE, C. & LE DOUARIN, N. (1973) Contribution du mésectoderme à la genèse des arcs aortiques chez l'embryon d'oiseau. *C. R. Hebd. Séances Acad. Sci. Sér. D Sci. Nat.* 276, 383–386

LE LIÈVRE, C. & LE DOUARIN, N. (1975) Mesenchymal derivatives of the neural crest: analysis of chimaeric quail and chick embryos. *J. Embryol. Exp. Morphol.* 34, 124–154

MAXIMOW, A. (1909) Untersuchungen über Blut und Bindegewebe. Über die Histogenese des Thymus bei Säugetieren. *Arch. Mikrosk. Anat. Entwicklungsmech.* 74, 525–621

METCALF, D. & MOORE, M.A.S. (1971) *Haemopoietic Cells*, North-Holland, Amsterdam

MOORE, M.A.S. & OWEN, J.J.T. (1965) Chromosome marker studies on the development of the haemopoietic system in the chick embryo. *Nature (Lond.)* 208, 956–957

MOORE, M.A.S. & OWEN, J.J.T. (1966) Experimental studies on the development of the bursa of Fabricius. *Dev. Biol.* 14, 40–51

MOORE, M.A.S. & OWEN, J.J.T. (1967) Experimental studies on the development of the thymus. *J. Exp. Med.* 126, 715–726

Norr, S.C. (1973) *In vitro* analysis of sympathetic neuron differentiation from chick neural crest cells. *Dev. Biol. 34*, 16–38

Owen, J.J.T. & Ritter, M.A. (1969) Tissue interaction in the development of thymus lymphocytes. *J. Exp. Med. 129*, 431–437

Pearse, A.G.E. (1969) The cytochemistry and ultrastructure of polypeptide hormone producing cells of the APUD series and the embryologic, physiologic and pathologic implications of the concept. *J. Histochem. Cytochem. 17*, 303–313

Pearse, A.G.E., Polak, J.M., Rost, F.W.D., Fontaine, J., Le Lièvre, C. & Le Douarin, N. (1973) Demonstration of the neural crest origin of Type I (APUD) in the avian carotid body, using a cytochemical marker system. *Histochemie 34*, 191–203

Polak, J.M., Pearse, A.G.E., Le Lièvre, C., Fontaine, J. & Le Douarin, N. (1974) Immunocytochemical confirmation of the neural crest origin of avian calcitonin producing cells. *Histochemistry 40*, 209–214

Raven, C.P. (1937) Experiments on the origin of the sheath cells and sympathetic neuroblasts in amphibia. *J. Comp. Neurol. 67*, 221

Strudel, G. (1953) Conséquences de l'excision de tronçons du tube nerveux sur la morphogenèse de l'embryon de poulet et sur la différenciation de ses organes: contribution à la genèse de l'orthosympathique. *Ann. Sci. Nat. Zool. Biol. Anim. 15*, 251–329

Taylor, J.H., Woods, P.S. & Hughes, W.L. (1957) The organization and duplication of chromosomes as revealed by autoradiographic studies using tritium-labeled thymidine. *Proc. Natl. Acad. Sci. USA 43*, 122–128

Teillet, M.A. (1971a) Recherches sur le mode de migration et la différenciation des mélanocytes cutanés chez l'embryon d'oiseau: étude expérimentale par la méthode des greffes hétérospécifiques entre embryons de caille et de poulet. *Ann. Embryol. Morphog. 4*, 95–109

Teillet, M.A. (1971b) Niveau d'origine de plusieurs dérivés des crêtes neurales cervicales postérieures, thoraciques et lombaires chez l'embryon d'oiseau. *C. R. Assoc. Anat. 152*, 543–550

Teillet, M.A. & Le Douarin, N. (1970) La migration des cellules pigmentaires étudiée par la méthode des greffes hétérospécifiques de tube nerveux chez l'embryon d'oiseau. *C. R. Hebd. Séances Acad. Sci. Sér. D Sci. Nat. 270*, 3095–3098

Teillet, M.A. & Le Douarin, N. (1974) Détermination par la méthode des greffes hétérospécifiques d'ébauches neurales de caille sur l'embryon de poulet, du niveau du névraxe dont dérivent les cellules médullo-surrénaliennes. *Arch. Anat. Microsc. Morphol. Exp. 63*, 51–62

Triplett, E.L. (1958) The development of the sympathetic ganglia, sheath cells, and meninges in amphibians. *J. Exp. Zool. 138*, 283–311

Turpen, J.B. & Volpe, E.P. (1975) On the origin of thymic lymphocytes. *Am. Zool. 15*, 51–61

Unna, P.G. (1913) *Virchows Arch. Pathol. Anat. Physiol. Klin. Med. 214*, 320 [Cited in Gabe, M. (1968) *Techniques Histologiques*, Masson, Paris]

Van Campenhout, E. (1930) Contribution to the problem of the development of the sympathetic nervous system. *J. Exp. Zool. 56*, 295–320

Weston, J.A. (1970) The migration and differentiation of neural crest cells. *Adv. Morphog. 8*, 41–114

Discussion

Saxén: Mammalian embryologists may also find this marker useful. For instance, we have done mouse–quail recombination experiments *in vitro* and it is a very good marker there, too.

Wolpert: How much of the neural crest is absolutely essential for the development of the many organs that are derived from it? If the neural crest is removed not all of those organs are lost, are they?

Le Douarin: If the neural crest cells are completely removed, the face and pharynx become extensively malformed. For instance, after the whole rhombencephalon and mesencephalon have been excised the skeleton of the face and of the branchial arches does not differentiate. There is no regulation from other embryonic primordia.

Gluecksohn-Waelsch: In amphibians, the origin of the visceral arch skeleton from the neural crest was proved by Harrison in transplantation experiments between two species of *Ambystoma* (for references see Hörstadius 1950).

Wolpert: Does a carotid body develop if the neural crest is removed?

Le Douarin: No.

Newth: But in the melanocyte population, for example, regulation can occur.

Le Douarin: Yes: after the excision of a fragment of the neural crest in a quail embryo the feather pigmentation pattern is not altered.

Newth: In urodeles, if not in chicks, total removal of the neural crest does not prevent melanocyte formation, presumed to be from the neural plate.

Cooke: If differentiation of cells is determined by the sites in which they end up, it seems odd that, in normal development, neural crest derivatives that differentiate differently come from very different regions, and by no means from levels adjacent to their position of settling. They sometimes migrate all along the length of the animal's body.

Le Douarin: Differentiation of neuroblasts into cholinergic or adrenergic neurons depends on which region of the animal the cells are in. I don't say that differentiation of all the neural crest derivatives depends on the same phenomenon. On the contrary it appears that some determination of neural crest cells happens before the onset of the migration. This is the case for the presumptive mesectodermal cells which give rise to connective elements even if cranial neural crests are grafted at the trunk level of the neural axis.

Cooke: When you did the heterotopic grafts the hosts and donors were at different stages of morphogenesis. How long after the operation did these particular types of cells have their origin in the neural crest? Was there time for the determination to have been altered according to the new relative position within the crest?

Le Douarin: We have to make heterochronic grafts in these experiments because migration begins in the head and afterwards progresses caudally. If neural crest cells of the posterior region are being grafted into the anterior region the two must be at different stages. But determination in the trunk neural crest is not very likely to be disturbed by being grafted in the head region, and the direct influence of the splanchnic mesoderm on differentiation of autonomic neurons has been demonstrated by the following experiment. We have shown (Le Douarin & Teillet 1973) that the autonomic neuroblasts reach the hindgut level during the 6th day of incubation in the chick. Thus, if taken before this stage and cultivated on the chorioallantoic membrane, the rectum develops without neurons. The hindgut is taken from a 4½-day chick embryo and associated on the chorioallantoic membrane with the dorsal level of the neural primordium of a 20 to 25-somite quail. The presumptive neuroblasts of the quail neural crest migrate into the chick gut, forming Auerbach's and Meissner's plexuses. In the latter plexus, the neurons are devoid of catecholamine and show a large amount of acetylcholinesterase (EC 3.1.1.7), suggesting that they are differentiated into cholinergic neurons.

Gardner: Dr Cooke asked whether the final site to which the neural crest cells migrate really determines the way that they differentiate or whether it could be something proximal to the spinal cord itself. I believe that Paul Weiss obtained fairly extensive chimerism after intravascular injection of cells into chick embryos. Would it be feasible to try this with neural crest cells as a way of answering that point?

Le Douarin: Yes, there is no objection to injecting neural crest cells into the bloodstream of the embryo except that this technique would not provide very normal conditions for differentiation of neural crest cells. Weiss & Andres (1952) in fact injected not pure melanocytes but a suspension of cells from embryos of a pigmented strain into a White Leghorn strain. They showed that there were melanocytes in the skin of the host. The melanocytes which were injected together with many other kinds of cells therefore went through the endothelium of the blood vessels and migrated throughout the skin. They located in the skin and differentiated into melanocytes.

We have done similar experiments with various types of cells to see whether those cells can recognize homologous tissue. For instance, if hepatocytes from an 8-day quail embryo are injected into a 6-day or 7-day chick embryo some colonies of quail liver cells are found in the liver of the host, but they also appear in many other places. In my opinion this technique provides results which are difficult to interpret for a number of reasons: blood flow is too rapid to allow cell recognition to occur and the injected cells seem to stop randomly in various locations according to the local circulatory conditions.

Škreb: Nicolet (1970) exchanged the primitive streaks of two chick embryos, one labelled with tritiated thymidine and the other unlabelled, and followed the migration of the endoderm. He proved in birds what we suspect in mammalian embryos, namely that the anterior part of the primitive streak always contains a large population of presumptive endodermal cells.

Le Douarin: With J. Fontaine (unpublished work) we did an experiment using a heterospecific combination of epiblast and hypoblast between quail and chick at the pre-streak stage. It appears that the hypoblast gives rise only to the extra-embryonic endoderm (yolk sac endoderm). The endoderm of the embryo is always of the epiblast type and thus is formed through the migration of cells in the primitive streak.

Škreb: The particles can move, while the labelled nuclei cannot. One can see that the endoderm has really migrated inside.

McLaren: What is the earliest stage of chick development at which cell movement or cell mingling has been demonstrated? In the mouse there seems to be rather little cell movement up to the blastocyst stage.

Le Douarin: It is likely that cell movement starts from the early stages of segmentation. However such movements cannot easily be investigated when the egg is still in the oviduct. They were studied essentially during gastrulation, by various methods—cell marking by vital dyes or microparticles of carbon, for instance, and time-lapse cinematography.

McLaren: Are there morphological correlates of cell movement? You know from your chimera experiments which cells had moved, but could you now tell from sections, by hindsight, which cells were moving? Do they look different?

Le Douarin: We have often observed quail cells with elongated shapes. However, cell morphology is not a sure criterion of the migrating state of a cell, because a moving cell may also be round at certain moments of the migration process.

Kelley: Do you see anything in the extracellular matrix that can be correlated with the direction of cell movement?

Le Douarin: The cells migrate preferentially on mucopolysaccharide-rich surfaces such as the external and internal sides of the circular muscle layer of the gut and the lateral sides of the neural tube.

Gropp: Are there any enzyme histochemical markers for migrating cells? For instance, in the bovine embryo, adenosinetriphosphatase (EC 3.6.1.3) gives a positive reaction in migrating melanoblasts, similar to that in migrating germ cells and other migrating cells (Ohno & Gropp 1965).

Le Douarin: To my knowledge no specific marker has been found in the neural crest during the migration process.

References

HORSTÄDIUS, S. (1950) *The Neural Crest*, Oxford University Press, London

LE DOUARIN, N. & TEILLET, M.A. (1973) The migration of neural crest cells to the wall of the digestive tract in avian embryo. *J. Embryol. Exp. Morphol. 30*, 31–48

NICOLET, G. (1970) Analyse autoradiographique de la localisation des differentes ébauches présomptives dans la ligne primitive de l'embryon de poulet. *J. Embryol. Exp. Morphol. 23*, 79–108

OHNO, S. & GROPP, A. (1965) Embryological basis for germ cell chimerism in mammals. *Cytogenetics (Basel) 4*, 251–260

WEISS, P. & ANDRES, G.M. (1952) Experiments on the fate of embryonic cells—chick—disseminated by the vascular route. *J. Exp. Zool. 121*, 449–487

General discussion I

DETERMINATION/DIFFERENTIATION

McLaren: We might find it useful to consider more closely how we define determination, differentiation and allocation. Imagine an initial undifferentiated state O, from which lead two alternative pathways of differentiation, X and Y, in two different environments, E_x and E_y. Imagine a third 'neutral' environment, E_o, in which neither type of differentiation takes place. One can distinguish three phases (see Fig. 1). In the first phase (I) transplantation of undifferentiated tissue from environment E_x into the neutral environment gives no differentiation, while transfer into E_y gives differentiation along pathway Y. In the second phase (II), transfer to E_y still gives Y, but now transfer to the neutral environment E_o gives X. Finally (III), determination is complete and whatever environment we put the tissue into we still get X. In the first phase the tissue can be called labile or undetermined, in the second it can be referred to as reversibly determined, and in the third as irreversibly determined. Of

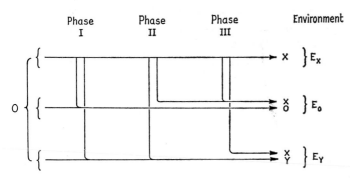

FIG. 1 (McLaren). Phases of differentiation in two environments, X and Y.

103

course these phases can be telescoped, so that the third follows immediately after the first.

Differentiation means 'becoming different', and Dr Gardner wisely referred to overt differentiation. Whether or not we recognize a state as 'differentiated' is a function of our methods of observation. If one had an all-seeing eye any determined state would perhaps also be a differentiated state, provided one were allowed to 'see' biochemical as well as morphological differences. Dr Gardner made the point that in the mouse there is a very short interval between determination and overt differentiation.

The phenomenon of allocation of cells is a different type of concept from differentiation or determination. It is concerned only with the *organization* of cells within the embryo and not with the *properties* of cells. It can involve specific organizational attributes, such as recognition via cell surface properties, or non-specific attributes like the cessation of movement. Cells can in principle be allocated at an early stage (e.g. in phase I), before any determination or differentiation has occurred.

Newth: What you said implies that full functional differentiation must be preceded by determination. If the Xs and Ys were allocated without overlap, there would of course be trouble in cases of metaplasia. The dorsal margin of the iris of the *Triturus* eye is determined at some point, and at a later point it is differentiated. If provoked, its cells can still produce an entirely different cell type, involving a complete chemical switch. The dorsal margin doesn't altogether like those categories. The problem of differentiation and determination is perhaps not quite so simple as we have thought.

McLaren: In your example, the tissue would have reached my phase II, i.e. one could say that it was determined but not irreversibly so.

Newth: But the implication of your phase II is that there is still some way to go to reach X or zero.

McLaren: X and Y were supposed to indicate pathways. I was regarding differentiation as arising at the same time as determination if only one could see it. The time at which one thinks that differentiation occurs is in part a function of one's techniques of observation.

Glueksohn-Waelsch: I am not sure that this is necessarily so. Even if the product of differentiation can be identified on the biochemical level, e.g. as enzyme X, the differentiation product of a particular cell might not be produced at the time of determination, before morphological differentiation. A cell may become determined in mammals as it does in *Drosophila*, i.e. long before differentiation products can be identified on any level. It is true that in the mouse the long interval between determination and differentiation, so characteristic of *Drosophila*, is much shortened but I think of it still in terms of an interval.

Wolpert: I think determination and differentiation *are* different. When I think of differentiation I think of overt differentiation. There are 150–200 different cell types in the body and from the point of view of differentiation there is no reason to believe that the cartilage in a digit is different from the cartilage in a humerus. But from the point of view of determination there is good reason to believe that the cells in a digit are different from the cells in a humerus. For example, the number of times cells in those two sites divide once they have decided whether they are going to become cartilage is different. I would like to think of determination as defining a cell state. Part of that definition of cell state is that it will differentiate into one of those terminal cell types. But other parameters are associated with that determination and an important feature is that of non-equivalence. That is, cells that have the same differentiated state may be very non-equivalent with respect to other properties, such as cell surface properties or how many times they are going to divide.

Bennett: Wouldn't you call that another state of differentiation? I think I would.

Wolpert: I would prefer not to. But it depends on your standpoint.

Bennett: In phase I, which you called a state of labile determination, Dr McLaren, are there truly any cells which are not, in a sense, determined? Don't you think that all cells are really at any given time determined to be something? Dr Gardner's and Dr Škreb's results made me think that, in general, determination of a cell may be a state in which it has one of two decisions to make. In other words, it has to make a binary decision to be either inner cell mass or trophectoderm. Once it has done that, it seems to arrive at another stage of determination in which it has again a binary decision to make to go in one of two directions.

McLaren: But at any particular point it may not have to take that decision yet. I would maintain that a 4-cell blastomere of a mouse was 'undetermined', i.e. in my phase I.

Bennett: I agree, but under normal conditions that cell, by dividing, will come to a point where a binary decision is needed.

Rutter: Why do you insist that it is binary?

Bennett: I can't think of any cells which clearly, without going through a stage in between, have three choices open to them.

Rutter: Can you think of any one cell for which a binary decision has been clearly determined?

Bennett: The cleaving mouse egg comes to the point of doing one of two things (i.e. forming trophoblast or remaining uncommitted inner cell mass), and the next few decisions that cells in the early embryo must make also appear to be based on just two choices.

Rutter: Maybe that is so in that particular case, but in most instances, binary decisions have not been demonstrated and ternary or quaternary decisions might be made. In the developing pancreas, for example, I believe that a pluripotent cell can give rise to an exocrine, to a duct, to an endocrine A, or to an endocrine B cell. Each of those decisions might be binary but each might also be quaternary. It is conceivable that a pluripotential cell might give rise to more than two cells by some stochastic mechanism.

Snow: There is a problem here with binary decisions. If you put it in those terms you are saying that when a cell reaches the point at which it is going to divide it is somehow saying to itself that the products of its forthcoming division are going to do one of those two things. In fact, in a stem cell population, where the division event gives rise to another stem cell and a product which is going to differentiate into some other cell type, one could say that after division these two cells are faced with different developmental paths: one is going to be a stem cell and one, by virtue of something that it has lost or gained, is going to develop, for epigenetic reasons, in another direction. That isn't a binary decision, unless of course you include death as an alternative.

Eguchi: From recent observations I have a similar impression to Dr Wolpert, that is that differentiation at the cellular level is a sort of state of the cell itself. The iris cells of the newt always transdifferentiate into lens cells, even in the presence of a potent carcinogen, nitrosoguanidine. It seems to me that the sequence of differentiation from pigment epithelial cell to lens cell is highly consistent. My speculation is that either the iris epithelium of the newt contains some cells which can easily transdifferentiate into lens cells by influences (unknown) from somewhere, or that such a cell population is more or less unstable so that the cells keep their heritability of differentiation and eventually transdifferentiate into lens cells, that is, to a more stable state of differentiation, after some repeats of DNA replications. The lens cells can be regarded as the terminal state of cell differentiation in this sequence because fully differentiated lens fibres no longer replicate.

Škreb: Dr McLaren, why did you propose three phases?

McLaren: For simplicity's sake. The process is presumably continuous.

Gardner: Where would your protodifferentiation fit in Dr McLaren's scheme, Dr Rutter?

Rutter: Protodifferentiation might be the immediate consequence of determination. It may be the first step of cytodifferentiation. Most embryologists consider determination to be different from cytodifferentiation but I wonder whether there is a dramatic difference between those two concepts. Maybe these represent two stages in cytodifferentiation. The first one would involve some aspect of differentiation, for example the cell surface, and the second would involve longer-term phenomena such as changes in organelle function and the production of specific products. If that were the case, and if the first stages were plastic, a certain amount of time would be needed for the products of a cell surface to be produced and for those functions to be accommodated in a natural way. It seems to me that we would have the basis for two or several progressive states of differentiation. The definitions are largely semantic, based on certain kinds of experimental embryological observations. There seems to be no terrific advantage, either conceptually or practically, in taking a firm stand one way or another.

Gurdon: On the question of binary decisions we should not forget the distinction between a single cell in development which will divide into two more and form two lines, and multiple cells, which take their decision together. With one cell whose daughter cells go in two different directions it is relatively easy to define the two directions so that one can always say that the cell is taking a binary decision. If we are thinking of 20 cells taking this decision simultaneously, it is a much more demanding test to require that the product of each of those divisions is binary. The second situation is therefore much more interesting than the first.

McLaren: Are there examples of single cells taking binary decisions, or do cells always differentiate in groups?

Pedersen: The differentiative capabilities of the isolated primary germ layers, as discussed by Drs Gardner and Škreb, suggest that primary ectoderm is a pluripotent cell type which makes a more complex decision in giving rise to embryonic ectoderm, endoderm and mesoderm. If the decisions are binary, then there must be a succession of them.

McLaren: I think that is the vital point. There is a distinction between a cell being pluripotent and a cell taking one of several alternative decisions at a single moment. One can envisage a succession of binary decisions.

Bennett: That is exactly what I meant by my comment. At each decision point, one cell will take one pathway and a cell remaining behind will make another decision. There are many forks.

Saxén: I am not too sure about ectoderm being a typical totipotent cell population. Japanese workers have separated the cells of the undifferentiated amphibian ectoderm electrophoretically into three bands. They suggest that each of these subpopulations already represents determined cells which have only one choice, to differentiate or not to differentiate, into ectoderm, mesoderm or endoderm (Ave *et al.* 1968).

Škreb: So they think the ectoderm is a heterogeneous population of cells?

Saxén: Yes.

Gluecksohn-Waelsch: I don't understand why the cells can be separated electrophoretically but not in terms of their potential for differentiation.

Saxén: According to their hypothesis, differentiation of the ectoderm seen in various experimental conditions is due to selection of one of these populations. It is very speculative, but the fact remains that there seem to be subpopulations of cells in the ectoderm.

Pedersen: One possible source of the electrophoretic variation in addition to surface charge could be cell size, which would vary with the cell cycle.

Škreb: Perhaps differences in cell cycle or in physiological age are responsible.

Gardner: On the question of decision-making in the mammalian embryo, I would not propose that for every $3\frac{1}{2}$-day inner cell mass cell one of the daughter cells becomes endoderm and the other becomes embryonic ectoderm. Within a group of cells, if something like a positional effect is operating which may depend on a gradient, then if we invoke the idea of three, four or five different categories of cells being produced within a single small population at that one time, it enormously complicates any gradient or similar type of mechanism that is going to lead to determination. The binary decision is just a simplistic idea. I would like to see good evidence for a greater number of choices at a particular time, like the inner cell mass going straight to three different types of determined cell. In other words there would perhaps be a stage of development where the inner cell mass cells would colonize all inner cell mass derivatives, and another stage where inner mass cells would go to A, B or C.

Wolpert: I agree with you. It would be much easier if there were binary choices. But in the insect egg, for example, where determination of the main regions occurs at a very early stage, it becomes difficult to see this in terms of binary choices.

Newth: In the classical mosaic egg with perfectly well-defined cytoplasmic areas one could go further. That there isn't a binary choice is shown by centrifugation experiments. The cells take what is allotted to them and the choice is between more than two. In fact, there are four in ascidians but perhaps this is a special case.

Cooke: I am surprised, Dr Wolpert, that you are troubled by the possibility of cellular decisions being more than 'binary'. If at any one time, across a sheet of cells within which this sort of spatial decision-taking process is to occur, there is a gradient with respect to some variable or other, then at first sight a binary choice would be easier because inside the cells the machinery that is interpreting relative cell position has only got to distinguish values above and below a certain threshold. But if more than one subsystem inside the cell is simultaneously responsive to levels of this same gradient variable, then one can assume within reason that separate threshold levels of the variable operate the binary switch of state in each responding subsystem. If such subsystems are in operation at the same time, then effectively a decision that comes out as more than binary can be made at any one time by cells according to position within the cell sheet, or gradient. The particular decision that has been made will be 'encoded' as a combination of the switch states of each of the binary subsystems (Kauffman 1973). If the subsystems operated sequentially in time, cells in the sheet would appear to take binary decisions sequentially, but if all were operating at once, it would require no intrinsically greater accuracy on the part of the cellular response system to give the appearance that a choice between many possibilities at once was being made. Yet I don't think one could push the idea too far—to encode, say, a 30-fold decision!

Hogan: What happens if you take the inner mass cell which has a layer of endoderm on the outside, and then strip that layer off? Will the cells that remain inside make a new layer of endoderm cells on the outside again? Could you go on repeating that?

Gardner: We have no information from *in vitro* studies, but from cell injections the embryonic ectoderm cells seem to be different. In other words, whether they are put directly into the inner cell mass or into the blastocoele, where they have to go through the endoderm layer, they will colonize the same regions later in development.

Hogan: So the cells which remain inside are really different, and are not capable of budding off or switching to form endoderm again?

Bennett: The question is, what do you think happens if you isolate an inner cell mass and it then makes endoderm all round the outside? If you then stripped that endoderm off, would the inner cell mass again make endoderm round the outside?

Gardner: At first we thought that what is called embryonic ectoderm was a reserve that could form other types of cells, but it doesn't seem to be that way *in vivo*. The data are, however, not compelling at present. We are trying to look at it *in vitro*.

McLaren: Janet Rossant (1975a, b) has done the equivalent experiment one step earlier, namely for the inner cell mass versus trophectoderm differentiation. She allowed the differentiation to occur, then put the inner cell mass back where it would have a chance to differentiate trophectoderm if it were able to do so; but it couldn't.

Škreb: Dr Wolpert, you emphasized the difference between determination and differentiation. Why is it necessary to have two terms for essentially the same process?

Wolpert: I think it is a convenient concept, because one needs a concept which defines the state of the cell. For example, one needs to distinguish between the mesenchyme of the wing bud and leg bud of the chick. These respond to the same signal in different ways. The number of determined states may be much larger than the number of differentiated states.

Škreb: The developmental capacities of the three germ layers in mammals are different. Generally speaking there are morphological, biochemical and developmental criteria for differentiation. In our special case of the mammalian germ layers, we can say that there are differences as far as morphological and developmental criteria are concerned. What would you call this step in a long process of development?

Wolpert: I would call the early stages determination. I would like to reserve differentiation for overt cytodifferentiation. Determination may precede differentiation by many hours.

ORIGIN OF THE GERM CELLS

Tarkowski: I would like to refer to the paper of my colleague, Dr W. Ożdżeński (1967) on the origin of primordial germ cells (PGCs) in the mouse. I have the impression that his work has been overlooked, at least by some students of this subject. As Chiquoine, Mintz and other authors did earlier, Dr Ożdżeński examined 7–9-day embryos histochemically, with alkaline phosphatase (EC 3.1.3.1). A detailed examination of a large series of embryos enabled him to detect PGCs for the first time in $7\frac{1}{2}$-day embryos at the stage when allantois is just starting to form; this is earlier than other authors have previously reported. At this early stage one can find a few cells positive for alkaline phosphatase located in the primitive streak or in the mesoderm which forms the core of the allantois and is continuous with the primitive streak. Later, these cells can be seen on the boundary between mesoderm and endoderm and, finally, in the endoderm of the yolk sac. Dr Ożdżeński's descriptive work and the experiments of Dr Gardner and his colleagues together provide good evidence for the origin of PGCs from the mesoderm rather than from the yolk sac endoderm—the tissue of their origin according to the textbooks and even the majority of papers on this subject. On *a priori* grounds alone it is most unlikely that PGCs could originate from the yolk sac endoderm, because at the stage when PGCs can be first visualized the endodermal cells are already highly differentiated.

Gluecksohn-Waelsch: Is that test entirely specific? Could another type of precursor cell perhaps react positively too?

Tarkowski: Not in the region where PGCs are first located, and not along the route of their migration.

Rutter: Do the cells which are positive occur in clones? That is, do all the cells in a particular region show positive tests, or is it just individual cells that are positive?

Tarkowski: At the very beginning there are just a few positive cells scattered in the mesoderm. It is not possible to say whether they represent a clone or have an independent origin.

McLaren: Dr Gardner, you said that the continuity of the germ line had been established in mammals. What did you mean?

Gardner: Of course, no one has produced complete sterility in mammals by damaging part of the cytoplasm of the uncleaved egg, as has been done in amphibia. I simply meant that there is now good evidence for continuity of the germ line from the embryo to the adult in mammals. In other words, the so-called primordial germ cells identified in postimplantation embryos form the entire population of definitive germ cells in the adult (Mintz 1960; Borum 1966; Peters 1970).

McLaren: So you were only referring to the period of mammalian development from about seven days onwards. 'Continuity of the germ line' could be interpreted as implying continuity throughout the entire life cycle.

Gardner: Once a germ-cell lineage can first be seen, the primordial germ cells of the embryo appear to give rise to the entire germ cell population of the adult. People used to talk about the germinal epithelium of the ovary, the idea being that oocytes could be produced according to demand from this epithelium. That doesn't seem to be so. I didn't mean any more than that.

Newth: The old problem, as you say, was whether somatic cells could become germ cells; but can primordial germ cells become somatic cells? This really is important because if the early segregation of the germ line has any developmental value, it is presumably to protect the germ-line cells from somatic influence. If the lost cells, the ones that don't get to the germinal epithelium, or the excess ones in the mammalian chimeras, undergo somatic differentiation, that would be one thing. If they just hang around, waiting for ovariectomy to give them a role, that is another matter. Or if they die that is yet another.

Bennett: The development of testicular teratocarcinomas from male germ cells indicates quite clearly that germ cells can become somatic cells, at least in the case of male primitive germ cells.

Tarkowski: My colleagues have tried to find out what is the fate of PGCs if they are prevented from colonizing the germinal ridges. The experiments consisted of dissecting the hindgut of the mouse embryo at the time when primordial germ cells are migrating along it, and placing it in various ectopic sites of adult mice or in the chick embryo (Ożdżeński 1969; Rogulska *et al.* 1971). In most grafts primordial germ cells were present for three to four days and then they quickly decreased in number and finally disappeared altogether. It remains unknown whether they degenerate or simply lose alkaline phosphatase to become indistinguishable from somatic cells. In the context of this discussion it may be interesting to add that none of the grafts examined after longer periods of time contained nests of undifferentiated embryonic cells or teratoma-like structures similar to testicular teratomas. It may be that PGCs require gonadal mesenchyme or stimuli from other tissues to proliferate and survive.

Cooke: I was interested in the circumstantial evidence Dr Gardner mentioned for the unequal partitioning of the germ plasm during cytokinesis as the germ cells pursue their lineage through the body. If this is going on, it might indicate a mechanism for giving extra protection to the chromosomes of the germ line, from the mutation load that would otherwise accrue as they go through successive divisions. There could even be a mechanism whereby the conservative strand of each chromosome replication was the one that went to the cell that was going to remain in the germ line, thus preventing the propagation of many classes of mutations.

Gardner: That is what happens in early stages, but by the late tail-bud stage the germ plasm moves to a perinuclear location, and appears thereafter to be partitioned equally between daughter cells, thereby expanding the germ cell population.

Cooke: Yes; if there is a mechanism for the unequal partitioning of cytoplasm there could possibly be one for directed partitioning of chromatids — a 'mitotic drive', as it were.

Gardner: Whittington & Dixon (1975) claim that in early stages the distribution of germ plasm resembles that of dye particles.

Pedersen: Can someone explain why in female mice the teratoma rarely becomes malignant, whereas in males these cells quite often develop into teratocarcinomas?

Bennett: It isn't clear whether teratocarcinomas really develop more readily in males than in females. In the mouse strains which have so far been studied, the development of teratocarcinomas in males is very frequent, especially in strain 129. On the other hand, Leroy Stevens (Stevens & Varnum 1974) now has a strain called LT which gives rise to ovarian teratocarcinomas in high frequency. This starts with a process of parthenogenesis in the ovary, with dividing eggs in the follicles at numerous stages of development—two cells, four cells, morulae and blastocysts. It is quite possible, therefore, that the apparent difference between males and females in the rate at which they generate teratocarcinomas may simply be due to sampling phenomena with respect to the mouse strains currently available.

Gluecksohn-Waelsch: Is teratocarcinoma more frequent in human females than in males?

Polani: No, it is more frequent in males.

Bennett: Benign teratoma is very frequent in human females, but these growths are rarely malignant.

Graham: One important difference between spontaneous teratocarcinomas and teratomas in male and female mice is that spontaneous testicular tumours develop without the formation of trophoblast (strain 129/J; Stevens 1959) while spontaneous ovarian tumours develop trophoblast early in their growth (LT strain; Stevens & Varnum 1974). I take this as evidence that trophoblast formation is not a necessary condition for subsequent cytodifferentiation.

Polani: What happens to the sex chromatin of female germ cells if they become malignant? In the female mouse the heterochromatic X chromosome cannot be recognized in the resting nucleus, but it can be recognized in prophase; and particularly with the bromodeoxyuridine labelling technique, one might identify it, though perhaps laboriously.

Bennett: To my knowledge that hasn't been studied.

Gardner: In classical textbooks on embryology we find general schemes in which haemopoietic stem cells give rise to the lymphoid line, to the granulocyte line and to the erythrocyte line. Then there is the neural crest, etc., and it appears that, superficially at least, there are a number of defined stem cell types which undergo progressive restriction. I wonder how important this is, developmentally. Does it mean that for an erythrocyte to be formed a very specific pathway of previous programming has to be followed? Or could it simply be a question of the cells being related in terms of the environment needed to support their differentiation? That is, is the existence of stem cell lineages trivial, or developmentally important?

References

AVE, K., KAWAKAMI, I. & SAMESHIMA, M. (1968) Studies on the heterogeneity of cell populations in amphibian presumptive epidermis, with reference to primary induction. *Dev. Biol. 17*, 617–626

BORUM, K. (1966) Oogenesis in the mouse: a study of the origin of the mature ova. *Exp. Cell Res. 45*, 39–47

KAUFFMAN, S.A. (1973) Control circuits for determination and transdetermination in *Drosophila* imaginal discs. *Science (Wash. D.C.) 181*, 310–318

MINTZ, B. (1960) Embryological phases of mammalian gametogenesis. *J. Cell Comp. Physiol. 56, suppl. 1*, 31–44

OŻDŻEŃSKI, W. (1967) Observations on the origin of primordial germ cells in the mouse. *Zool. Pol. 17*, 65–78

OŻDŻEŃSKI, W. (1969) Fate of primordial germ cells in the transplanted hind gut of mouse embryos. *J. Embryol. Exp. Morphol. 22*, 505–510

PETERS, H. (1970) Migration of gonocytes into the mammalian gonad and their differentiation. *Philos. Trans. R. Soc. Lond. B Biol. Sci. 259*, 91–101

ROGULSKA, T., OŻDŻEŃSKI, W. & KOMAR, A. (1971) Behaviour of mouse primordial germ cells in the chick embryo. *J. Embryol. Exp. Morphol.* 25, 155–164

ROSSANT, J. (1975a) Investigation of the determinative state of the mouse inner cell mass. I. Aggregation of isolated inner cell masses with morulae. *J. Embryol. Exp. Morphol. 33*, 979–990

ROSSANT, J. (1975b) Investigation of the determinative state of the mouse inner cell mass. II. The fate of isolated inner cell masses transferred to the oviduct. *J. Embryol. Exp. Morphol. 33*, 991–101

STEVENS, L.C. (1959) Embryology of testicular teratomas in strain 129/J mice. *J. Natl. Cancer Inst. 23*, 1249–1295

STEVENS, L.C. & VARNUM, D.S. (1974) The development of teratomas from parthenogenetically activated ovarian mouse eggs. *Dev. Biol. 37*, 369–380

WHITTINGTON, P.McD. & DIXON, K.E. (1975) Quantitative studies of germ plasm and germ cells during early embryogenesis of *Xenopus laevis*. *J. Embryol. Exp. Morphol. 27*, 467–479

Genetic variation of β-glucuronidase expression during early embryogenesis

VERNE M. CHAPMAN, DAVID ADLER, CESAR LABARCA
and LINDA WUDL

Department of Molecular Biology, Roswell Park Memorial Institute, Buffalo, New York

Abstract To determine when embryonic genes begin to function during mammalian embryogenesis, the expression of β-glucuronidase (EC 3.2.1.31) in preimplantation mouse embryos has been examined. β-Glucuronidase is especially useful as a tool for early developmental studies because: (1) it is a biochemically well-characterized gene product with genetic variants between inbred strains of mice, (2) its activity can be measured in individual embryos with a microfluorometric assay, and (3) it increases more than 100-fold during preimplantation development. The increase in activity is most pronounced after 60 hours of development but a significant increase occurs between 30 and 60 hours. Strain C3H has a genetic variant of glucuronidase (Gus^h) which results in activity levels six- to tenfold lower than in adult C57BL/6 (Gus^b) tissues. β-Glucuronidase activities in C3H embryos were also lower than those in C57BL/6 during preimplantation development. C3H glucuronidase is also more heat-labile than that from C57BL/6. Heat denaturation kinetics of glucuronidase in F1 embryos from C3H females × C57BL/6 males were intermediate to homozygous C3H and C57BL/6 embryos at 84 hours, indicating that paternally derived genes were expressed in the 100-fold increase in activity.

Increases in glucuronidase activity between 30 and 60 hours were higher in F1 embryos than in C3H, suggesting that embryonic genes are expressed before 60 hours. However, because strains differ in their patterns of cleavage and overall development, glucuronidase expression in a congenic C57BL/6 strain with the C3H glucuronidase gene was also examined. Congenic C57BL/6 embryos had lower glucuronidase activity than C57BL/6. Heterozygous ($Gus^{h/b}$) embryos from congenic females and C57BL/6 males had significantly higher activity than homozygous congenic embryos (Gus^h) at 30 hours and a greater increase in activity between 30 and 60 hours. The findings indicate that embryonic genes are transcribed and translated as early as 30 hours (2-cell stage) and that embryonic gene function may begin soon after fertilization or by the first cleavage.

During the time between fertilization and implantation a number of morphological and biochemical changes occur in mammalian embryos. Morphologically there is a gross transition from the zygote through cleavages to a blastocyst with trophectoderm and inner cell mass. Numerous fine structural changes, including the elaboration of organelles, rough endoplasmic reticulum and intercellular junctions, also occur during this period (Calarco & Epstein 1973).

At the molecular level, RNA synthesis has been initiated by the 2-cell stage in the mouse (Knowland & Graham 1972) and protein is synthesized at all embryonic stages (Brinster 1971; Epstein & Smith 1973; Van Blerkom & Brockway 1975). The qualitative pattern of proteins synthesized in 1-cell embryos appears to be similar to that of proteins synthesized by the ova. By the 2-cell stage (day 2) the pattern is markedly different from the 1-cell pattern. Additional changes in the electrophoretic pattern occur between day 2 and day 3 but the distribution of proteins being synthesized remains fairly constant between day 3 and the remainder of the preimplantation period (Van Blerkom & Brockway 1975; Epstein & Smith 1974). Inhibitors of RNA synthesis also block cell divisions as early as the first cleavage, indicating that RNA synthesis is essential for preimplantation development (Golbus et al. 1973).

The activities of numerous enzymes have been characterized during the preimplantation period. Some enzymes have relatively high activity in unfertilized ova, persisting through early cleavages and markedly decreasing at about 60 hours of development. Notable examples are lactate dehydrogenase (EC 1.1.1.27) (Brinster 1965) and glucose-6-phosphate dehydrogenase (EC 1.1.1.49) (Epstein et al. 1969). Other enzymes show a pronounced increase in activity beginning around 60 h; these include uridine kinase (EC 2.7.1.48) (Daentl & Epstein 1971), hypoxanthine phosphoribosyltransferase (EC 2.4.2.8) (Epstein 1970) and β-glucuronidase (EC 3.2.1.31) (Chapman & Wudl 1975). The transcription and translation of embryonic genes has been shown by using genetic variants for glucosephosphate isomerase (EC 5.3.1.9) (Chapman et al. 1971; Brinster 1973) and β-glucuronidase (Chapman & Wudl 1975). Thus, embryonic genes are functioning when the initial morphogenetic events occur that separate trophectoderm from inner cell mass in the mouse, and there is evidence from the arrested development of t^{12}/t^{12} homozygotes in the morulae stage that embryonic gene function is required for this differentiation (Mintz 1964; Calarco & Brown 1968). A more comprehensive review of preimplantation embryonic development has been published recently by Epstein (1975).

A number of features recommend glucuronidase as a useful model system for the study of gene expression at the onset of mouse embryogenesis. First, there is a 100-fold increase in activity during the first 84 h of development, primarily between 60 and 84 h. Second, a simple, sensitive microfluorometric assay technique is available which measures activities of single embryos and potentially single blastomeres. Third, among inbred strains of mice genetic variants for glucuronidase are available which have been biochemically and genetically characterized in different tissues at various stages of development, particularly in the proximal tubule cells of kidney where glucuronidase is induced by testosterone (Swank *et al.* 1974) and in adult livers where developmental differences in glucuronidase activity have been characterized (Paigen *et al.* 1975).

MATERIALS AND METHODS

Inbred mouse strains C3H/HeJ, C57BL/6J (B6) and SWR/J from the Jackson Laboratory were used for this work. In addition a congenic C57BL/6 strain with the *Gus^h* glucuronidase allele from C3H was obtained from Dr Elizabeth Russell. These mice were originally established from the transfer of the light ear (*le*) mutation which arose spontaneously in C3H to the C57BL/6 background. The *le* locus maps close to *rd* on chromosome 5 at about 18 map units from the *Gus* locus. Thus, about 20% of chromosome 5 in the congenic stock carries C3H genes.

In our initial work with B6, C3H and SWR mice, females were induced to ovulate by injections of gonadotropin, 4 i.u. (pregnant mare's serum—Pregnyl, Ayerst), followed 48 h later by 4 i.u. human chorionic gonadotropin (HCG; Sigma). Injections of HCG were given at noon. The females were paired with stud males late in the afternoon and checked the following morning for vaginal plugs.

In the experiments with congenic C57BL/6 *Gus^h* mice we attempted to standardize the initiation of development by artificially inseminating females early in the morning after ovulation. The insemination procedures are similar to those described by Leckie *et al.* (1973). For these experiments, gonadotropin injections were given at 1700 hours.

Embryos were flushed from the reproductive tract with phosphate-buffered saline (GIBCo), pH 7.2, containing 0.3% bovine serum albumin. Embryos were separated from contaminating cells and enzyme by being transferred in small volumes to fresh medium three times.

A single-cell microfluorometric assay technique (Wudl & Paigen 1974) was used to assay β-glucuronidase activity in single embryos. In outline, the assay procedure consists of placing the embryos in enzyme assay mixture containing the fluorogenic substrate, 4-methylumbelliferyl-β-D-glucuronic acid. The embryos are picked up in the assay mixture with finely drawn polyethylene tubing (0.3 to 0.4 mm inside diameter) and deposited singly in microdroplets of 1 to 10 nl under oil on a glass microscope slide. The slides are alternately frozen and thawed in an atmosphere of nitrogen to disrupt the cells, and they are then incubated for 60 min at 37°C. The enzyme reaction is stopped by placing the slide in a closed chamber with a reservoir of triethylamine, which diffuses through the oil and raises the pH of the droplet to 10. The fluorescence of droplets was measured with a Leitz MPV-2 fluorescence microscope equipped with Ploem illumination; interference filters were used to obtain monochromatic light at the excitation (365 nm) and emission (455 nm) maxima for the product, 4-methylumbelliferone (4MU). At pH 10 the excitation and emission maxima of 4MU are at much higher wavelengths than the substrate and in these conditions the relative fluorescence of 4MU is several thousand times greater than that of the substrate. Control experiments have shown that the fluorescence of a droplet is directly proportional to the number of moles of product contained in the droplet (Wudl & Paigen 1974).

RESULTS

β-Glucuronidase activity in single C57BL/6 embryos was measured between 36 and 84 h of development (Fig. 1). Activity increased 100-fold during this period, primarily between 57 and 84 h, though it also increased slightly but significantly between 36 and 57 h. The increase in activity after 57 h represents a substantial increase in activity per cell as well as in the entire embryo.

To determine whether the increase in glucuronidase activity at this time results from the translation of messenger RNA that is transcribed before or after fertilization, we examined glucuronidase activities in embryos from strains C3H and B6 and in F1 hybrids from C3H females and B6 males. C3H and B6 have different glucuronidase alleles, Gus^h and Gus^b respectively, which have different heat denaturation kinetics and different adult tissue activity levels (Ganschow

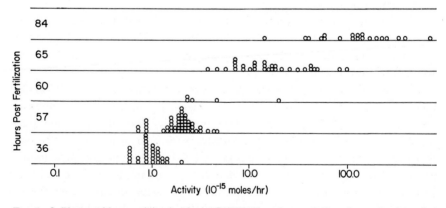

Fig. 1. β-Glucuronidase activity in single C57BL/6J embryos during the preimplantation period. Midnight of the day of mating is used as zero time of development.

TABLE 1

β-Glucuronidase activity (10^{-15} mol h^{-1} embryo^{-1}) in C57BL/6J, (C3H × C57BL/6)F1 embryos and C3H/HeJ

Strain	Hours of development		
	36	57	84
C57BL/6J	0.8 ± 0.05[a] (32)[b]	1.8 ± 0.1 (49)	150 ± 31.2 (20)
(C3H × C57BL)F1[c]	0.2 ± 0.03 (16)	1.0 ± 0.2 (19)	98 ± 9.5 (34)
C3H/HeJ	0.1 ± 0.01 (16)	0.4 ± 0.02 (19)	66 ± 6.4 (29)

[a] ± standard error.
[b] No. of embryos measured.
[c] C3H/HeJ × C57BL/6J.

& Paigen 1968). If paternally derived genes are functioning in early embryogenesis the enzyme of F1 embryos should have heat denaturation kinetics different from C3H kinetics. Conversely, if the increase in glucuronidase activity results from the translation of stored message, the activation of stored enzyme or the preferential transcription and translation of maternal genes, then C3H and F1 embryos should have the same enzyme activity, and that activity should have similar heat denaturation kinetics.

The mean glucuronidase activities at 36, 57, and 84 h for C3H, B6 and F1 hybrid embryos are shown in Table 1. At each time point B6 embryos had higher activity than C3H. Activity levels of F1 embryos were significantly higher than those of C3H at 36 h and subsequent time points. This significant difference between C3H and F1 embryos suggests either that the Gus^b paternal allele has been transcribed and translated or that the developmental increase in glucuronidase activity has been accelerated in the hybrid by the action of other genes.

The difference in activity between C3H and B6 is consistent with differences observed in activity levels in adult tissue, where the ratio of B6 to C3H activity in liver was 7. Immunological titrations showed that the numbers of enzyme molecules contained in C3H and B6 were proportional to their respective enzyme activities. The basis for there being more enzyme in B6 is that the rate of synthesis is higher. The ratio of the rate of synthesis of glucuronidase in B6 adult liver to that in C3H is 6.9 (Ganschow 1975; Paigen et al. 1975). Our observations that the increase in activity during early development was greater in B6 than C3H and that the initial activity levels were lower in C3H are consistent with a difference in rate of synthesis for the two Gus alleles.

To establish the expression of the paternal Gus^b allele in F1 embryos qualitatively we compared the heat inactivation kinetics of B6, C3H and F1 embryonic glucuronidase in pooled samples of embryos at 84 h of development (Chapman & Wudl 1975). We observed that the activity surviving after 30 min at $70\,^\circ$C was 50, 40 and 12% for B6, F1 and C3H, respectively. The heat denaturation differences are similar to adult values for these Gus genotypes. The difference between F1 and C3H glucuronidase demonstrates that the paternal Gus^b has been transcribed and translated during the 100-fold increase in activity.

The significant difference in activity between C3H and F1 embryos at 36 hours is consistent with the expression of the paternal Gus^b allele which has a greater rate of synthesis. However, if the increase in activity during the pre-implantation period is a function of the overall rate of development then the differences in glucuronidase activity between strains may not be the direct result of differences in Gus allelic activities. Differences in C3H and B6 preimplantation development have been reported where the timing of fertilization and subsequently the first cleavage is delayed by about 4 h in C3H compared with B6 (Nicol & McLaren 1974; McLaren & Bowman 1973).

The effect of a slower rate of overall development on glucuronidase activity is indicated by the developmental pattern observed in strain SWR/J, which has the same Gus^b genotype as B6 and similar levels of adult glucuronidase activity. However, the preimplantation expression of glucuronidase in SWR relative to C3H (Table 2) is quite different from that of B6 relative to C3H. At 32 and 57 h SWR embryos have significantly more glucuronidase activity than C3H, but by 81 hours C3H, (C3H × SWR) F1 and SWR embryos do not differ. By 90 h, F1 embryos have significantly higher glucuronidase activity than SWR.

TABLE 2

β-glucuronidase activity (10^{-15} mol h^{-1} embryo^{-1}) in SWR, (C3H × SWR)F1 and C3H embryos

Strain	Hours of development			
	32	57	81	90
SWR/J	1.4 ± 0.07^a (51)[b]	2.2 ± 0.13 (42)	50 ± 6.3 (40)	155 ± 3.0 (46)
F1	0.5 ± 0.04 (71)	2.8 ± 0.31 (33)	67 ± 6.0 (44)	194 ± 7.0 (66)
C3H	0.4 ± 0.04 (27)	0.45 ± 0.03 (41)	65 ± 5.0 (32)	175 ± 11.0 (74)

[a] $\pm$ standard error.
[b] No. of embryos measured.

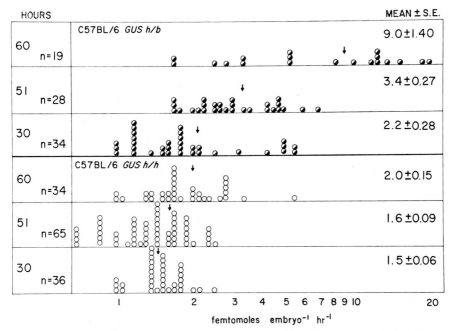

FIG. 2. β-Glucuronidase activity in single heterozygous $Gus^{h/b}$ and homozygous Gus^h embryos from congenic C57BL/6 females at 30, 51 and 60 h. Arrows indicate the mean values at each time. Time of insemination is zero time of development.

From a direct count under the dissecting microscope of blastomeres in embryos at 57 h, the average cell number in C3H, SWR and (C3H × SWR) F1 embryos was estimated to be 10.4, 5.1 and 12.0 for the three genotypes, respectively. C3H cleaves more rapidly than SWR during initial development, as does the F1 hybrid from the C3H mother, so that the number of cells available for glucuronidase synthesis in SWR increases more slowly than in C3H or the hybrid. The greater levels of glucuronidase activity in F1 embryos at 90 h compared with that in either parental strain represents the combined effects of the C3H rate of cleavage and the greater rate of synthesis for the Gus^b allele from SWR.

We used a congenic C57BL/6 strain, in which a segment of chromosome 5 carried the Gus^h allele from C3H, to evaluate the embryonic expression of different Gus alleles on a common genetic background. Since Gus^b has a greater rate of synthesis than Gus^h we reasoned that an early expression of the paternal Gus^b allele would produce a greater increase in glucuronidase activity in $Gus^{h/b}$ heterozygotes than in Gus^h homozygotes during early cleavage stages.

Glucuronidase activity in homozygous Gus^h and heterozygous $Gus^{h/b}$ embryos was measured at 30, 51, and 60 h after artificial insemination (Fig. 2).

Artificial insemination at 0700 h the day after gonadotropin (HCG) injection was used in this study to ensure a relatively uniform time of fertilization. β-Glucuronidase activity in $Gus^{h/b}$ heterozygotes was higher than in homozygotes by 30 h (2-cell stage), and between 30 and 60 h the increase in $Gus^{h/b}$ activity was 10 times greater than the increase in Gus^h homozygotes. These findings clearly show that the *Gus* gene is transcribed and translated by 30 h of development. Glucuronidase activity was not measured before the first cleavage because cumulus cells have β-glucuronidase activity, which is difficult to remove entirely by hyaluronidase activity or mechanical means. Thus, whether synthesis of message for glucuronidase begins before or after the first cleavage has not been determined. Also, it is possible that if enzyme were made during the 1-cell stage it would not be sufficient to determine differences between genotypes or to measure it as a difference from residual activity present in the egg from prefertilization synthesis.

The apparent 'activation' of glucuronidase after 57 to 60 h of development which results in an increased activity per cell corresponds to the timing of an increased incorporation of amino acids into protein (Brinster 1971; Epstein & Smith 1973; Van Blerkom & Brockway 1975) and to an increase in the uptake of nucleotides into RNA (Daentl & Epstein 1971). Whether these factors are rate-limiting in glucuronidase synthesis earlier than 57 h or merely reflect an increased metabolic activity of the embryo after 60 h has not been determined. Alternatively, it is possible that the marked increase in activity after 57 to 60 h results from (1) an increase in the number of cells transcribing message, (2) an accumulation of relatively long-lived mRNA for glucuronidase, and (3) an accumulation of glucuronidase which is not degraded until later in development.

In summary, β-glucuronidase in the mouse is synthesized by the 2-cell stage of development from mRNA transcribed from the embryo genome rather than from stored messenger RNA of oogenetic origin. A pronounced increase in activity (100-fold) occurs in the 24-hour period after 57 to 60 h in strains C3H and C57BL and somewhat later in SWR. The amount of increase in activity during the preimplantation period is affected by at least two factors: (1) the relative rate of synthesis of glucuronidase by different *Gus* alleles, and (2) the overall rate of development of the embryo, particularly the rate of cleavage.

ACKNOWLEDGEMENTS

Kenneth Paigen provided helpful suggestions and criticisms in the preparation of the manuscript.

This work was supported by grants GM-19521 and HD08768-01 from the National Institutes of Health.

References

BRINSTER, R. L. (1965) Lactate dehydrogenase in the preimplantation mouse embryo. *Biochim. Biophys. Acta 110*, 439–441

BRINSTER, R. L. (1971) Uptake and incorporation of amino acids by the preimplantation mouse embryo. *J. Reprod. Fertil. 27*, 329–338

BRINSTER, R. L. (1973) Parenteral glucose phosphate isomerase activity in three day mouse embryos. *Biochem. Genet. 9*, 187–191

CALARCO, P. G. & BROWN, E. H. (1968) Cytological and ultrastructural comparisons of t^{12}/t^{12} and normal mouse morulae. *J. Zool. Proc. Zool. Soc. Lond. 168*, 169–186

CALARCO, P. G. & EPSTEIN, C. J. (1973) Cell surface changes during preimplantation development in the mouse. *Dev. Biol. 32*, 208–213

CHAPMAN, V. M. & WUDL, L. (1975) The expression of β-glucuronidase during mouse embryogenesis, in *III Int. Conf. Isozymes* (Markert, C. L., ed.), p. 57, Academic Press, New York

CHAPMAN, V. M., WHITTEN, W. K. & RUDDLE, F. H. (1971) Expression of paternal glucose phosphate isomerase-1 (GPI-1) in preimplantation mouse embryos. *Dev. Biol. 26*, 153–158

DAENTL, D. L. & EPSTEIN, C. J. (1971) Developmental interrelationships of uridine uptake, nucleotide formation and incorporation into RNA by early mammalian embryos. *Dev. Biol. 24*, 428–442

EPSTEIN, C. J. (1970) Phosphoribosyltransferase activity during early mammalian development. *J. Biol. Chem. 245*, 3289–3294

EPSTEIN, C. J. (1975) Gene expression and macromolecular synthesis during preimplantation embryonic development. *Biol. Reprod. 12*, 82–105

EPSTEIN, C. J. & SMITH, S. A. (1973) Amino acid uptake and protein synthesis in preimplantation mouse embryos. *Dev. Biol. 33*, 171–184

EPSTEIN, C. J. & SMITH, S. A. (1974) Electrophoretic analysis of proteins synthesized by preimplantation mouse embryos. *Dev. Biol. 40*, 233–244

EPSTEIN, C. J., WEGIENKA, E. A. & SMITH, C. W. (1969) Biochemical development of preimplantation mouse embryos: *in vivo* activities of fructose 1, 6 diphosphate aldolase, glucose 6-phosphate dehydrogenase, and lactate dehydrogenase. *Biochem. Genet. 3*, 271–281

GANSCHOW, R. (1975) Simultaneous genetic control of the structure and rate of synthesis of murine β-glucuronidase, in *III Int. Conf. Isozymes* (Markert, C. L., ed.), Academic Press, New York

GANSCHOW, R. & PAIGEN, K. (1968) Glucuronidase phenotypes of inbred mouse strains. *Genetics 52*, 335–349

GOLBUS, M. S., CALARCO, P. G. & EPSTEIN, C. J. (1973) The effects of inhibitors on RNA synthesis (amanitin and actinomycin D) on preimplantation mouse embryogenesis. *J. Exp. Zool. 186*, 207–216

KNOWLAND, J. & GRAHAM, C. (1972) RNA synthesis at the two-cell stage of mouse development. *J. Embryol. Exp. Morphol. 27*, 167–176

LECKIE, P. A., WATSON, J. G. & CHAYKIN, S. (1973) An improved method for the artificial insemination of the mouse *(Mus musculus)*. *Biol. Reprod. 9*, 420–425

McLAREN, A. & BOWMAN, P. (1973) Genetic effect on the timing of early development in the mouse. *J. Embryol. Exp. Morphol. 30*, 491–497

MINTZ, B. (1964) Gene expression in the morula stage of mouse embryos, as observed during development of t^{12}/t^{12} lethal mutants *in vitro*. *J. Exp. Zool. 157*, 267–272

NICOL, A. & McLAREN, A. (1974) An effect of the female genotype on sperm transport in mice. *J. Reprod. Fertil. 39*, 421–424

PAIGEN, K., SWANK, R. T., TOMINO, S. & GANSCHOW, R. E. (1975) The molecular genetics of mammalian glucuronidase. *J. Cell Physiol. 85*, 379–392

SWANK, R.T., PAIGEN, K. & GANSCHOW, R.E. (1974) Genetic control of glucuronidase induction in mice. *J. Mol. Biol. 81*, 225–243

VAN BLERKOM, J. & BROCKWAY, G.O. (1975) Qualitative patterns of protein synthesis in the preimplantation mouse embryo 1. Normal pregnancy. *Dev. Biol. 44*, 148–157

WUDL, L. & PAIGEN, K. (1974) Enzyme measurements on single cells. *Science (Wash. D.C.) 184*, 992–994

Discussion

Gurdon: You got a 100-fold increase in β-glucuronidase activity. How different is that in activity per cell compared to the 1-cell stage? How many cells are there at that point?

Chapman: By the time it has gone up 100-fold in activity there are about 32 cells. It is three or four times higher per cell than it was originally.

Gurdon: If eggs are assayed for a whole range of metabolic enzyme activities, allowing for the possibility that these may be a fewfold down on typical values, do they contain all kinds of activities that can be measured? You have a specially sensitive assay but have people done this kind of thing with 1000 eggs or 100 eggs?

Chapman: Probably 15 or 20 enzyme assays have been used during pre-implantation development (Epstein 1975).

Gurdon: Do mouse eggs lack a significant level of *general* enzyme activities which other cells possess?

Chapman: It is not a consistent picture. For instance lactate dehydrogenase starts out with very high activity and by 60 to 84 hours of development it decreases in activity in the whole embryo. Glucose-6-phosphate dehydrogenase and glucosephosphate isomerase do the same. On the other hand, other enzymes (uridine kinase, HGPRT, APRT) increase in activity at about the same time as glucuronidase is increasing (Epstein 1975). However, the relative increase in activity of those enzymes does not really represent an increase in activity per cell, whereas the increase in glucuronidase activity does. Our preliminary studies on β-galactosidase (EC 3.2.1.23) suggest that this enzyme has about 10 times the activity that glucuronidase has initially, and it has the same pattern of increase in activity as glucuronidase (D. Adler & V. M. Chapman, unpublished).

Gurdon: Is it known, in any of these cases, whether the new enzyme activity arises from new activation of inherited molecules or whether it arises from newly synthesized enzyme molecules?

Chapman: The case of glucosephosphate isomerase is a peculiar one. Activity is diminishing between the third and fourth days of development. At the 8-cell stage, it is possible to identify paternal gene products qualitatively. Synthesis is going on and protein is being synthesized from paternal message at this stage.

Kelley: Where is the glucuronidase within each blastomere?

Chapman: I don't know. Glucuronidase in adult tissues is associated with the microsomal fraction and with the lysosomal fraction.

Kelley: What benefit is the embryo deriving from this enhanced function?

Chapman: Lysosomal function is beginning and the coordinate increase in β-galactosidase suggests that biogenesis of lysosomes has probably begun at this stage of development. Lysosomes are known to be present in trophecto-derm, for instance.

Kelley: Would you comment on your reference to growth rates or cleavage rates in the different strains?

Chapman: A difference in the rate of cleavage may result in differences in the rate at which enzyme activity increases during preimplantation development. With a slower rate of cleavage there is a slower increase in the activity of β-glucuronidase. This has been largely ignored in most work on the preimplantation stage, but it may be significant when absolute levels of enzyme activity at various stages are being compared.

Kelley: So you are making a quantitative statement rather than suggesting a cause and effect?

Chapman: Initially when we saw this we weren't convinced that glucuronidase was synthesized before 60 hours. We thought that our assay was not sensitive enough to pick it up and that maybe the enzyme was coming in with the sperm. We very much hoped that glucuronidase expression came on at 60 h of development and that there was developmental induction. It was a very naive assumption. We were then going to look for genetic variants in the timing of glucuronidase expression. We found that SWR and C57BL/6, even though they had the same structural gene, differed in the time at which the activity increased. Rather than some profound genetic explanation for that, I think it is just a matter of cleavage.

Wolpert: Do all adult tissues have β-glucuronidase?

Chapman: All that we have measured do.

Wolpert: Are you quite sure that it is always synthesis that you are measuring when you measure changes in activity?

Chapman: No, we are only inferring that it is synthesis.

Pedersen: Do your observations on the difference in cleavage rates of hybrids between C3H and SWR confirm Whitten & Dagg's (1961) observation of a paternal effect on cleavage rate as early as the 2-cell stage?

Chapman: No, I don't think they do. I think they suggest that cleavage rate may be a maternally-inherited condition. F1 cleaves at about the same rate as

C3H, or if anything it is faster than the C3H. With a paternal effect one would expect to have an intermediate rate of cleavage. There is an apparent effect on the cleavage but it is not a simple genetic determinant.

McLaren: Are you satisfied that embryos of one strain are actually cleaving faster than those of the other, rather than merely starting earlier? When we saw a difference in the timing of cleavage between C3H and C57BL embryos, I thought initially that it would involve a difference in cleavage rate but it turned out not to be so (McLaren & Bowman 1973).

Chapman: We haven't determined cleavage rate yet. We are trying to develop a DNA assay so that we can make a specific activity measurement per unit of DNA during development rather than trying to do cell counts on whole embryos.

Graham: Are differences in β-glucuronidase activity apparent in sperm? Could the increase in β-glucuronidase activity that you see in the F1 embryos be due to stored messenger RNA of sperm?

Chapman: Glucuronidase activity is apparently associated with sperm preparations but we don't know yet whether it is closely enough associated with the sperm to come into the egg at the time of fertilization. We are trying to do single sperm assays but there are difficulties in doing these. There is no evidence that stored messenger RNA comes into the egg with the sperm but it is a possibility. The findings are consistent with the expression of the embryonic genes but alternative explanations may be possible.

McLaren: Do the Gus^b/Gus^h activity differences show up in every tissue?

Chapman: Yes, but the amount of difference is not the same from tissue to tissue. For instance, in spleen the difference between the C3H and C57BL/6 strains was not as pronounced as in liver.

McLaren: Has it been examined in sperm?

Chapman: Attempts have been made. It is very difficult to quantitate the specific activity. Rough estimates can be made of the total number of sperm and of the amount of activity, but we don't know whether the activity comes specifically with the sperm or simply from the semen preparation.

Gardner: The idea of ooplasmically inherited messenger RNA is generally accepted, but in discussing the question of time of paternal genome expression, this possibility has not really been thought about in relation to sperm. The sort of approach adopted by Alfred Gropp (this volume, pp. 155–171) and Charles Ford (1971) might settle this question. The aim would be to obtain male mice heterozygous for a metacentric chromosome that carries, for example, the β-glucuronidase gene. Through meiotic non-disjunction, such males should yield monosomic embryos lacking the paternal allele for the enzyme, when mated with normal females of *Mus musculus*. The findings of Charles Ford

(1971, 1975) suggest that such embryos develop until at least implantation. Hence, providing the assay for the enzyme was sufficiently sensitive to be carried out on single embryos, you should be able to settle this question for β-glucuronidase. Admittedly, there is not much RNA in sperm. Nevertheless, I think this possibility should be examined.

Chapman: Van Blerkom & Brockway (1975) showed that a lot of proteins have been synthesized by the 2-cell stage. The mouse genome may certainly be functioning by the 2-cell stage of development. If the sperm brings in mRNA it means that the paternal genome is contributing to development. This is slightly different from the strategy proposed if there is a lot of message of oogenetic origin that might direct early development. If it can bring in message for glucuronidase it can bring in message for a lot of other things, potentially.

Gluecksohn-Waelsch: Has the regulatory gene for glucuronidase been identified? If so, are alleles of that regulatory gene known and do the various strains used carry different alleles?

Chapman: The situation is not clear-cut. The regulatory gene for glucuronidase that Paigen has proposed is in the liver (Paigen *et al.* 1975). If the activity per gram wet weight of liver is plotted postnatally in mice of strains DBA and C3H, then between 10 and 30 days of age activity in C3H decreases compared with that in DBA. Paigen proposes that this is evidence for a regulatory gene for glucuronidase activity that is associated with a structural gene. He has done a cross showing that liver activity segregates with the structural gene.

Gluecksohn-Waelsch: Are the activity differences you observed inherent in the structural gene in your system?

Chapman: It is not known for sure. Heat lability is a complicating factor, and the difference in rate of synthesis was measured specifically in the liver, so if the difference in rate of synthesis really reflects a regulatory gene in liver it biases my evidence for gene expression. Conversely it says that the regulatory gene that affects liver development is also functioning very early. Obviously we haven't determined rates of synthesis for glucuronidase at those levels of activity. We would like to.

McLaren: Are the structural and the regulatory genes very closely linked?

Chapman: Yes; the developmental pattern segregates with a structural gene.

Gropp: I understand that β-glucuronidase is coded by a gene on chromosome 5. It might be interesting to study this enzyme phenotype in fetal trisomy 5. But there is at the moment no access to this chromosome. Results on the developmental capacity of haploid embryos and observations by Ford (1971) and ourselves (see Gropp 1973) on the developmental capacity of monosomic or trisomic preimplantation embryos lead to the assumption that they can apparently develop until implantation, irrespective of whether they are singly or multiply aneusomic. This could make one think that the enzymes activated during early embryogenesis have no great importance. On the other hand, from recent observations in our group we got the impression that there is also a more or less important loss of aneuploid preimplantation embryos. At least, if we compare exactly the rates of malsegregation in male and female meiotic anaphase I, the number of corpora lutea, and the total number of implants with the number of euploid and aneuploid late preimplantation embryos, we must assume a loss.

Chapman: Swank *et al.* (1973) in our laboratory have obtained further data on regulatory genes associated with structural genes. This work concerns the androgen induction of β-glucuronidase and it is another reason why we are using this particular gene as a marker. In the mouse the kidney is a target organ for androgen in terms of glucuronidase production. For some reason, males have more glucuronidase activity in the kidneys than females. A large dose of androgens given to females induces glucuronidase specifically in the proximal tubule cells of the kidney, but not in the liver or any other place that we have looked. Strains C57BL/6 and A/J both have the same basal level of activity, about 20 units per gram wet weight of kidney but different induction levels of activity. Activity levels in all the adult tissues are the same. The F1 hybrids have intermediate levels of activity between the two strains. A back-cross of F1 with the low-inducing C57BL/6 gives two kinds of offspring: on androgen induction there are some like the C57BL/6 and some like the F1. Linkage analysis with the electrophoretic variants of the structural gene shows that those with intermediate androgen induction have heterozygous electrophoretic mobility, while those that have low induction have the C57BL/6 gene. This is evidence that the regulation of androgen induction segregates with the structural gene. From back-crosses in the original study it looked as if there might be some recombination between the structural and regulatory genes. There were two out of about 200 chromosomes tested. We are now doing back-crosses with 1000 mice but as yet we have no confirmed recombinations.

Paigen *et al.* (1975) looked at the electrophoretic mobility of F1 and found that instead of there being a nice intermediate pattern between the fast and the slow electrophoretic mobility, the pattern was like the fast electrophoretic mobility, indicating that the regulation is *cis*, which is consistent with the linkage of this control gene to the structural gene.

Graham: Dr Gropp, is the difference between your results and Charles Ford's results on preimplantation death of monosomics due to the fact that you are working with different monosomics or that you have more extensive observations?

Gropp: Our first paper referred to a more complex system in the mouse, the tobacco mouse and its F1 hybrid, which is a multiple heterozygote with seven metacentrics. We are now repeating this work with single and double metacentric heterozygotes which allow us to compare in more detail anaphase I malsegregation in the male and the female with the rates of euploid and aneuploid pre- and postimplantation embryos in simpler systems. According to this study it can be assumed that at least *some* unbalanced zygotes, perhaps mainly multiple monosomics, are so heavily damaged that they are eliminated before implantation (unpublished work).

Graham: Even if there was very little preimplantation death, I would not conclude that the changes in enzyme activity which have been described are unimportant, because often a developmental defect might take time to express itself.

Rutter: There were 100-fold differences in activity between some of those embryos, Dr Chapman. It is a mean activity, of course, but why is there such a large dispersion when you have what is apparently a highly precise assay? Are you getting very different growth rates which haven't been normalized on a per cell basis?

Chapman: It is partly that, and partly because most of the observations on enzyme activity changes during the preimplantation period were done on pooled samples. We are among the few people who have actually looked at single embryos and some dispersion comes from that. Discrepancies in development do occur and sometimes we are not as careful at keeping those out as we should be. Sometimes there are mistakes in the assay, with foreign substances in the droplets.

Rutter: In some of your results where the differences were relatively small and the dispersion was relatively large, a substantial number of the points overlapped. Much of your evidence might depend on just a few embryos.

Polani: Did you have greater variability in the heterozygotes?

Chapman: Yes. The difference at 30 h is probably due largely to a few embryos with high activity. At this particular time we have probably caught the developmental increase just as it is beginning. A few of the embryos have begun to increase in activity but most have not. Between 30 and 51 h there is clearly a shift in the distribution of F1 embryos to higher activity. Four embryos at 51 h have very low activity in the homozygous class but I don't know why. If we took out those four the distribution would be essentially the same as in the sample at 30 h.

McLaren: But are those four embryos statistical outliers, in the sense that they lie significantly outside the normal distribution of the rest of the population? If not, you have no reason to exclude them.

Chapman: The difference in the sample size is 65 compared with 36, so differences may occur because the sample size is greater.

Wolpert: It is a fairly big range.

Rutter: Could a process which is as orderly as the early stages of development must be express itself so randomly as this? Or does some other ancillary function give that huge variation?

Chapman: When we first compared C57BL/6 with SWR it was not really clear what the real mean activity was. It looked as though we had caught some that had gone through a cleavage stage and some that had not. When we do a very careful time course and catch them sometimes right after they have gone through a cleavage, there almost seems to be a slight decrease in activity compared to the previous time point.

Graham: The orderliness of development has been questioned. Is there any biochemical evidence at all on enzyme expression by single cells in an orderly tissue such as the liver? Is this the kind of variation which all biochemists ignore?

Chapman: We are going to study the expression of glucuronidase at different levels of ploidy but that requires the DNA assay that we haven't got yet.

Bennett: I have seen many hundreds of litters of preimplantation and post-implantation embryos. The embryos in a given litter do not march forward in step, so there are very wide variations in stage of development within litters. Therefore I am not at all surprised at your findings, Dr Chapman.

Chapman: These are induced ovulations. We get 20 to 30 embryos, not the 50 or 80 that can be obtained by superovulation. We use more mature females and that might affect the results.

Bennett: If you categorized them by stage of development, or even roughly counted the number of cells, rather than going by age, I am sure you would find much closer distributions.

Chapman: I am sure that when we do it with the DNA assay it will come out better.

References

EPSTEIN, C.J. (1975) Gene expression and macromolecular synthesis during preimplantation embryonic development. *Biol. Reprod. 12*, 82–105

FORD, C.E. (1971) Gross genome unbalance in mouse spermatozoa: does it influence the capacity to fertilize? in *Edinburgh Symposium on The Genetics of the Spermatozoon* (Beatty, R.A. & Gluecksohn-Waelsch, S., eds.), pp. 359–368, published by the organizers (editors)

FORD, C.E. (1975) The time in development at which gross genome unbalance is expressed, in *The Early Development of Mammals (2nd Symp. Br. Soc. Dev. Biol.)* (Balls, M. & Wild, A.E., eds.), pp. 285–304, Cambridge University Press, London

GROPP, A. (1973) Reproductive failure due to fetal aneuploidy in mice, in *Fertility and Sterility (Proc. VII World Congr.)* (Hasegawa, T. *et al.*, eds.), ICS 278, Excerpta Medica, Amsterdam

GROPP, A. (1976) Morphological consequences of trisomy in mammals, in this volume, pp. 155–171

McLAREN, A. & BOWMAN, P. (1973) Genetic effects on the timing of early development in the mouse. *J. Embryol. Exp. Morphol. 30*, 491–498

PAIGEN, K., SWANK, R.T., TOMINO, S. & GANSCHOW, R.E. (1975) The molecular genetics of mammalian glucuronidase. *J. Cell Physiol. 85*, 379–392

SWANK, R. T., PAIGEN, K. & GANSCHOW, R. E. (1973) Genetic control of glucuronidase induction in mice. *J. Mol. Biol. 81*, 225–243

VAN BLERKOM, J. & BROCKWAY, G.O. (1975) Qualitative patterns of protein synthesis in the preimplantation mouse embryo 1. Normal pregnancy. *Dev. Biol. 44*, 148–157

WHITTEN, W.K. & DAGG, C.P. (1961) Influence of spermatozoa on the cleavage rate of mouse eggs. *J. Exp. Zool. 148*, 173–183

Genetic effects on mammalian development during and after implantation

ROGER A. PEDERSEN and AKIKO I. SPINDLE

Laboratory of Radiobiology, University of California, San Francisco, California

Abstract   The effects of gene expression on early mouse embryo differentiation were investigated by measuring the developmental rate of embryos homozygous for the yellow allele (A^y) of the agouti locus and by determining the growth response of normal embryos treated with 5-bromodeoxyuridine (BrdU).

The earliest effect of A^y homozygosity observed in cultured embryos was a delay in cleavage from the 2-cell to the 4-cell stage. A^y/A^y embryos also reached the blastocyst stage later than their normal littermates and had fewer cells but showed no gross alteration in the rate of DNA synthesis. Although A^y/A^y embryos were capable of some post-blastocyst development *in vitro* if the zona pellucida was removed, their inner cell masses disappeared during attachment and trophoblast outgrowth. The period of gene expression that is responsible for the abnormal development of A^y/A^y embryos may thus be between the 2-cell stage and implantation.

A more precise determination of critical periods for gene expression was made by continuous or 24-hour treatments of embryos with BrdU. Embryos cultured for five days beyond the blastocyst stage in 10^{-9} to 10^{-7} M-BrdU formed trophoblast outgrowths, but the extent of their inner cell mass growth varied inversely with BrdU concentration. At 5×10^{-8} M-BrdU, inner cell mass growth was less than 50% of controls, and there was almost no differentiation of endoderm and ectoderm, although this treatment did not grossly interfere with DNA or RNA synthesis. When embryos were treated for 24-hour intervals between the morula and late blastocyst stages with 1×10^{-7} M-BrdU, inner cell mass growth and differentiation into endoderm and ectoderm were particularly sensitive to BrdU; hatching and trophoblast development were sensitive to BrdU only when embryos were treated at the morula stage.

It is therefore suggested that gene expression necessary for *in vitro* hatching, attachment, trophoblast outgrowth and inner cell mass development occurs between the morula and late blastocyst stages.

The sensitivity of early mammalian embryos to drugs that block RNA and protein synthesis (Thomson & Biggers 1966; Golbus *et al.* 1973) suggests that they begin to rely on products of their own genome during the preimplantation

period. In the mouse a paternal effect on the cleavage rate can be recognized
at the 2-cell stage (Whitten & Dagg 1961); synthesis of ribosomal, transfer
and heterogenous DNA-like RNA is detectable in 2- to 4-cell mouse embryos
(Woodland & Graham 1969; Knowland & Graham 1972); and synthesis of
enzymes specified by paternal genes can be recognized in 8-cell embryos
(Brinster 1973; Wudl & Chapman 1976; Chapman et al., this volume, pp. 115–
124). These findings indicate that expression of the embryonic genome begins
to affect development during cleavage stages. We therefore attempted to determine at what time gene expression must occur if implantation and early postimplantation differentiation of mouse embryos in vitro are to take place.

For this purpose we used two perturbations of normal development: homozygosity for a recessive mutation, the yellow (A^y) allele of the agouti locus
and treatment with 5-bromodeoxyuridine (BrdU), a thymidine analogue that
interferes with differentiation of cultured cells (Stellwagen & Tomkins 1971)
and embryos (Tencer & Brachet 1973).

In vivo, homozygous yellow (A^y/A^y) embryos die during implantation but
evoke a normal uterine decidual response (Kirkham 1919; Robertson 1942;
Eaton & Green 1963). In vitro, presumed A^y/A^y embryos become conspicuously
abnormal at the morula or blastocyst stage due to the earlier arrest of one or
more blastomeres (Pedersen 1974). These disorganized embryos fail to hatch
when cultured further but are capable of forming trophoblast outgrowths if
the zona pellucida is removed experimentally (Pedersen 1974). However, A^y/A^y
outgrowths are completely devoid of inner cell masses and have fewer trophoblast cells than normal. We therefore observed A^y/A^y embryos by time-lapse
cinematography to determine when abnormalities appear, since these effects
are an indication of the expression of both maternal and paternal alleles of the
$+A^y$ gene.

Mouse blastocysts exposed to BrdU at appropriate concentrations also
have impaired inner cell mass growth after attachment in vitro but, unlike
homozygous yellow embryos, BrdU-treated embryos hatch and form trophoblast outgrowths (Sherman & Atienza 1975). It is therefore of interest to compare these two cases of perturbations of normal development.

In many types of differentiated cells, BrdU prevents the expression of
differentiated functions at concentrations that do not greatly affect other
cellular processes, such as cell division and growth (Wessells 1964; Abbott &
Holtzer 1968; Coleman et al. 1970). In preimplantation mouse embryos, BrdU
at concentrations of 10^{-5} to 10^{-4} M interferes with both cleavage and blastocyst
formation (Garner 1974; Golbus & Epstein 1974). Lower concentrations of
BrdU (10^{-8} to 10^{-6} M) allow blastulation, hatching and trophoblast outgrowth
(Garner 1974) but interfere with inner cell mass growth (Sherman & Atienza

1975; Pedersen & Spindle, unpublished work). We therefore treated mouse embryos with BrdU in an attempt to determine whether sensitive periods exist and whether the effects of BrdU incorporation into DNA indicate an interference with gene expression.

The processes of blastocyst hatching and trophoblast outgrowth *in vitro* have been compared with embryonic development *in vivo* at the time of implantation (Gwatkin 1966; Menke & McLaren 1970). Although the flattening of trophoblast cells on the substrate and exposure of the inner cell mass directly to the medium occur only *in vitro*, many ultrastructural and biochemical characteristics of embryos developing *in vivo* and *in vitro* are similar (Solter *et al.* 1970, 1974; Chew & Sherman 1975). The advantages of *in vitro* analysis are that the environment of the embryos can be controlled, their nutritional requirements can be defined, and the consequences of various treatments can be determined by direct observation of the embryos without interference from maternal factors.

MATERIALS AND METHODS

Two-cell embryos of C57BL 6J-A^y/a mice (Jackson Laboratories, Bar Harbor, Maine) and of randomly bred DUB/ICR mice (Flow Laboratories, Dublin, Virginia) were cultured to the blastocyst stage in the egg culture medium of Biggers *et al.* (1971) with slight modifications (Goldstein *et al.* 1975). Blastocysts were transferred to Eagle's Basal Medium (BME, Eagle 1955), modified to contain increased concentrations of several essential amino acids (Spindle & Pedersen 1973) and 102 mM-NaCl, and supplemented with 5% fetal calf serum and 5% newborn calf serum (Grand Island Biological Co., Grand Island, New York). Each lot of serum was tested for toxicity and for stimulatory effects on post-blastocyst development before being used. When grown in this medium, more than 90% of blastocysts hatched, attached and formed trophoblast outgrowths on the substrate. Approximately 90% of the outgrown embryos had inner cell masses, and more than half of these differentiated into endoderm and ectoderm during five days of culture beyond the blastocyst stage. Attachment of embryos to the substrate *in vitro* was considered to be the stage equivalent to implantation *in vivo*.

Identification of presumed A^y/A^y embryos and enzymic removal of the zona pellucida were accomplished as previously described (Pedersen 1974). Embryos were incubated at 37 °C on a heated microscope stage (Steier 1975) for time-lapse cinematographic observations.

For continuous BrdU treatment, blastocysts were incubated in eight-chamber culture slides (Lab-Tek, Naperville, Illinois; 15 embryos per chamber) in modified BME containing various concentrations of BrdU, 10% dialysed serum (5% fetal calf serum and 5% newborn calf serum). For 24-hour treatment, 2-cell embryos were cultured to the appropriate stage (see Table 3) and treated with 1×10^{-7} M-BrdU. After treatment, the embryos were washed once with fresh medium and cultured for the remainder of the 5-day post-blastocyst culture period in BrdU-free medium. Embryos were scored for hatching, trophoblast outgrowth, inner cell mass growth, and differentiation into endoderm and ectoderm.

Embryos from A^y/a parents and embryos treated with BrdU were pulse-labelled with [^{3}H]methylthymidine (1 µCi/ml, 40 Ci/mmol) or [^{3}H]uridine (0.1 µCi/ml, 20.4 Ci/mmol) for 2 h and then fixed on microscope slides (Tarkowski 1966). Slides were soaked in 5% trichloroacetic acid at 4 °C for 30 min, washed in 95% ethanol, air dried, and exposed to Kodak NTB emulsion for autoradiography.

RESULTS AND DISCUSSION

Culture requirements for early postimplantation growth

In contrast to the simple ions and carbon sources needed for preimplantation growth of mouse embryos (Cholewa & Whitten 1970; Wales 1970; Biggers *et al.* 1971), fixed nitrogen sources, in the form of specific essential amino acids and non-dialysable component(s) from serum are required for growth beyond the blastocyst stage (Gwatkin 1966; Hsu 1971; Spindle & Pedersen 1973). These requirements are fulfilled by several serum-supplemented tissue culture media that allow trophoblast outgrowth on a suitable substrate (Gwatkin 1966; Hsu 1971; Jenkinson & Wilson 1973; Pienkowski *et al.* 1974; Solter *et al.* 1974; Salomon & Sherman 1975). However, our approach has been to define the conditions for growth in a simple medium, BME, by altering the concentrations of components or by adding potentially stimulating factors. By doing this we found (Spindle & Pedersen 1973) that elevated concentrations of cystine, histidine, leucine, methionine, phenylalanine, threonine, tryptophan, and valine improve hatching, attachment and trophoblast outgrowth. The non-essential amino acids—alanine, asparagine, aspartic acid, glutamic acid, glycine, proline, and serine—do not stimulate growth at all. Although collagen coating of the substrate promotes growth at low amino acid concentrations (Hsu 1971), it is not necessary for obtaining a high incidence of trophoblast outgrowth or inner cell mass differentiation into endoderm and ectoderm at higher amino acid concentrations (Spindle & Pedersen 1973).

In order to obtain a high incidence of inner cell mass growth and differentiation, addition of 10% or more serum is necessary (Hsu 1971; Spindle & Pedersen 1973). This effect is not obtained when fetal calf serum is replaced with bovine serum albumin (0.5–4 mg/ml) or linoleic acid (10^{-8} to 10^{-4} M) (Spindle, unpublished work), which substitutes for serum requirements of some cultured cell types (Ham 1963). The steroids present in serum do not appear to be responsible for its stimulatory effects (Salomon & Sherman 1975). A growth-promoting, low-molecular-weight protein like those affecting other cultured cells (Temin et al. 1972) may therefore be the active serum factor. However, in mouse embryos, fetal calf serum stimulates trophoblast outgrowth (Spindle, unpublished work), whereas human cord serum (Hsu et al. 1974) or newborn calf serum (Spindle, unpublished work) stimulates inner cell mass differentiation into endoderm and ectoderm, so it is possible that serum factors required for embryo growth vary from stage to stage and are different from those required by other cells in tissue culture.

Development beyond endoderm and ectoderm differentiation can be obtained by using higher serum concentrations (15–20%) and by gradually replacing the calf serum with heat-inactivated human cord serum, as described by Hsu et al. (1974). Under these conditions, about 5% of the blastocysts form yolk sac blood islands and a beating heart-like structure after 9–14 days of culture (Hsu 1973; Hsu et al. 1974; Pedersen & Spindle, unpublished work). It is clear, however, that further work is necessary to define the requirements for a higher incidence of successful development to the stage of early organogenesis. Nevertheless, the early post-blastocyst processes of hatching, attachment, trophoblast outgrowth and inner cell mass differentiation into endoderm and ectoderm occur with high enough frequencies in vitro to enable us to examine the effects of perturbations that act during and after implantation.

Development of homozygous yellow A^y/A^y embryos

Although histological studies rarely recognize abnormalities of presumed A^y/A^y embryos in vivo as early as the blastocyst stage (Kirkham 1919; Robertson 1942; Eaton & Green 1963), in vitro studies reveal abnormalities in 17% of morulae and blastocysts cultured overnight from the 8-cell stage and in 24% of embryos flushed from the uterus as morulae and blastocysts (Pedersen 1974). These abnormalities range from arrest of a single blastomere at the 4-cell or 8-cell stage to extensive disorganization at the morula stage, accompanied by abortive blastocoele formation and fragmentation or disintegration of arrested blastomeres. However, a majority of the abnormal morulae and blastocysts have only one to three arrested blastomeres, and these are excluded from the remaining cells. The remaining cells form small blastocysts that have both inner cell mass and trophoblast cells (Calarco & Pedersen 1976). The hatching failure of these abnormal presumed A^y/A^y blastocysts that is observed after prolonged culture (Pedersen 1974) may be a failure of trophoblast function, since trophoblast cells appear to be involved in the hatching process (Bergstrom 1972). Death at the blastocyst stage due to hatching failure does not typify the potential for growth *in vivo*, where embryos implant before the cells die; embryos *in vivo* are probably able to escape hatching failure because of the oestrogen-dependent zona lysis that occurs in the uterus on day 4 of gestation (McLaren 1970; Mintz 1971).

However, after enzymic removal of the zona pellucida and five days of culture, presumed A^y/A^y embryos form a trophoblast layer that varies from small outgrowths with only a few cells to moderate-sized outgrowths with up to half the normal number of trophoblast giant cells (Pedersen 1974). The trophoblast outgrowths from presumed A^y/A^y embryos lack any inner cell mass cells at the end of the 5-day post-blastocyst culture period, although most of the normal littermates, like embryos of control cultures, have an inner cell mass when they grow out on the substrate after pronase treatment (Pedersen 1974). This pattern of trophoblast outgrowths by abnormal, presumed A^y/A^y, embryos resembles their growth *in vivo* (Eaton & Green 1963), where they appear to form trophoblastic vesicles lacking inner cell mass cells (Gardner 1972).

To obtain more information about when the $+A^y$ allele affects development, we observed embryos by time-lapse cinematography during preimplantation and early postimplantation periods. Preliminary results indicate that homozygosity caused a 2- to 4-h delay in cleavage as early as the second division (2-cell to 4-cell) and that the homozygotes lagged behind their normal littermates during subsequent preimplantation development, including blastulation. This effect is consistent with the participation of both maternal and paternal genomes in determination of the rates of early cleavage, as suggested by the work of Whitten & Dagg (1961). Blastocyst stage A^y/A^y embryos underwent cycles of expansion and collapse typical of normal blastocysts of several strains that have been observed in culture (Borghese & Cassini 1963; Cole & Paul 1965). Before they attached to the glass substrate, the A^y/A^y embryos occasionally extended blunt cytoplasmic protrusions that differed from the slender pseudopodia of normal blastocysts at the same stages. Later, attachment and trophoblast cell migration resembled that of normal blastocysts, except for irregular thickenings in the ruffled membrane during outgrowth. However, in spite of the presence of inner cell masses in the A^y/A^y blastocysts (Calarco & Pedersen 1976), no inner cell mass cells were observed by the time the embryo had flattened into a trophoblast layer. Thus, the exact fate of the A^y/A^y inner cell mass cells remains obscure: they may disintegrate or be sloughed off into the culture medium as intact cells, or they may be incorporated into the flattened trophoblast layer.

In view of the sensitivity of post-blastocyst inner cell mass development to a variety of perturbations, including acute X-irradiation (Goldstein *et al.* 1975) and the interference with DNA, RNA and protein synthesis by metabolic inhibitors (Rowinski *et al.* 1975; Sherman & Atienza 1975; R.H. Glass, A.I. Spindle & R.A. Pedersen, unpublished work), it seems likely that the death of the A^y/A^y of the inner cell mass is secondary to some other primary function specified by the $+A^y$ gene. For example, most A^y/A^y morulae and blastocysts are smaller and contain fewer inner cell mass cells than controls (Calarco & Pedersen 1976) and may for these reasons have impaired inner cell mass survival during postimplantation growth *in vitro*. But such a decrease in mass alone certainly would not account for lethal A^y/A^y effects *in vivo*, since normal fetuses are obtained even when one blastomere of a mouse embryo is destroyed at the 2-cell stage (Tarkowski 1959). It is also possible that the early cleavage delay and arrest of some blastomeres could indicate a malfunction in DNA replication that differentially affects the inner cell mass cells due to their high rate of proliferation (Barlow *et al.* 1972). To evaluate this possibility, abnormal blastocysts were labelled with [³H]thymidine and their cell numbers and labelling index were compared with those of normal littermates (Table 1). Presumed A^y/A^y embryos had fewer cells, as expected from the cleavage delay and partial arrest, but the proportion of labelled nuclei was not significantly different from that of normal littermates ($\chi^2 = 1.86$, $P \leqslant 0.15$). This result indicates that there was no difference in the relative length of the S-phase of the cell cycle and therefore there were probably no major differences in the overall rates of DNA synthesis.

Any unifying hypothesis about the primary biochemical alteration specified by the A^y allele should account not only for recessive lethality in the embryo but also for the dominant heterozygous effects in the adult. These effects

TABLE 1

DNA synthesis in mouse embryos from $A^y/a \times A^y/a$ matings

Presumed genotype	No. of embryos	Mean no. of nuclei ± S.E.	% of [³H]thymidine-labelled nuclei ± S.E.[a]
A^y/A^y	15	33 ± 5	54.5 ± 5.8
$A^y/a + a/a$	36[b]	60 ± 4	66.6 ± 4.5

[a] Embryos were labelled with [³H]thymidine (1 μCi/ml) for 1 h at the blastocyst stage and then exposed to emulsion for 1 week.
[b] Eight other embryos in this category were excluded because of poor fixation or loss.

include the production of phaeomelanin by hair follicle melanocytes but of eumelanin by retinal melanocytes (Markert & Silvers 1956; Galbraith 1971; Mayer & Fishbane 1972), obesity and a diabetes-like syndrome (Hummel *et al.* 1972), and mating deficiencies, particularly the inability of A^y/a males to induce oestrus synchrony in females (Bartke & Wolff 1966). At present there is not enough information for a useful hypothesis integrating these diverse symptoms to be formulated. However, in view of the presence of several stage-specific surface antigens in preimplantation development (Artzt *et al.* 1973; Wiley 1974), the possibility of membrane alterations in A^y/A^y embryos should be considered in addition to possible deficiencies in RNA or protein synthesis.

Finally, it is useful to consider some implications of the time of occurrence of A^y/A^y defects. The early cleavage delay suggests that some crucial early function is impaired and continues to be impaired during subsequent cleavage with a high probability of arrest of several blastomeres before the 16-cell stage. The differentiation into inner cell mass and trophoblast by many A^y/A^y embryos indicates that blastomeres that escape arrest are able to complete preimplantation development in spite of their defects. Subsequent failure of hatching and inner cell mass development may indicate that there is a second critical period for expression of the defective gene during and after implantation or may reflect the deficiencies accumulated by A^y/A^y cells throughout the preimplanta-

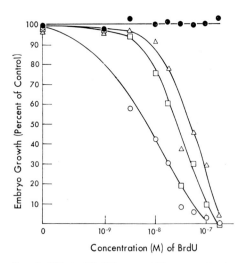

FIG. 1. Effect of BrdU on post-blastocyst development of mouse embryos *in vitro*. Blastocysts were cultured for 5 days in modified BME containing 10% dialysed serum and different concentrations of BrdU. Growth is shown as percentage of control for each end-point (data from Table 2). (●) trophoblast outgrowth, (△) inner cell mass growth, (□) inner cell mass differentiation into endoderm and ectoderm (normal and abnormal combined), (○) inner cell mass differentiation into endoderm and ectoderm (normal only).

TABLE 2

Effect of continuous BrdU treatment of blastocysts on postimplantation development

Concentration of BrdU (m)	No. of replicates[a]	Mean no. of trophoblast outgrowths ± S.E.	Mean no. of inner cell masses ± S.E.	Mean no. of all 2-layer inner cell masses ± S.E.	Mean no. of normal 2-layer inner cell masses ± S.E.
0	18	14.3 ± 1.1	12.7 ± 2.1	7.3 ± 2.6	6.9 ± 2.4
1 × 10⁻⁹	5	14.1 ± 1.0	12.6 ± 1.3	7.6 ± 1.3	7.2 ± 0.8
5 × 10⁻⁹	10	14.8 ± 0.8	12.3 ± 2.2	6.9 ± 1.9	4.0 ± 1.8
1 × 10⁻⁸	12	14.3 ± 1.1	11.6 ± 2.0	5.0 ± 3.0	2.9 ± 2.4
2.5 × 10⁻⁸	16	14.5 ± 0.6	9.9 ± 2.4	4.4 ± 2.6	2.1 ± 2.1
5 × 10⁻⁸	16	14.4 ± 1.1	4.8 ± 3.7	1.4 ± 2.1	0.6 ± 1.1
7.5 × 10⁻⁸	9	14.3 ± 0.9	4.8 ± 3.7	1.2 ± 2.3	0.4 ± 0.7
1 × 10⁻⁷	9	14.4 ± 1.0	3.7 ± 2.4	0.7 ± 0.7	0.2 ± 0.4

[a] Fifteen embryos were treated per replicate and the average response of trophoblast and inner cell mass tissues for n replicates was determined.

tion period. However, since homozygous yellow embryos are continuously defective during this time for the product specified by the $+A^y$ allele, a more precise definition of critical periods for gene expression affecting early postimplantation development requires a perturbation, such as BrdU, that can be applied at specific stages.

Effect of 5-bromodeoxyuridine on postimplantation development

In order to determine whether BrdU-sensitive processes occur between blastulation and primary germ layer formation, we cultured blastocysts continuously for 5 days in low concentrations (10^{-9} to 10^{-7} M) of BrdU, and scored the growth of trophoblast and inner cell mass tissues (Fig. 1, Table 2). There was a dose-dependent inhibition of inner cell mass development, but there was no effect on either trophoblast giant cell formation or the gross appearance of trophoblast outgrowths at these concentrations (Fig. 2). Sherman & Atienza (1975) also observed a difference between trophoblast and inner cell mass sensitivity when blastocysts were cultured at higher BrdU concentrations in NCTC-109 or Dulbecco's modified Eagle's medium, and Garner (1974) reported resistance of trophoblast outgrowth to 1×10^{-7} M-BrdU in medium containing 5% serum. It is unlikely that this relative resistance of trophoblast development to BrdU is due to decreased trophoblast cell permeability to the drug, since trophoblast cells incorporate [³H]BrdU into acid-insoluble material (Sherman & Atienza 1975) and since approximately 80% of all nuclei in our experiments incorporated [³H]BrdU in 1 24-h period at the early or late blastocyst stage, when the difference between trophoblast and inner cell mass sensitivity is greatest (Pedersen & Spindle, unpublished work). Apparently, processes that are necessary for trophoblast development during and after implantation are sensitive to these BrdU concentrations before, but not after, the blastocyst stage.

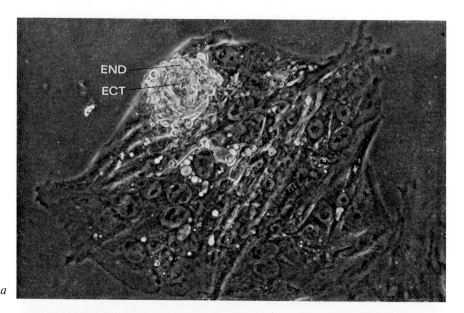

a

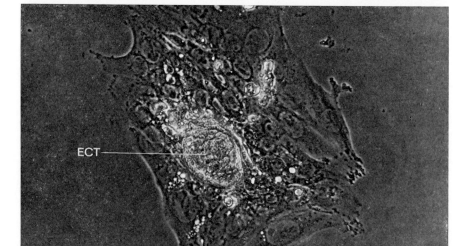

b

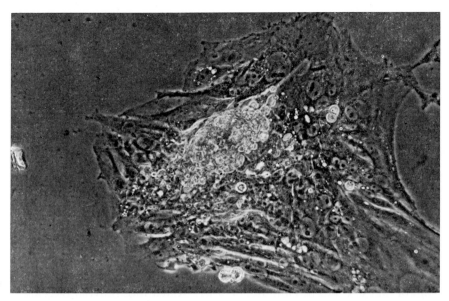

c

FIG. 2. Effect of BrdU on inner cell mass growth and differentiation into endoderm and ectoderm *in vitro*. Blastocysts were grown continuously for 5 days in modified BME containing 10% dialysed serum and BrdU as indicated. (*a*) In control cultures trophoblast cells have grown out and the inner cell mass has differentiated into endoderm (END) and ectoderm (ECT). Phase contrast, $\times$ 127. (*b*) In 1×10^{-8} M-BrdU trophoblast cells have grown out and the inner cell mass has formed two primary germ layers, but the ectoderm is underdeveloped. Phase contrast, $\times$ 100. (*c*) In 5×10^{-8} M-BrdU trophoblast cells have grown out and inner cell mass tissue is present but not differentiated into endoderm and ectoderm. Phase contrast, $\times$ 127.

However, the BrdU inhibition of inner cell mass growth and differentiation into endoderm and ectoderm (Fig. 1, Table 2) indicates that processes necessary for inner cell mass development are sensitive both before and after the blastocyst stage. Another indication that critical events occur after the blastocyst stage is that in $(1-5) \times 10^{-8}$ M-BrdU up to half of the 2-layer inner cell masses had an underdeveloped ectodermal layer (Fig. 2*b*). Although the basis for this effect is not clear, it is reminiscent of interference with ectoderm differentiation by lithium chloride treatment of amphibian embryos (Masui 1961) and the reported effects of several recessive lethal mutations on primary germ layer differentiation (Glucksohn-Schoenheimer 1940; Dunn 1972).

In order to determine whether there is a shorter critical period of inner cell mass sensitivity, we treated embryos with BrdU (1×10^{-7} M) for 24 hours after culturing them for 2 days (morula), 3 days (blastocyst), 4 days (late blastocyst), 5 days (attachment), 6 days (early outgrowth), or 7 days (mid-outgrowth) (Table 3). When embryos were treated at the morula, blastocyst or late blasto-

TABLE 3

Effect of 24-hour BrdU treatment on postimplantation development of mouse embryos[a]

Stage treated	No. of embryos	Growth response (% of controls)			
		Hatching	Trophoblast outgrowth	Inner cell mass growth	2-layer differentiation
Morula	150	67.6	69.9	24.8	1.7
Blastocyst	150	104	99.3	36.4	5 4
Late blastocyst	75	95.8	98.7	26.7	2.3
Attachment	60	—	100	60.0	27.8
Early outgrowth	60	—	—	91.7	77.3
Mid-outgrowth	60	—	—	103	103

[a] Embryos were cultured from the 2-cell stage to the appropriate stage and then exposed to BrdU (1×10^{-7} M) for 24 h. After BrdU treatment, embryos were washed once and cultured for the remainder of the 5-day post-blastocyst culture period in BrdU-free medium.

cyst stage, the differentiation into endoderm and ectoderm was less than one-tenth of that in controls. However, embryos treated with BrdU at the attachment stage were considerably less sensitive, and their inner cell masses differentiated into two layers at nearly one-third of the control level, although their cells incorporated BrdU into DNA at a rate similar to that of earlier stages (Pedersen & Spindle, unpublished work). When embryos were treated at outgrowth stages, neither inner cell mass growth nor endoderm–ectoderm differentiation was greatly impaired. These results indicate that the peak of the critical period for postimplantation inner cell mass development lies between the morula and late blastocyst stages. There was a 30% reduction in hatching and trophoblast outgrowth when embryos were cultured for 24 h from the morula to the blastocyst stage in 10^{-7} M-BrdU, which suggests that events just before blastocyst formation are critical for hatching and postimplantation trophoblast function.

Although the precise mechanism of BrdU interference with differentiation is still unknown, the well-known effects of BrdU in preventing the synthesis of specific products by cultured cells (Abbott & Holtzer 1968; Stellwagen & Tomkins 1971) suggest that BrdU inhibits gene expression, perhaps by influencing the binding of regulatory proteins to the DNA (Lin & Riggs 1972; David et al. 1974) or by altering the base composition of messenger RNAs (Hill et al. 1974). In an attempt to elucidate the mechanism of BrdU effects on inner cell mass development, we labelled embryos with [³H]thymidine or [³H]-uridine after five days of continuous culture in BrdU at concentrations that depressed endoderm–ectoderm differentiation. There was no decrease in the percentage of inner cell mass nuclei labelled with [³H]thymidine at concentrations of either 1×10^{-8} M- or 5×10^{-8} M-BrdU, nor was there a decrease in [^{3}H]uridine incorporation into acid-insoluble material localized in the nucleoli or the nucleoplasm as determined by grain counting (Table 4). Thus, incorporation of BrdU into inner cell mass cells impairs their development without grossly altering the rates of DNA replication or general RNA synthesis. However, subtle changes in messenger RNA synthesis would be beyond the resolution of these autoradiographic techniques and may in fact be the most important consequences of BrdU incorporation. Although these observations do not rule out the possibility of an effect of BrdU on proliferation at a level other than DNA replication or an effect of unincorporated BrdU (Meuth & Green 1974), the results are consistent with the interpretation that BrdU exerts its effects by interfering with specific gene expression during certain critical periods.

CONCLUSIONS

Homozygous effects of the A^y allele, as shown by time-lapse cinematography, occur during the second cleavage division, which confirms that the zygote genome is activated at or before this time. Presumptive A^y/A^y blastocysts had about half as many cells as A^y/a and a/a embryos, yet they showed almost the same incidence of pulse-labelling with [^{3}H]thymidine, which rules out a major change in the rate of DNA synthesis as the primary action of the $+A^y$ gene at the blastocyst stage. Although most A^y/A^y blastocysts had an inner cell mass, inner cell mass cells disappeared during the trophoblast outgrowth that occurred

TABLE 4

Effect of BrdU on DNA and RNA synthesis

Concentration of BrdU (m)	DNA synthesis		RNA synthesis			
	No. of nuclei	% of [^{3}H]-thymidine-labelled nuclei per embryo $\pm$ S.E.[a]	No. of nuclei	Grain counts[b] $\pm$ S.E.		
				Nucleolus	Nucleoplasm	Whole nucleus[c]
0	697	73.4 ± 1.4	45	27.5 ± 2.4	33.4 ± 3.1	57.1 ± 4.9
1×10^{-8}	770	72.0 ± 2.8	25	25.3 ± 2.4	34.0 ± 3.5	55.7 ± 5.4
5×10^{-8}	689	71.4 ± 1.5	59	29.9 ± 3.0	34.1 ± 3.2	61.7 ± 5.9

[a] After 5 days of continuous culture in BrdU at the indicated concentrations, embryos were labelled for 2 h with [^{3}H]thymidine (1 µCi/ml) and then exposed to emulsion for 7 days.
[b] After 5 days of continuous culture in BrdU at the indicated concentrations, embryos were labelled for 2 h with [^{3}H]uridine (0.1 µCi/ml) and then exposed to emulsion for 3 days.
[c] Total nuclear grain counts after correction for background.

when the zona pellucida was removed experimentally. Thus, the defects of A^y/A^y embryos occur over a long period of time during preimplantation and early postimplantation development and a more precise determination of the timing of gene expression necessary for early development requires the use of a perturbing substance, such as BrdU, that can be applied at specific stages.

The mechanisms by which BrdU inhibits development of mammalian embryos are not well defined. However, since we found that continuous exposure of post-blastocyst stage mouse embryos to BrdU did not significantly alter the rate of general DNA and RNA synthesis, although it inhibited inner cell mass growth and differentiation, we suggest that BrdU affects implantation and postimplantation development by interfering with specific gene expression needed for subsequent development. Our results suggest that the gene expression required for trophoblast development and function occurs before the blastocyst stage and that the critical period of gene expression for inner cell mass growth and differentiation into endoderm and ectoderm extends from the morula stage through the late blastocyst stage.

ACKNOWLEDGEMENTS

We thank Kitty Wu for her technical assistance, Miriam Zeiger for her editorial assistance and Patricia Calarco, Charles Epstein and Mitchell Golbus for their comments on the manuscript. We are grateful to Michael Sherman and Sue Bi Atienza for showing us their unpublished results. This work was performed under the auspices of the US Energy Research and Development Administration.

References

ABBOTT, J. & HOLTZER, H. (1968) The loss of phenotypic traits by differentiated cells, V. The effect of 5-bromodeoxyuridine on cloned chondrocytes. *Proc. Natl. Acad. Sci. USA* 59, 1141–1151

ARTZT, K., DUBOIS, P., BENNETT, D., CONDAMINE, H., BABINET, C. & JACOB, F. (1973) Surface antigens common to mouse cleavage embryos and primitive teratocarcinoma cells in culture. *Proc. Natl. Acad. Sci. USA 70*, 2988–2992

BARLOW, P., OWEN, D.A.J. & GRAHAM, C. (1972) DNA synthesis in the preimplantation mouse embryo. *J. Embryol. Exp. Morphol. 27*, 431–445

BARTKE, A. & WOLFF, G.L. (1966) Influence of the lethal yellow (A^y) gene on estrous synchrony in mice. *Science (Wash. D.C.) 153*, 79–80

BERGSTROM, S. (1972) Shedding of the zona pellucida in normal pregnancy and in various hormonal states in the mouse: A scanning electron microscope study. *Z. Anat. Entwicklungsgesch. 136*, 143–167

BIGGERS, J.D., WHITTEN, W.K. & WHITTINGHAM, D.G. (1971) The culture of mouse embryos *in vitro*, in *Methods in Mammalian Embryology* (Daniel, J.C., Jr., ed.), pp. 86–116, Freeman, San Francisco

BORGHESE, E. & CASSINI, A. (1963) Cleavage of mouse egg, in *Cinemicrography in Cell Biology* (Rose, G.G., ed.), pp. 263–277, Academic Press, New York

BRINSTER, R.L. (1973) Parental glucose phosphate isomerase activity in three-day mouse embryos. *Biochem. Genet. 9*, 187–191

CALARCO, P.G. & PEDERSEN, R.A. (1976) Ultrastructural observations of lethal yellow (A^y/A^y) mouse embryos. *J. Embryol. Exp. Morphol*, in press

CHAPMAN, V.M., ADLER, D., LABARCA, C. & WUDL, L. (1976) Genetic variation of β-glucuronidase expression during early embryogenesis, in this volume, pp. 115–124

CHEW, N.J. & SHERMAN, M.I. (1975) Biochemistry of differentiation of mouse trophoblast: $\Delta^5,3\beta$-hydroxysteroid dehydrogenase. *Biol. Reprod. 12*, 351–359

CHOLEWA, J.A. & WHITTEN, W.K. (1970) Development of two-cell mouse embryos in the absence of a fixed-nitrogen source. *J. Reprod. Fertil. 22*, 553–555

COLE, R.J. & PAUL, J. (1965) Properties of cultured preimplantation mouse and rabbit embryos, and cell strains derived from them, in *Preimplantation Stages of Pregnancy (Ciba Found. Symp.)*, pp. 82–112, Churchill, London

COLEMAN, A.W., COLEMAN, J.R., KANKEL, D. & WERNER, I. (1970) The reversible control of animal cell differentiation by the thymidine analog, 5-bromodeoxyuridine. *Exp. Cell Res. 59*, 319–328

DAVID, J., GORDON, J.S. & RUTTER, W.J. (1974) Increased thermal stability of chromatin containing 5-bromodeoxyuridine-substituted DNA. *Proc. Natl. Acad. Sci. USA 71*, 2808–2812

DUNN, G.R. (1972) Embryological effects of a minute deficiency in linkage group II of the mouse. *J. Embryol. Exp. Morphol. 27*, 147–154

EAGLE, H. (1955) Nutrition needs of mammalian cells in tissue culture. *Science (Wash. D.C.) 122*, 501–504

EATON, G.J. & GREEN, M.M. (1963) Giant cell differentiation and lethality of homozygous yellow mouse embryos. *Genetica (The Hague) 34*, 156–161

GALBRAITH, D.B. (1971) Expression of genes at the agouti locus and mitotic activity of the hair bulb of the mouse. *Genetics 67*, 559–568

GARDNER, R.L. (1972) An investigation of inner cell mass and trophoblast tissues following their isolation from the mouse blastocyst. *J. Embryol. Exp. Morphol. 28*, 279–312

GARNER, W. (1974) The effect of 5-bromodeoxyuridine on early mouse embryos *in vitro*. *J. Embryol. Exp. Morphol. 32*, 849–855

GLUECKSOHN-SCHOENHEIMER, S. (1940) The effect of an early lethal (t^0) in the house mouse. *Genetics 25*, 391–400

GOLBUS, M.S. & EPSTEIN, C.J. (1974) Effect of 5-bromodeoxyuridine on pre-implantation mouse embryo development. *Differentiation 2*, 143–149

GOLBUS, M.S., CALARCO, P.G. & EPSTEIN, C.J. (1973) The effects of inhibitors of RNA synthesis (α-amanitin and actinomycin D) on preimplantation mouse embryogenesis. *J. Exp. Zool. 186*, 207–216

GOLDSTEIN, L.S., SPINDLE, A.I. & PEDERSEN, R.A. (1975) X-ray sensitivity of the preimplantation mouse embryo *in vitro*. *Radiat. Res. 62*, 276–287

GWATKIN, R.B.L. (1966) Amino acid requirements for attachment and outgrowth of the mouse blastocyst *in vitro*. *J. Cell. Comp. Physiol. 68*, 335–343

HAM, R.G. (1963) Albumin replacement by fatty acids in clonal growth of mammalian cells. *Science (Wash. D.C.) 140*, 802–803

HILL, B.T., TSUBOI, A. & BASERGA, R. (1974) Effect of 5-bromodeoxyuridine on chromatin transcription in confluent fibroblasts. *Proc. Natl. Acad. Sci. USA 71*, 455–459

HSU, Y-C. (1971) Post-blastocyst differentiation *in vitro*. *Nature (Lond.) 231*, 100–102

HSU, Y-C. (1973) Differentiation *in vitro* of mouse embryos to the stage of early somite. *Dev. Biol. 33*, 403–411

HSU, Y-C., BASKAR, J., STEVENS, L.C. & RASH, J.E. (1974) Development *in vitro* of mouse embryos from the two-cell stage to the early somite stage. *J. Embryol. Exp. Morphol. 31*, 235–245

HUMMEL, K.P., COLEMAN, D.L. & LANE, P.W. (1972) The influence of genetic background on expression of mutations at the diabetes locus in the mouse. I. C57BL/KsJ and C57BL/ 6J strains. *Biochem. Genet. 7*, 1–13

JENKINSON, E.J. & WILSON, I.B. (1973) *In vitro* studies on the control of trophoblast outgrowth in the mouse. *J. Embryol. Exp. Morphol. 30*, 21–30

KIRKHAM, W.B. (1919) The fate of homozygous yellow mice. *J. Exp. Zool. 28*, 125–135

KNOWLAND, J. & GRAHAM, C. (1972) RNA synthesis at the two-cell stage of mouse development. *J. Embryol. Exp. Morphol. 27*, 167–176

LIN, S-Y. & RIGGS, A.D. (1972) *Lac* operator analogues: Bromodeoxyuridine substitution in the *lac* operator affects the rate of dissociation of the *lac* repressor. *Proc. Natl. Acad. Sci. USA 69*, 2574–2576

McLAREN, A. (1970) The fate of the zona pellucida in mice. *J. Embryol. Exp. Morphol. 23*, 1–19

MARKERT, C.L. & SILVERS, W.K. (1956) The effects of genotype and cell environment on melanoblast differentiation in the house mouse. *Genetics 41*, 429–450

MASUI, Y. (1961) Mesodermal and endodermal differentiation of the presumptive ectoderm of *Triturus* gastrula through influence of lithium ion. *Experientia (Basel) 17*, 458–463

MAYER, T.C. & FISHBANE, J.L. (1972) Mesoderm-ectoderm interaction in the production of the agouti pigmentation pattern in mice. *Genetics 71*, 297–303

MENKE, T.M. & McLAREN, A. (1970) Mouse blastocysts grown *in vivo* and *in vitro*: Carbon dioxide production and trophoblast outgrowth. *J. Reprod. Fertil. 23*, 117–127

MEUTH, M. & GREEN, H. (1974) Induction of deoxycytidineless state in cultured mammalian cells by bromodeoxyuridine. *Cell 2*, 109–112

MINTZ, B. (1971) Control of embryo implantation and survival, in *Schering Symposium on Intrinsic and Extrinsic Factors in Early Mammalian Development (Advances in the Biosciences 6)* (Raspé, G., ed.), pp. 317–340, Pergamon Press/Vieweg, Oxford

PEDERSEN, R.A. (1974) Development of lethal yellow (A^y/A^y) mouse embryos in vitro. *J. Exp. Zool. 188*, 307–319

PIENKOWSKI, M., SOLTER, D. & KOPROWSKI, H. (1974) Early mouse embryos: Growth and differentiation in vitro. *Exp. Cell Res. 85*, 424–428

ROBERTSON, G.G. (1942) An analysis of the development of homozygous yellow mouse embryos. *J. Exp. Zool. 89*, 197–231

ROWINSKI, J., SOLTER, D. & KOPROWSKI, H. (1975) Mouse embryo development in vitro: Effects of inhibitors of RNA and protein synthesis on blastocyst and post-blastocyst embryos. *J. Exp. Zool. 192*, 133-142

SALOMON, D.S. & SHERMAN, M.I. (1975) Implantation and invasiveness of mouse blastocysts on uterine monolayers. *Exp. Cell Res. 90*, 261–268

SHERMAN, M.I. & ATIENZA, S.B. (1975) Effects of bromodeoxyuridine, cytosine arabinoside and Colcemid upon *in vitro* development of mouse blastocysts. *J. Embryol. Exp. Morphol. 34*, 467–484

SOLTER, D., DAMJANOV, I. & ŠKREB, N. (1970) Ultrastructure of mouse egg-cylinder. *Z. Anat. Entwicklungsgesch. 132*, 291–298

SOLTER, D., BICZYSKO, W., PIENKOWSKI, M. & KOPROWSKI, H. (1974) Ultrastructure of mouse egg-cylinders developed in vitro. *Anat. Rec. 186*, 263–280

SPINDLE, A.I. & PEDERSEN, R.A. (1973) Hatching, attachment, and outgrowth of mouse blastocysts in vitro: Fixed nitrogen requirements. *J. Exp. Zool. 186*, 305–318

STEIER, H. (1975) Heated microscope stage: A temperature control for live-cell microscopy. *Lab. Pract.* p. 417.

STELLWAGEN, R.H. & TOMKINS, G.M. (1971) Preferential inhibition by 5-bromodeoxyuridine of the synthesis of tyrosine aminotransferase in hepatoma cell cultures. *J. Mol. Biol. 56*, 167–182

TARKOWSKI, A.K. (1959) Experiments on the development of isolated blastomeres of mouse eggs. *Nature (Lond.) 184*, 1286–1287

TARKOWSKI, A. K. (1966) An air-drying method for chromosome preparations from mouse eggs. *Cytogenetics (Basel)* 5, 394–400

TEMIN, H. M., PIERSON, R. W. JR. & DULAK, N. C. (1972) The role of serum in the control of multiplication of avian and mammalian cells in culture, in *Growth, Nutrition, and Metabolism of Cells in Culture* (Rothblat, G. H. & Cristofalo, V. J., eds.), vol. 1, pp. 49–81, Academic Press, New York

TENCER, R. & BRACHET, J. (1973) Studies on the effects of bromodeoxyuridine (BUdR) on differentiation. *Differentiation* 1, 51–64

THOMSON, J. L. & BIGGERS, J. D. (1966) Effects of inhibitors of protein synthesis on the development of preimplantation mouse embryos. *Exp. Cell Res. 41*, 411–427

WALES, R. G. (1970) Effects of ions on the development of the pre-implantation mouse embryo *in vitro*. *Aust. J. Biol. Sci. 23*, 421–429

WESSELLS, N. K. (1964) DNA synthesis, mitosis, and differentiation in pancreatic acinar cells *in vitro*. *J. Cell Biol. 20*, 415–433

WHITTEN, W. K. & DAGG, C. P. (1961) Influence of spermatozoa on the cleavage rate of mouse eggs. *J. Exp. Zool. 148*, 173–183

WILEY, L. D. (1974) Presence of a gonadotrophin on the surface of preimplanted mouse embryos. *Nature (Lond.) 252*, 715–716

WOODLAND, H. R. & GRAHAM, C. F. (1969) RNA synthesis during early development of the mouse. *Nature (Lond.) 221*, 327–332

WUDL, L. & CHAPMAN, V. (1976) The expression of β-glucuronidase during preimplantation development of mouse embryos. *Dev. Biol. 48*, 104–109

Discussion

Gluecksohn-Waelsch: Having advocated for a long time the use of mutations as tools for the causal analysis of development, I would like to call attention here to a new mutation that may be of interest for studies of inner cell mass and trophectoderm differentiation, since it seems to interfere with interactions between trophoblast and inner cell mass.

Susan Lewis in our laboratory has studied embryos homozygous for one of the radiation-induced alleles at the albino locus in the mouse. These alleles are distinguished by their multiple effects on enzyme differentiation as well as on morphogenesis. We are interested in them as tools for studying the correlation of biochemical and structural, particularly ultrastructural, cell differentiation. One of these mutations appears interesting in connection with both Dr Gardner's work and Dr Pedersen's work on the yellow mutant.

The homozygous c^{6H} embryo is characterized by a spear-shaped extension of the parietal, distal endoderm into the maternal decidua at the stage of the $6\frac{1}{2}$–$7\frac{1}{2}$-day egg cylinder. This is the most characteristic feature of the embryo, which in addition is retarded in growth and development. The embryonic ectoderm looks normal but its growth is reduced. Primitive streak and mesoderm differentiation are absent in the $7\frac{1}{2}$-day egg cylinder and the ectoplacental cone is severely defective. The extension of the parietal endoderm is several times the length of the embryo. The abnormal ectoplacental cone has a network of vacuolated cells with enlarged nuclei and prominent nucleoli; mitosis is still evident. The proximal endoderm is abnormal in its differentiation.

In summary, trophoblastic derivatives as well as inner cell mass derivatives are severely affected in the mutant embryos. Because of the nature of the developmental abnormalities we feel that this mutant may lend itself to further studies of inductive interaction between trophoblast and inner cell mass.

Tarkowski: Those mutant embryos closely resemble the parthenogenetic embryos which we obtained in the mouse. Development of both is checked at the same stage, and some of the parthenogenetic egg cylinders have a similar endodermal extension.

Škreb: A similar situation seems to arise in the spontaneous parthenogenetic embryos which Dr L.C. Stevens (1975) described during the Roche Symposium on Teratomas and Differentiation in May 1975.

Gardner: In the yellow mutant, the time of appearance of anomalies might depend on genetic background. We wanted to transplant inner cell masses derived from heterozygous yellow matings to normal blastocysts and vice versa, to see which of the two tissues was defective. We obviously wanted to be able to identify the mutants. Clearly with the genetic background you use, Dr Pedersen, you can sometimes identify them as early as the 2-cell stage. But we use both natural matings and superovulations, getting perfect blastocysts formed. We looked at the blastocysts very closely—trophoblast junctions, size of blastocysts and so on—trying to sort them on a whole lot of criteria. When these blastocysts from yellow by yellow matings were transplanted to uterine fostermothers we found the expected excess of early postimplantation deaths over what was seen in the yellow by extreme non-agouti controls. We couldn't find any evidence of any abnormalities before implantation. We haven't tried stressing the embryos by culturing them from earlier cleavage stages but as recovered blastocysts there is nothing wrong (V.E. Papaioannou & R.L. Gardner, unpublished work). As discussed later (p. 232), our results suggest that both homozygous yellow inner cell mass and trophoblast continue to develop when combined with non-yellow tissue.

Pedersen: This is certainly fascinating. Of course we would like to have a linked recessive genetic marker which would enable us to know for sure that cells of the homozygous embryo have survived. The genes undulated (*un*) and wellhaaring (*we*) are nearby on chromosome 2, but are recognizable only after birth. One would prefer a linked marker that could be identified soon after implantation.

McLaren: The difference between your findings and Dr Gardner's is probably due to a difference in genetic background between the two substrains, rather than to the culture stress, Dr Pedersen. Our yellow embryos resemble yours (H. Paterson, personal communication), even when they are taken directly out of the uterus.

Gardner: The difference between our yellow stock and Dr Pedersen's is that our mice are yellow by extreme non-agouti heterozygotes. They are also of entirely different origin (AG/Cam; Staats 1972).

Pedersen: The expression of the A^y allele in the homozygous condition does appear to vary with strain background. Although embryos from C57-A^y/a parents frequently showed arrested blastomeres before the blastocyst stage, homozygous yellow embryos from hybrid parents (C57BL × SEC F1) could be recognized primarily by their collapse during culture beyond the blastocyst stage, but not before (Pedersen 1974). The reported histological observations also vary from strain to strain. Kirkham (1919) saw a few abnormalities in his strain at the morula stage, but Robertson (1942a) in another strain did not observe any until implantation.

Gluecksohn-Waelsch: Robertson (1942b) transplanted ovaries from heterozygous yellow females into ovariectomized homozygous normal mice. The homozygous mutant embryos that originated from matings to heterozygous males of these normal females carrying heterozygous yellow ovaries developed much further than usual. In comparison with homozygous yellow embryos in heterozygous mothers, the homozygous yellow embryos in normal mothers had about twice the number of cells, they developed a small ectoplacental cone, and implantation proceeded to a more advanced stage. I find this very interesting in view of the suggestion that normal development might be achieved in chimeras with normal inner cell mass and homozygous yellow trophoblast, and the reciprocal combination. How far exactly did these homozygotes get in normal mothers, Dr Pedersen?

Pedersen: Some of the homozygous yellow embryos that developed from Robertson's (1942a) ovarian transplants formed an ectoplacental cone, Reichert's membrane and a larger inner cell mass than homozygous embryos that developed in the heterozygous yellow mother. Even though the abnormalities initially appeared at about the same time in both environments, Robertson (1942a) interpreted this result as indicating a detrimental effect of the A^y/a uterine environment on development. Whatever the case, the *in vitro* failure of homozygotes shows that they have an inherent developmental problem, as well.

Gluecksohn-Waelsch: The normal mother may provide something that neither *in vitro* conditions nor the heterozygous mother can provide.

Rutter: Is there complementation between the normal and the yellow mice? A soluble factor might be involved. Could you put a filter between them, or place them contiguously after they begin developing?

Pedersen: The way to do that is to make a chimera, either as Dr Gardner has done, or by aggregating whole embryos. Mintz (1964) used this approach with t^{12}/t^{12} embryos and found no evidence for any obvious improvement of the homozygous lethal cells.

Rutter: Has the restriction in development anything to do with restricted cleavage in two particular blastomeres? Is it simply an aspect of development of any of the blastomeres?

Pedersen: It seems unlikely that cleavage delay and arrest are due to localization of determinants in certain blastomeres, since there are ample data now which show convincingly that the blastomeres' fates are labile up to about the morula stage. I think that we are seeing the effect of a random process in the A^y/A^y embryo with each blastomere having a certain probability of arrest. The pattern of arrest we see may thus reflect a Poisson distribution: some embryos have no arrested blastomeres, others have one or even several arrested or disintegrating blastomeres.

Rutter: You might get at that problem by using Burns' micro beam to destroy blastomeres *in situ* (Burns 1971). It should be possible to decide whether all irradiated cells produced your result or only a few of them.

Pedersen: One could look at normal postimplantation development *in vitro* as a function of mass by disaggregating 4-cell or 8-cell embryos and seeing whether the failure of inner cell mass development in homozygous yellow embryos is partly a result of their small size.

McLaren: It struck me also, from your BrdU results, that the two indices of differentiation that you are using—the reduction in inner cell mass relative to trophectoderm and the reduction of ectoderm relative to endoderm—both involve inside-outside differentiations. If there were a reduction in the total number of cells one would expect to have relatively fewer 'inside' cells, and hence less inner cell mass and less ectoderm. Have you done any cell counts?

Pedersen: We have observed a decrease in cell numbers at the late blastocyst stage when embryos are treated for 24-hour periods during preimplantation development (A.I. Spindle, unpublished work, 1975), but we have not counted cells of the inner cell mass after treatment at the post-blastocyst stages. I think this is necessary if we are to resolve whether the reduced incidence of endoderm and ectoderm formation is an effect of BrdU on proliferation or specifically on differentiation.

Hensleigh: In the embryos with reduced numbers of ectoderm cells how does development proceed between the endoderm–ectoderm stage and the egg-cylinder stage?

Pedersen: We have not gone beyond the point of endoderm–ectoderm differentiation with our BrdU treatments because the incidence of successful development in our controls drops below 50% after about the fifth day of post-blastocyst culture. There is clearly a need for improvement in our capabilities for prolonged, organized *in vitro* development.

Hensleigh: It would be interesting to see what percentage of embryos treated with BrdU would develop embryonic and extra-embryonic structures *in vitro*.

Pedersen: We have attempted to repeat Hsu's (1973) success in obtaining postimplantation development *in vitro*. By following his protocol of gradually increasing the concentration of human cord serum to 20% we can get a low incidence, about 5%, of beating heart-like structures and about the same percentage of embryos with blood islands. We have not observed any definite somite structures, neural folds, or blood circulation as Hsu has, but our control cultures are healthy at the end of the culture period and are capable of developing beyond germ layer formation if the serum is appropriately modified.

Graham: You have identified a critical period of development which is sensitive to BrdU. Could you comment on the possibility that your critical period is simply a time when there is rapid cell multiplication and DNA synthesis in your system?

Pedersen: Even with concentrations of 10^{-9}–10^{-8} M-BrdU continuously present after the blastocyst stage there is still substantial survival of inner cell mass, and we looked specifically at these cells by dissecting off the inner cell mass. Although we were primarily interested in the effect of a continuous post-blastocyst BrdU treatment on DNA and RNA synthesis, we also wondered whether cells at different stages incorporate different amounts of BrdU as a result either of changes in their rates of division or of alterations in their membranes. Between the 2-cell and the morula stages the amount of BrdU incorporated (per nucleus) during a 24-h incubation increased eightfold; there was a further twofold increase in incorporation (per nucleus) from the morula to the blastocyst stage, and very little change between blastocyst and late blastocyst or early outgrowth stages. Between the morula and late blastocyst stages there is relatively little change in inner cell mass sensitivity, but endoderm–ectoderm differentiation becomes increasingly resistant to BrdU treatment after attachment in spite of continued incorporation (A. I. Spindle & R. A. Pedersen, unpublished work, 1975).

Graham: Was there any evidence of differences in uptake of BrdU between outside cells and inside cells of the embryo? If there was, and if the effect depends on BrdU concentration, then one would expect the perhaps more rapidly dividing inner cell mass cells to be more sensitive than the outside cells.

Pedersen: We did not look at histological sections so we could not distinguish inside from outside cells. However, at the morula, blastocyst and late blastocyst stages 70–80% of all nuclei were labelled, so it is unlikely that trophoblast cells as a class had failed to take up BrdU. Also, these are the stages when the difference in the BrdU sensitivity of trophoblast and of inner cell mass is the greatest. Sherman & Atienza (1975) also have evidence that the relative resistance of post-blastocyst trophoblast differentiation is not due to lack of uptake or incorporation of BrdU.

References

BURNS, M.W. (1971) A simple and versatile argon laser microbeam. *Exp. Cell Res. 65* 470–473

HSU, Y.-C. (1973) Differentiation *in vitro* of mouse embryos to the stage of early somite. *Dev. Biol. 33*, 403–411

KIRKHAM, W.B. (1919) The fate of homozygous yellow mice. *J. Exp. Zool. 28*, 125–135

MINTZ, B. (1964) Formation of genetically mosaic mouse embryos and early development of 'lethal (t^{12}/t^{12})-normal' mosaics. *J. Exp. Zool. 157*, 273–292

PEDERSEN, R.A. (1974) Development of lethal yellow (A^y/A^y) mouse embryos *in vitro*. *J. Exp. Zool. 188*, 307–319

ROBERTSON, G.G. (1942a) An analysis of the development of homozygous yellow mouse embryos. *J. Exp. Zool. 89*, 197–231

ROBERTSON, G.G. (1942b) Increased viability of homozygous yellow mouse embryos in new uterine environments. *Genetics, 27*, 166–167

SHERMAN, M.I. & ATIENZA, S.B. (1975) Effects of bromodeoxyuridine, cytosine arabinoside and Colcemid upon *in vitro* development of mouse blastocysts. *J. Embryol. Exp. Morphol. 34*, 467–484

STAATS, J. (1972) Standardised nomenclature for inbred strains of mice: fifth listing. *Cancer Res. 32*, 1609–1646

STEVENS, L.C. (1975) Comparative development of normal and parthenogenetic mouse embryos, early testicular and ovarian teratomas, and embryoid bodies, in *Teratomas and Differentiation* (Sherman, M.I. & Solter, D., eds.), pp. 17–32, Academic Press, New York

Morphological consequences of trisomy in mammals

A. GROPP

Abteilung für Pathologie der Medizinischen Hochschule Lübeck

Abstract   An experimental model of trisomy has been built up in the mouse and used for a systematic evaluation of teratological profiles. Autosomal trisomy (Ts) in the mouse is almost invariably connected with prenatal death of the embryo (before day 20). Differences in the manifestation of an individual trisomic condition are due to the allelic heterogeneity of mouse stocks. The placenta exhibits concomitant changes of hypoplasia and retardation.

In some trisomic conditions (Ts 4, 8, 11, 15, 17) only a minute unorganized mass or an extremely retarded, dwarf-like embryo is formed which dies before day 12. Ts 1, 6 and 10 display mostly moderate to more severe retardation and hypoplasia. They die before or around day 15. Gross morphological malformation has been observed only with Ts 19 (isolated cleft palate) and with Ts 1 and 12. Ts 1 produces cyclopia in the most heavily affected embryos, suggesting that the more frequent minor manifestations also belong to this malformation complex. This trisomy can be considered as a mouse model of Ts 13 in man. Ts 12 in the mouse fetus is always connected with exencephaly. In contrast to similar defects caused by exogenous agents, the malformation produced by Ts 12 affects exclusively the anterior neural tube and the embryos die around day 15 – 17. There is evidence that the morphogenetic abnormalities produced by Ts 1 and Ts 12 are the consequence of transient and punctual defects in the inductive capacity of parts of the prechordal plate.

It is assumed that the failure and final breakdown of development inherent in all trisomic conditions is in part due to impairment of growth. However, *in vitro* studies of growth characteristics and cell cycle have not yet revealed major differences between trisomic and normal cells.

Autosomal trisomy (Ts) makes up an important part of the total incidence of chromosomal disorders observed in mammalian species. This is most obvious in man if surveys of pre- and postnatal chromosomal anomalies are considered.

According to a synopsis by Friedrich & Nielsen (1973) of several population surveys covering a total of about 31 800 newborn children, the total incidence of numerical plus balanced and unbalanced structural chromosomal anomalies is about 0.57%, or 0.36% if only the numerically and structurally unbalanced conditions are considered. About a third of these are autosomal trisomic conditions. The average incidence of the three most common types of autosomal trisomy in man is 0.1% in Down's syndrome (G-21 trisomy), 0.014% in Patau's syndrome (D-13 trisomy) and 0.011% in Edward's syndrome (E-18 trisomy). On the other hand, chromosomal aberrations have been found to be a frequent cause of early fetal death, and thus of spontaneous abortion. In about 1500 consecutive karyotyped human abortuses studied by Boué et al. (1974), chromosomal anomalies were detected in 61.5%. Moreover, by extrapolation from their observations, Boué et al. believe that in man about 50% of all conceptuses are chromosomally unbalanced and prone to earlier or later fetal death. The largest group of chromosomal errors in earlier pregnancy is represented by the autosomal trisomies. They come to about 45–54% of all chromosomal errors in recognized abortuses in man, though the relative frequencies of the individual autosomes involved differ markedly (from 0.7% for B group trisomy to about 14% for Ts 16) (Boué et al. 1974).

It follows that in general trisomy is more common in the early embryo but becomes less frequent thereafter by a process of gradual selective elimination. The chances certain types of trisomic conceptuses have of reaching the postnatal period, in comparison with two other frequent anomalies, X-monosomy and triploidy, are shown in Table 1. It can be concluded that specific trisomic conditions display differences in the temporal course of their developmental capacity as well as in their phenotypic or teratogenic profiles of development.

TABLE 1

Approximate postnatal survival rates of chromosomally abnormal zygotes

	Incidence (%)		Survival rate (based on a supposed incidence of 10% spontaneous abortions among all conceptuses)
	In spontaneous abortion[a]	Among newborns[b]	
45, XO	7.5–1.5	~0.015	~1:50–1:100
D-Trisomy (unspecified)	6	0.014	~1:40
Trisomy 18	2.0–2.5	0.011	~1:20
Trisomy 16	~8	0	1:>100
G-Trisomy (unspecified)	3.5	0.1	~1:3.5
Triploidy	3.3–9.0	Rare	1:>100

[a] Based on joint data of Carr (1965), Dhadial et al. (1970), Boué et al. (1974), not ascertained by banding procedures.
[b] Based on Friedrich & Nielsen 1973, and other available sources.

EXPERIMENTAL BASIS OF A SYSTEMATIC STUDY
OF TRISOMY IN THE MOUSE

Due to this situation in man, an experimental system was felt to be needed
for studying the morphological consequences of trisomy. Morphology, in the

TABLE 2

Characteristics of currently available Robertsonian centric fusion metacentrics in the mouse

Designation of metacentric chromosome	Origin	Composition of arms designated according to the numbering system for mouse chrosomes	Linkage group
Rb 1 Bnr		$\dfrac{3}{1}$	- XIII
Rb 2 Bnr		$\dfrac{6}{4}$	XI VIII
Rb 3 Bnr		$\dfrac{15}{5}$	VI XVII
Rb 4 Bnr		$\dfrac{13}{11}$	XIV VII
Rb 5 Bnr	Feral (Gropp et al. 1972)	$\dfrac{12}{8}$	XVI XVIII
Rb 6 Bnr		$\dfrac{14}{9}$	III II
Rb 7 Bnr		$\dfrac{17}{16}$	IX -
Rb 8 Bnr		$\dfrac{11}{10}$	VII X
Rb 9 Bnr		$\dfrac{12}{4}$	XVI VIII
Rb 10 Bnr		$\dfrac{10}{1}$	X XIII
Rb 1 Ald	Laboratory (Léonard & Deknudt 1967)	$\dfrac{15}{6}$	VI XI
Rb 163 H	(Evans et al. 1967)	$\dfrac{19}{9}$	XII II
Rb 1 Wh	(White & Tjio 1968)	$\dfrac{19}{5}$	XII XVII
Rb 1 JeM	(Baranov & Dyban 1971)	$\dfrac{17}{8}$	IX XVIII

sense of maintenance or breakdown of gross embryological and histological patterns, can be considered as an integral whole, including many diverging and distinct (cellular, biochemical, molecular and other) expressions of a triplicate autosome. The mouse has been found particularly convenient for the experimental approach to a systematic study of the effects of trisomy. There is, in fact, no other mammalian species for which so much is known about gene mutants and linkage. In addition, it was certainly a great advance when new procedures for the staining of specific chromosome banding patterns were introduced in the fields of chromosomal cytology and reproductive biology. In particular, these procedures allow normal or rearranged autosomes to be unequivocally identified and linkage groups to be assigned to these chromosomes (Miller 1973; Gropp & Zech 1973).

The experimental systems used in attempts to study trisomy systematically are based on the observation that, at least in the mouse, structural heterozygotes with one or more metacentric chromosomes may enhance irregular meiotic segregation (Tettenborn & Gropp 1970). In consequence, chromosomally unbalanced hypo- or hypermodal gametes are produced which are responsible for monosomy or trisomy of the embryo.

It is now well established that in the mouse, particularly in feral populations, there is a rather comprehensive reservoir of different metacentrics (Gropp et al. 1972; Capanna et al. 1975), at least some of which can be made available for experimental use by being introduced into laboratory mouse strains (Cattanach et al. 1972). Table 2 records the 14 metacentrics at present available (10 of feral and 4 of laboratory origin), the identification of their arms, and the assignment of known linkage groups.

Two different designs for breeding heterozygous animals are suitable for the study of trisomy in their progeny (Gropp et al. 1974, 1975): one design uses back-crosses of single metacentric heterozygotes, and the other uses crosses of double metacentric heterozygotes. In both cases monosomic offspring may occur as well as trisomics. However, as shown in earlier studies (Ford 1971; Gropp 1973), monosomics, in contrast to trisomics, do not survive day 9 or 10 of embryonic development, so that as a rule trisomics are the only unbalanced offspring after day 10.

In the first type of experiment, single metacentric heterozygotes are back-crossed with normal all-acrocentric mice. Depending on the rate of meiotic non-disjunction produced by a given heterozygote, up to about 20% trisomic embryos may be observed in the progeny of female heterozygotes, although the incidence is much lower in the progeny of male heterozygotes. According to the design in Fig. 1, two types of trisomy can be expected, corresponding to the arms involved in the formation of a metacentric. In this case, ascertainment of

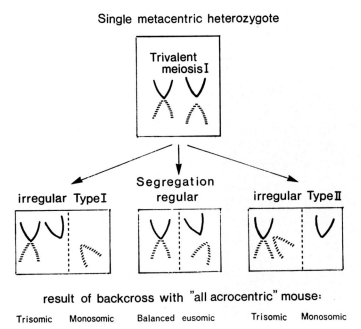

FIG. 1. Segregational pattern of single metacentric heterozygotes in the mouse and design of back-cross breeding producing mono- and trisomic offspring.

either of the two trisomics depends on the identification of the extra chromosome in a banded karyotype of the affected embryo.

The second type of approach is more specific. It is based on the use of double metacentric heterozygotes with monobrachial homology. In such an association of metacentrics a quadrivalent is formed in meiosis I (Fig. 2) by which anaphase I malsegregation is enhanced. Two examples of double metacentric combinations of this type are shown in the schematic drawing of Fig. 3. Among the hypermodal haploid products of the abnormal meiotic segregation, the type with two metacentrics resulting from joint metacentric non-disjunction (H. Winking, personal communication) is noticeably prevalent (Fig. 2b). In fact, it has been shown that almost all trisomic embryos observed after day 10 were produced by such gametes. This particular type of trisomy is easy to ascertain by simple cytogenetic procedures demonstrating the presence of two metacentrics, for example in fetal membranes. The specific kind of trisomy in the fetal progeny can be predetermined by selection of the special double heterozygote combination, because the triplicate chromosome necessarily corresponds to the arm shared by both metacentrics. Thus, as demonstrated by the examples of Fig. 3, Ts 1 occurs in the progeny of the Rb1/Rb10Bnr heterozygote whose

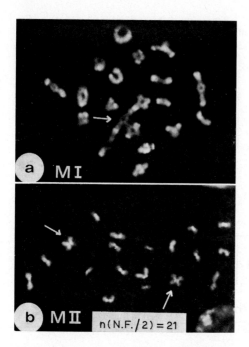

FIG. 2. Meiotic figure from doubly metacentric heterozygous male mouse with monobrachial homology (see Fig. 3), Rb(8.*12*)5/Rb(4.*12*)9Bnr: *a* = diakinesis/metaphase I with quadrivalent; b = metaphase II figure; hypermodal unbalanced segregation product—N.F./2 = 21—due to non-disjunction of the metacentrics.

Double metacentric heterozygote with monobrachial homology

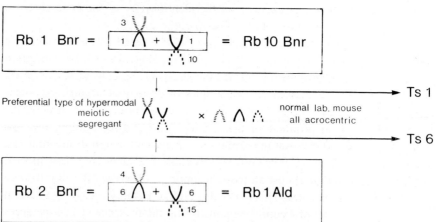

FIG. 3. Design of induction of specific trisomies (for example Ts 1 and Ts 6) by breeding double metacentric heterozygotes.

metacentrics are partially homologous for a chromosome arm corresponding to mouse chromosome no. 1, and Ts 6 is observed in the progeny of Rb2Bnr/-

RblAld heterozygotes. These and other combinations are being used in our laboratory in a systematic investigation of 10 of the possible 19 autosomal trisomies in the mouse, namely Ts 1, 4, 6, 8, 9–12, 15 and 17.

DEVELOPMENTAL CHARACTERISTICS OF TRISOMY IN THE MOUSE

The developmental profiles in autosomal trisomy may differ considerably according to which autosome is involved. However, autosomal trisomy in the mouse is almost invariably connected with earlier or later prenatal death, even though brief postpartum survival is possible in Ts 19 according to White *et al.* (1974).

Morphological features of certain individual trisomies

Some specific trisomies are characterized by severe hypoplasia, extreme developmental retardation or inhibition, and comparatively early death around day 11 or 12. This is true for Ts 4, 8, 11, 15 and 17. They usually form only a minute unorganized mass, as in Ts 11 and 15, or an extremely retarded dwarf-

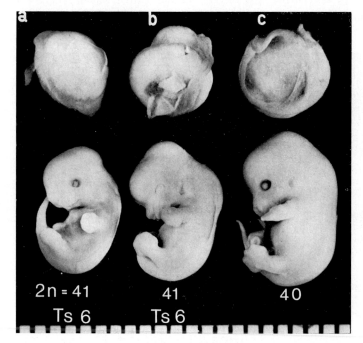

FIG. 4. Embryos (on mm scale) with placentas (day 14). ♂Rb2Bnr/RblAld × ♀NMRI offspring (see Fig. 3): 'littermates', normal (*c*) and Ts 6 (*a*, *b*).

like embryo, although there is sometimes more advanced differentiation, mainly of the neural tube.

Ts 6 and 10 in the fetal mouse produce a rather unspecific syndrome of slight to moderate, sometimes severe, retardation and hypoplasia. This type of developmental impairment and the differences in individual manifestations are demonstrated for Ts 6 in Fig. 4. The embryos| may range from near-normality to extreme hypoplasia or dwarfishness. Usually the placenta is also affected and shows concomitant changes of hypoplasia and retardation. Similar variations are also observed in other trisomies. Apparently, they are due to the allelic heterogeneity of mouse stocks to which the introduction of metacentrics has been limited.

Defined malformation syndromes have been observed only for Ts 19, described by White *et al.* (1974), and for Ts 1 and 12, which have been studied recently in our laboratory. According to White *et al.*, Ts 19 was consistently associated with isolated cleft palate when there was a special chromosomal constitution with three metacentrics. This demonstrates clearly the effects of the genic background on the morphological expression of trisomy. A significant decrease in fetal and placental weights at all stages of development has also been found with Ts 19, but the only further specific feature was degeneration of oocytes in some ovaries. With Ts 1 (Fig. 5) the phenotypic expression varies

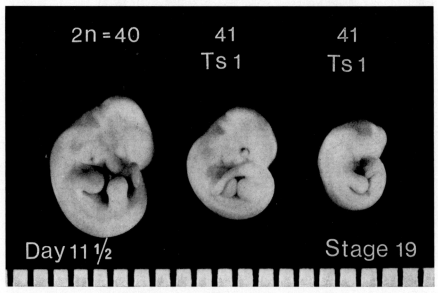

FIG. 5. Embryos (on mm scale; day 11½). ♂Rb1/Rb10Bnr × ♀NMRI offspring: 'littermates', normal (*a*) and Ts 1 (*b*, *c*). Embryo *c* represents an early stage of cyclopia (see Fig. 6).

a

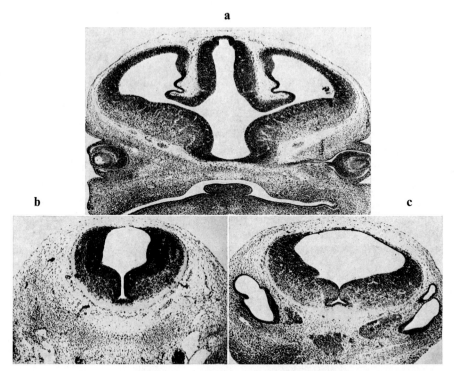

FIG. 6. Frontal sections of head: *a*, normal (=embryo Fig. 5*a*); *b* and *c*, early cyclops (=embryo Fig. 5*c*). Horizon of section *b* more anterior, in section *c* more posterior: absence of ocular primordia, otic vesicles present; primitive stage of holoprosencephalic development.

within a remarkably broad range, from slight retardation and hypoplasia to rather severe impairment of fetal development. The more severely affected embryos already exhibit variable degrees of craniofacial hypoplasia and dysmorphy on day 12 and 13, but this particular feature becomes more frequent with further fetal development until day 15, on which the embryos with Ts 1 usually die.

The real nature of the developmental anomaly of Ts 1 can be understood by analysing the more severely affected embryos, like that on the right in Fig. 5, where oculo-facial development is almost absent. Histological examination of frontal sections of the head (Fig. 6*b*, *c*) reveals that development of the prosencephalon is impaired. In contrast to normal embryos of this stage (Fig. 6*a*), the ocular bulbs are absent and the primitive forebrain vesicle is at best slightly subdivided into a diencephalic and telencephalic area. These changes correspond to an early developmental stage of a cyclops, indicating that the malformation syndrome observed with Ts 1 belongs to the holoprosencephaly–cyclopia complex. In fact, a few other specimens of TS 1 exhibiting the almost classical features of cyclopia with proboscis have also been found on day 15. It should be emphasized that a parallel can be drawn with the Patau syndrome in man, which is similarly caused by an endogenous and chromosomal anomaly, in this case by trisomy 13. Also in man, cyclopia represents the most severe manifestation of Ts 13, while milder forms show only minor malformations like microcephaly, defects of the corpus callosum, etc.

A third type of trisomy with specific fetal malformation is Ts 12. It rather uniformly exhibits exencephaly and microphthalmia, but only slight to moderate hypoplasia or retardation (Fig. 7). Most of these embryos die between days 15 and 17. Histologically, the brain is extroverted, but it shows mostly a quasi-normal though everted morphogenetic development of its parts (Fig. 8). Only in a minority of embryos is more severe impairment of brain development, similar to anencephaly, observed.

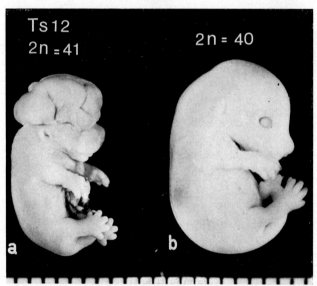

FIG. 7. Embryos (on mm scale; day 17). ♂Rb5/Rb9Bnr × ♀NMRI offspring: normal (*b*) and Ts 12 (*a*) with exencephaly; note small eyes.

Trisomy and exogenous teratogen

A comparison of the endogenous syndrome of Ts 12 with exencephaly induced by exogenous agents seemed to be a useful approach to a closer study of the mode and developmental mechanism of phenotypic expression of both these causative factors. Among the teratogens which can produce exencephaly in the fetal mouse, excess vitamin A (12 500 units intraperitoneally on day 9) has been

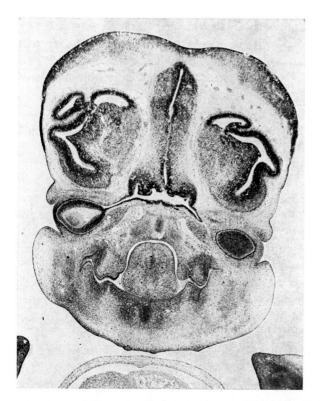

FIG. 8. Frontal head section of exencephalic embryo (Ts 12), developmental age day 15. Note eversion of encephalon, inward displacement of eyes, but otherwise normal development of facial skull.

used in animals of the same genetic background as in the breeding experiment for trisomy (B. Putz and A. Gropp, unpublished work). Ts 12 and the vitamin A-induced condition can be clearly distinguished. In the syndrome caused by the exogenous agent exencephaly is usually accompanied by spina bifida, which means that there is also a defect of closure of the caudal part of the neural tube, and by exophthalmia rather than microphthalmia. Histological examination reveals that in both cases the cartilaginous skull base is markedly hypoplastic. Moreover, detailed measurements (B. Putz, unpublished work) show an abnormal downward inclination of the basisphenoid which entails a similar downward move of the angle of the axis of the optic nerve and of the ocular bulbs. In the Ts 12 syndrome these changes are responsible for an inward displacement of the eye bulb suggesting microphthalmia (Fig. 8). Conversely, exophthalmia as observed in the vitamin-A-induced syndrome is caused by an outward movement of the ocular bulbs resulting from concomitant extensive textural changes of the facial structures and primordia. Such changes, which are responsible for a reduction in size of the orbita, are most evident in the region of the oropharynx. Their main features are hypoplasia and partial atresia as well as irregular cartilage formation. The differences between Ts 12 and the vitamin-A-induced malformation syndrome can be explained by the assumption that in Ts 12 a rather limited region is involved in the course of the development of the head, whereas the damage exerted by the exogenous agent affects more extensive areas of the skull base and of the face.

COMPARATIVE DEVELOPMENTAL ASPECTS

The comparison with human disease has some interest with respect to the fact that in man autosomal trisomies constitute the largest group of chromosomal errors in recognized abortuses and that the clinical importance of postnatally observed trisomy syndromes is very great. On the other hand, only incomplete data are available on the teratological profiles and developmental capacity of the individual trisomic conditions in man. In the animal model, such profiles and the biochemical properties of trisomic embryos and placentas can be studied experimentally in appropriate conditions of preservation.

With regard to individual trisomies in the mouse model and in man, it has become clear that the developmental anomaly in mouse Ts 1 has a counterpart in human Ts D 13. This comparison is, of course, meaningful only in the sense of morphogenetic steps of the developmental anomaly. As in some other trisomies, the expression of the trisomic condition varies greatly, with cyclopia at the end of the scale. In this context, the interest in and the need to use isogenic mouse strains with a defined genetic background for the systematic study of the expression of the genes located on a triplicate chromosome have to be underlined.

Exencephaly as observed in Ts 12 in the mouse also has counterparts in man, even though in the human species genetic or chromosomal mutations play a minor role among the causes of craniorhachischisis. There are only isolated observations of neural tube defects in man with a presumed chromosomal aetiology (Wright *et al.* 1974) or with autosomal recessive inheritance. The more important aspect of a comparative analysis of this group of malformations is the observation in the mouse that the endogenous chromosomal anomaly of Ts 12 affects a much more defined area and a more limited developmental unit than exogenous factors do. Normally, the various phases of the formation and closure of the neural tube are induced by the notochord and the parachordal mesoderm. At the anterior extremity of the neural anlage, corresponding to the presumptive prosencephalon, this process of induction is mediated by the prechordal plate. These relations are shown in the schematic drawing of Fig. 9 (based on Tuchmann-Duplessis 1974). In the Ts 12 syndrome in the fetal mouse, the target of the time-limited (around day 8½–9) teratological effect of the chromosomal anomaly seems to be restricted to the prechordal plate, and even more specifically to its notochordal constituent and the adjacent anterior part of the notochord. This assumption would be in agreement with the fact that the exencephalic malformation is strictly limited to the cranium. The teratogenic period is the same in exencephaly induced by exogenous factors, but in this case the damage seems to affect more extended areas, including the adjacent endodermal constituent of the prechordal plate, the parachordal mesoderm and segments of the caudal notochord.

It is probable that the cyclopic malformation in mouse Ts 1 is also due to a defective process of induction, but confined to a slightly later period around day 9 to 9½, when the inductive capacity of the prechordal plate causes the telencephalon to subdivide into two hemispheres. The degree and completeness of the impairment of this induction determines the severity of the malformation complex. Similar attempts at analysing the developmental anomaly in Ts 6 and 10 are in progress.

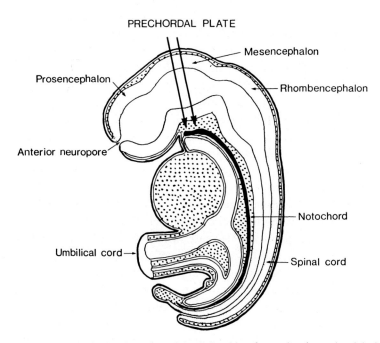

FIG. 9. Schematic drawing of spatial relationship of notochord, prechordal plate and neural tube. (Based on Tuchmann-Duplessis *et al*. 1974)

DEVELOPMENTAL ANOMALY AND IMPAIRMENT OF GROWTH

It appears questionable whether malformation *per se* can explain the developmental failure inherent in trisomy. It is more likely that gross malformation indicates rather localized and limited developmental damage in specialized blastemata, produced only when the embryo has a longer survival span, whereas earlier breakdown of growth and differentiation characterizes the more severe phenotypic expression of the triplication of an autosome. It seems reasonable to suppose that the failure of development of trisomic embryos is at least in part due to impairment and slowing down of growth, leading eventually to death. In fact, one of the main features of the development of trisomic embryos is the lag in weight increase, which might, however, be of different severity depending on the type of trisomy. For example, in Ts 12, the delay in weight increase becomes noticeable only after day 13 (B. Putz, unpublished work).

In tissue culture experiments, an increased doubling time of trisomic fibroblasts cultured *in vitro* has been found in cases of Down's syndrome by Schneider & Epstein (1972), and in cultures of fetal tissues of other trisomic and triploid conditions by Cure *et al.* (1973). Studies of the length of the cell cycle, mainly of G-21 trisomic cells, by Paton *et al.* (1974) among others, seem to indicate that in trisomic cells the S- or G_2-period is slightly longer than in normal cells. Evidence has been presented, on the other hand, that in the affected tissues of 'splotch' mutant mouse embryos with neural tube defects, the S-phase, the mitotic period and G_1 are prolonged (Wilson 1974).

The results accumulated so far in this field are at best ambiguous. We have therefore begun a systematic comparative study of the growth pattern of *in vitro* cultured fetal cells of Ts 1, Ts 12 and of normal mouse embryos using different parameters, namely measurements of the growth areas of apposed solid explants, mitotic index, cell population dynamics of mixed trisomic/normal cultures, and, with the aim of analysing the cell cycle, we are also doing pulse and permanent labelling of cultures with [^{3}H]thymidine as well as double labelling with [^{3}H]- and [^{14}C]thymidine (joint experiments with P. Citoler, Cologne). Surprisingly, no definite or specific impairment or decrease in the overall growth could be found in cultures of trisomic tissues. An example of this behaviour is given in Fig. 10, showing explants from normal embryos grown in the same culture vessel as Ts 1 explants. Additional experiments destined to exclude the effect of complementation between normal and trisomic cultures are in progress. The labelling experiments did not reveal disturbances or an increase in the duration of the S-phase or of the total cell cycle in either mouse trisomy 1 or Ts 12. The proportion of cells participating in the growth fraction does not differ signifi-

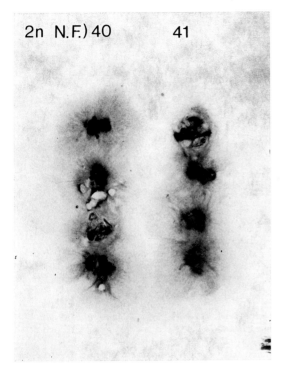

FIG. 10. Apposing rows of *in vitro* explants from 14-day embryos: left normal, right trisomic (Ts 1) embryo, outgrowth after 9 days in culture.

cantly between normal and trisomic cells. According to these preliminary experiments, it can be stated that the attempts to evaluate growth characteristics and growth kinetics in trisomic cells *in vitro* were not successful in elucidating the nature and the mechanism of the growth lag and developmental retardation which are certainly the main features of trisomy *in vivo*.

Finally, the observation that the trisomic placenta is also involved in the impairment of growth and differentiation raises the question of whether a disproportionate manifestation of such effects in the placenta could initiate the developmental breakdown of the embryo, for example by means of an impaired permeability for essential metabolites, or an insufficiency in fetal blood supply. The evaluation of the incorporation of tritium-labelled phenylalanine, serine and thymidine in the placenta and in the embryo against the background of measurements of the free compound and of the dry weight of these tissues lead to the conclusion (P. Citoler *et al.*, unpublished work) that there is no impairment of placental permeability, at least not for the amino acids. On the other hand, the incorporation of the amino acids in trisomic embryos decreases at variable rates.

This observation, however, can be interpreted as another expression of the impairment of cellular growth and growth-related metabolic activities.

ACKNOWLEDGEMENTS

I wish to thank Miss B. Putz and Mr U. Zimmermann, assistants in the Department of Pathology, Lübeck, for their collaboration and for allowing me to quote unpublished material, Mrs U. Kolbus, Miss G. Noack and Miss A. Sachon for technical assistance, and Mrs E. Hüttenhain for help in preparing the manuscript. This work is supported by a research grant from Deutsche Forschungsgemeinschaft, BN-Bad Godesberg (SPP 'Pränatale Diagnose').

References

BARANOV, V. & DYBAN, A.P. (1971) A new marker Robertsonian translocation (centric fusion of autosomes) in the laboratory mouse *Mus musculus*. *Tsitologiya 13*, 820–829

BOUÉ, J., BOUÉ, A. & LAZAR, P. (1974) The epidemiology of human spontaneous abortions with chromosomal anomalies, in *Aging Gametes* (Blandau, R.J., ed.), pp. 330–348, Karger, Basle

CAPANNA, E., CRISTALDI, M., PERTIONE, P. & REZZONI, M. (1975) Identification of chromosomes involved in the 9 Robertsonian fusions of the Apennine mouse with a 22-chromosome karyotype. *Experientia (Basel) 31*, 294–296

CARR, D.H. (1965) Chromosome studies in spontaneous abortions. *Obstet. Gynecol. 26*, 308–326

CATTANACH, B.M., WILLIAMS, C.E. & BAILEY, H. (1972) Identification of the linkage groups carried by the metacentric chromosomes of the tobacco mouse *(Mus poschiavinus)*. *Cytogenetics (Basel) 11*, 412–423

CURE, S., BOUÉ, A. & BOUÉ, J. (1973) Consequence of chromosome anomalies on cell multiplications, in *Chromosomal Errors in Relation to Reproductive Failure*, pp. 95–109, INSERM, Paris

DHADIAL, R.K., MACHIN, A.M. & TAIT, S.M. (1970) Chromosomal anomalies in spontaneously aborted human foetuses. *Lancet 2*, 20–21

EVANS, E.P., LYON, M.F. & DAGLISH, M. (1967) A mouse translocation giving a metacentric marker chromosome. *Cytogenetics (Basel) 6*, 105–119

FORD, C.E. (1971) Gross genome unbalance in mouse spermatozoa: does it influence the capacity to fertilize? in *Edinburgh Symposium on The Genetics of the Spermatozoon* (Beatty, R.A. & Gluecksohn-Waelsch, S., eds.), published by the organizers (editors)

FRIEDRICH, U. & NIELSEN, J. (1973) Chromosome studies in 5049 consecutive newborn children. *Clin. Genet. 4*, 333–343

GROPP, A. (1973) Reproductive failure due to fetal aneuploidy in mice, in *Fertility and Sterility (Proc. VII World Congr.)* (Hasegawa, T. *et al.*, eds.), ICS 278, Excerpta Medica, Amsterdam

GROPP, A. & ZECH, L. (1973) Identification of metacentric marker chromosomes in the mouse by use of banding techniques. *Nobel Symp. 23*, 118–123

GROPP, A., WINKING, H., ZECH, L. & MÜLLER, H.J. (1972) Robertsonian chromosomal variation and identification of metacentric chromosomes in feral mice. *Chromosoma (Berl.) 39*, 265–288

GROPP, A., GIERS, D. & KOLBUS, U. (1974) Trisomy in the fetal backcross progeny of male and female metacentric heterozygotes of the mouse. I. *Cytogenet. Cell Genet. 13*, 511–535

GROPP, A., KOLBUS, U. & GIERS, D. (1975) Systematic approach to the study of trisomy in the mouse, II. *Cytogenet. Cell Genet.* 14, 42–62

LÉONARD, A. & DEKNUDT, G.H. (1967) A new marker for chromosome studies in the mouse. *Nature (Lond.)* 214, 504–505

MILLER, O.J. (1973) The karyotype and chromosome map of the mouse. *Nobel Symp.* 23, 132–144

PATON, G.R., SILVER, M.F. & ALLISON, A.C. (1974) Comparison of cell cycle time in normal and trisomic cells. *Humangenetik* 23, 173–182

SCHNEIDER, E.L. & EPSTEIN, C.J. (1972) Replication rate and lifespan of cultured fibroblasts in Down's syndrome. *Proc. Soc. Exp. Biol. Med.* 141, 1092–1094

TETTENBORN, U. & GROPP, A. (1970) Meiotic non-disjunction in mice and mouse hybrids. *Cytogenetics (Basel)* 9, 272–283

TUCHMANN-DUPLESSIS, H., AUROUX, M. & HAEGEL, P. (1974) *Illustrated Human Embryology*, vol. 8: *Nervous System and Endocrine Glands*, Springer, New York

WHITE, B.J. & TJIO, J.H. (1968) A mouse translocation with 38 and 39 chromosomes but normal N.F. *Hereditas* 58, 284–296

WHITE, B.J., TJIO, J.H., VAN DE WATER, L.C. & CRANDALL, V. (1974) Trisomy 19 in the laboratory mouse, I and II. *Cytogenet. Cell Genet.* 13, 217–231; 232–245

WILSON, D.B. (1974) Proliferation in the neural tube of the splotch (Sp) mutant mouse. *J. Comp. Neurol.* 154, 249–255

WRIGHT, Y.M., CLARK, W.E. & BREG, W.R. (1974) Craniorhachischisis in a partially trisomic fetus in a family with reproductive failure and a reciprocal translocation (6p + ; 11q −). *J. Med. Genet.* 11, 69–75

Discussion

Škreb: In most of these cases growth of the embryos was retarded. Could this be due to retarded placental growth rather than to fetal retardation?

Gropp: We studied the permeation of labelled thymidine, serine and phenyl-alanine through the placenta, and there was no indication that impairment of placental function is responsible for the death of the embryo (P. Citoler & A. Gropp, unpublished work).

Škreb: Head malformations can be obtained not only with vitamin A but also with high temperature, X-rays and so on. One can time the exact stage of development when this kind of malformation is obtained. If an embryo is put in a higher temperature or treated with X-rays at the stage of mesoderm formation, different head and brain malformations, including exencephaly, can be obtained. It would be interesting to see whether there were any changes during mesoderm formation or on, say, day 15 of development. Have you seen any changes earlier than at the end of gestation?

Gropp: With trisomy 12, exencephaly is regularly observed. So far, we have studied only the later stages when exencephaly has already developed, but other experiments on the earlier stages of the malformation are in progress.

Škreb: There must be damage at the earlier stages of development.

Saxén: I agree that there is probably a defective interactive mechanism during the earlier stages. For instance, all those central nervous system defects you showed, Dr Gropp, can be produced in amphibian embryos by experimental interference with primary induction. I would also agree with Dr Škreb that one would expect to see changes at that early stage, especially an abnormal relationship between the prechordal mesoderm and the neural plate. That is where I would look for the primary defect.

Gropp: We are trying to do that mainly in Ts 12 by labelling the area of the prechordal plate and the neural tube.

Tarkowski: Which monosomies are compatible with survival to the seventh or eighth day?

Gropp: We have not yet studied the monosomics separately and in detail, and I don't think that Dr C.E.Ford has either. Certainly, some few monosomics can survive until day 10. Monosomy 6 may do so, but that is only an assumption drawn from preliminary studies.

Snow: I get a small percentage of tetraploid mouse embryos through to late gestation. At 14½ and 16½ days they weigh about half as much as corresponding diploids. They show a variety of abnormalities but they are really remarkably normal considering that, though the cells are double the size of diploid cells, they have less than a quarter as many abnormalities (Snow 1975).

Polani: This is true in man of course, where triploids survive reasonably well. They have a longer gestation age than aneuploids and a small proportion survive up to term.

Gardner: You presumably transplant only tetraploids to a uterine fostermother, Dr Snow, which may be rather different from when normal embryos compete with embryos that are retarded.

Snow: I think that is true, but I don't think one can necessarily associate abnormalities with a slow growth rate and the implied paucity of cells. In these cases, no matter how they are derived, they are making an essentially normal embryo with very few cells.

Gardner: Similarly, if you cut blastocysts in half you get quite a lot that are retarded and resorb at mid-gestation.

Snow: There is an acceleration in growth rate in the diploids which may to a certain extent compensate for any initial lack of cells at the blastocyst stage. That doesn't happen with the tetraploids.

Gardner: But presumably in Dr Gropp's situation where there are normal embryos it could partly be a competition phenomenon.

Gluecksohn-Waelsch: Are there effects on other characters which are not quite as obvious as the development of the face? Two of the trisomics apparently had no eye pigment.

Gropp: That was because we used mice of an undefined genetic background.

We have only recently been able to start introducing the metacentrics in defined inbred lines.

Gluecksohn-Waelsch: As to the failure to survive, have you looked at any internal organs or any biochemical parameters to see whether there is anything abnormal other than the external features?

Gropp: Apart from the morphological abnormalities in the head area in some of these syndromes, no other organ malformations could be found. Dr White and her associates (1974), studying trisomy 19, observed some deterioration of oocytes but otherwise they too found no malformations of the internal organs. We looked at some other phenotypes, for example haemoglobin (C. P. Claussen & A. Gropp, unpublished work). So far, we can only say that there is some maturation inhibition: the adult haemoglobin does not appear when it should appear. This work has been done in Ts 1, 12 and 13.

Gluecksohn-Waelsch: Which linkage groups or chromosomes are involved in the α and β haemoglobin chain genes?

Gropp: That is mostly unknown for the embryonic haemoglobins, except for the adult α-chain (LG VII) which is involved in E II and E III (Russell 1973).

Chapman: Haemoglobin alpha is on chromosome 11. Haemoglobin beta is linked with albino, on the seventh chromosome.

McLaren: At what stage of development do these haemoglobins appear?

Gropp: Embryonic haemoglobins are built between days 9 and 14 of development; adult haemoglobin appears first at day 11, but is mainly formed after day 14. So there is a good chance of studying these conditions in fetal trisomy syndromes.

Morriss: Your trisomies were associated with facial malformation, Dr Gropp, and it is interesting that all major human chromosomal anomalies are associated with maldevelopment of the face. The vitamin A-induced malformations of course include facial malformation as well as exencephaly when vitamin A is given at the primitive streak stage (Morriss 1972). Although there are major effects on all cells at an ultrastructural level (Morriss 1973) the important effect for subsequent morphogenesis seems to be the translation of these ultrastructural changes into abnormal cell migration, which of course affects mesenchyme more than anything else. Mesenchyme migration is slowed down so that less primary mesenchyme moves into the future head region and therefore there is late induction of neural plate. Migration of neural crest cells is also retarded and this is probably even more important, in relation to facial development. It certainly affects cartilage development in the pharyngeal arch. Is cell migration also abnormal in the trisomics? In the cultured trisomic cells you seemed to have less outgrowth from your explants than in the control cultures, which might indicate a slowing of cell migration.

Gropp: I wouldn't think that there is less outgrowth from the trisomic than from the normal tissues. We made extensive measurements of normal and trisomic explants cultured in the same vessel without observing major differences of growth. But these are only preliminary results. We have to exclude complementation of defects of the trisomic tissue grown in the same culture.

Morriss: Have you looked at earlier stages of the malformation in your trisomics? In histological sections you should be able to see whether there is less primary mesenchyme or neural crest-derived mesenchyme than in control embryos.

Gropp: Yes, there seems to be a hypoplasia of the mesenchymal structures of the skull base. Dr Le Douarin's work on the neural crest cells may also help to explain the differences between the type of the malformation in trisomy 12 and that caused by vitamin A. The exogenous agent may impair the movement of the neural crest derivatives, while trisomy 12 does not. It is a very limited area of malformation in trisomy 12 and a more extensive malformation with vitamin A.

Bennett: Is there usually an inverse correlation between the size of the chromosome and the length of life of trisomics?

Gropp: No, I don't think so. For example, trisomy may affect the largest autosome of the mouse, chromosome no. 1, but embryos with this trisomy survive for a fairly long time. In contrast, with trisomy of the small chromosomes, nos. 15 or 17, there is early death. Certainly, the correlations are more complicated.

Pedersen: When embryos from matings with X-irradiated males are grown *in vitro*, there is a high death rate during the preimplantation period if the male germ cells were exposed as spermatocytes or spermatids (L. S. Goldstein & A. I. Spindle, unpublished work, 1975). The induction of these dominant lethal events by X-rays is probably a result of chromosome breakage, translocations and aneuploidy. I think it is interesting, then, that their pattern of failure resembles that of the monosomics.

Gluecksohn-Waelsch: Or even haploidy?

Pedersen: There may have been haploids. These embryos were not studied cytogenetically. Whatever their deficiencies, the embryos developed more like monosomics than trisomics.

References

MORRISS, G. M. (1972) Morphogenesis of the malformation induced in rat embryos by maternal hypervitaminosis A. *J. Anat. 113*, 241–250

MORRISS, G. M. (1973) The ultrastructural effects of excess maternal vitamin A on the primitive streak stage rat embryo. *J. Embryol. Exp. Morphol. 30*, 219–242

RUSSELL, E. S. (1973) *Mouse Newsl. 49*, 33

SNOW, M. H. L. (1975) Embryonic development of tetraploid mice during the 2nd half of gestation. *J. Embryol. Exp. Morphol. 34*, 707–722

WHITE, B. J., TJIO, J.-H., VAN DE WATER, L. C. & CRANDALL, C. (1974) Trisomy 19 in the laboratory mouse, I & II. *Cytogenet. Cell Genet. 13*, 217–231; 232–245

The appearance of cell-surface antigens in the development of the mouse embryo: a study of cell-surface differentiation

MICHAEL EDIDIN

Biology Department, The Johns Hopkins University, Baltimore, Maryland

Abstract   The expression of cell-surface antigens determined by genes of the major histocompatibility complex, *H*-2, of the mouse has been studied in embryos. Antigens of this complex may be present on gametes but are undetectable on embryos up to six days of development. *H*-2 expression may also be studied in two different types of cell lines: teratomas and the blastocyst-derived MB lines. The former lines have been shown to be *H*-2-negative, both serologically and by grafting; they bear antigens which are present in embryos at stages lacking *H*-2, and one of these antigens may be physically associated with *H*-2 on tumour cell surfaces. The second set of lines, the MB lines, partially express H-2 antigens; only some structural features of their H-2 molecules are accessible to antibody. Two models are described for this partial expression which have more general application to expression of the properties of cell surfaces in development. One model suggests that specific associations of membrane molecules may alter their reactions with ligands in the medium or on other cells. A second model proposes that constraints on the diffusion of membrane proteins in the plane of the membrane can radically affect the interactions of these proteins with the external environment.

Work in our laboratory is focused on the antigens of the major histocompatibility system of the mouse, H-2 antigens. In the following pages I hope to use examples taken mainly from work on H-2 but also from a study of tumour-cell antigens to show a history of cell-surface changes in mouse development. I hope that this history, besides being of interest in its own right, may exhibit some general principles of cell-surface differentiation. The history will also serve as the starting point for speculation on the extent to which epigenetic changes in physical properties of the cell surface and other membranes may affect the expression of new membrane functions.

GENES AND PRODUCTS OF THE MOUSE HISTOCOMPATIBILITY-2 COMPLEX

The genetics of tissue transplantation was first established by grafting tumours between inbred strains of mice (reviewed in Snell 1966). These experiments indicated that many genes affected the survival of tissue grafts. Further work (Gorer 1938; Gorer *et al.* 1948) established an association between erythrocyte antigens, detected with an alloantiserum, and a single histocompatibility 'gene', termed *Histocompatibility-2*, or *H-2*. When, some years later, graft rejection was shown to be an immune response (reviewed in Medawar 1958), the characteristics established for *H-2* were translated into immunological language: the *H-2* products are transplantation antigens which provoke both humoral antibody responses and cellular immunity leading to graft rejection. The humoral antibodies formed after rejection of allogeneic tissue were thought to react with antigens, shared by tissue cells and erythrocytes, which were strong transplantation antigens. Further experiments showed that H-2 antigens were the strongest of all histocompatibility antigens (Snell 1966). Analyses since then, of inbred strains, of congenic resistant strains bred to differ at a single chromosome region containing *H-2*, and of recombinant progeny of crosses between such strains, have developed a far more complex picture (cf. Klein 1975). The *H-2* complex has been dissected into four or five tightly linked regions (Klein *et al.* 1974, 1975; Shreffler & David 1975; David *et al.* 1975), each of which may in turn contain more than a single gene (Table 1). A particular combination of alleles of each region is termed a 'haplotype'. The products or functions associated with these regions can roughly be grouped as: (1) provoking mainly humoral immunity and reacting with serum antibodies, (2) provoking mainly lymphocyte responses, for example blast transformation, and (3) affecting lymphocytes and quite possibly functions of other cells; these genes were first defined in terms of the control of immune responses to synthetic polypeptide antigens (Benacerraf & McDevitt 1972; Démant 1973; Meruelo & Edidin 1975). The close linkage of the seven regions and similar tight linkages of *H-2* homologues in other species have allowed some degree of serotyping for grafting; that is, the survival of allografts may be predicted from the reaction of defined antisera with donor and recipient lymphocytes. However, the genes and products actually responsible for graft rejection are still unknown. The best data available suggest that differences in at least two *H-2* regions are required

TABLE 1

Regions of the mouse *H-2* complex

K	I		(on chromosome 17)		Ss	G	D
	Ir-1A	Ir-1B	I-C				

Data from Shreffler & David (1975), David *et al.* (1975), and Klein *et al.* (1975). The total recombinational length of the complex is 0.5 map units (centimorgans).

for lymphocyte activation and lymphocyte-mediated cell killing *in vitro* (Alter *et al.* 1973).

Further characteristics of the *H-2* complex that concern us here are: (1) its extreme polymorphism, the large number of haplotypes being a function both of the number of permutations possible for seven regions, and of the allelic polymorphism of regions coding for antigens detectable with immune sera, and (2) the number of *H-2* regions determining these antigens (Shreffler & David 1975).

Anti-H-2 antisera react with products of at least three *H-2* regions. The classical H-2 antigens prove to be product of the D and K regions. Antisera to these products detect several antigenic determinants on each product. All these determinants are aspects of polypeptides of around 45 000 mol. wt. (Nathenson & Cullen 1974). These antigens are widely distributed in tissues of adult animals and are also represented on erythrocytes.

Recently, antisera have been made against products of the I region. These sera have quite limited reactions against tissue cells, reacting predominantly with a subpopulation of lymphocytes but also with epidermal cells, macrophages, fetal liver cells and sperm. Ia antigens are lacking on many tumours, erythrocytes, brain, liver and kidney (Delovitch & McDevitt 1975; Hämmerling *et al.* 1975). When putative anti-H-2D and H-2K antisera are absorbed on D- and K-positive, Ia-negative cells, and tested on Ia-positive cells, they are often found to contain anti-Ia activity as well. Positive reactions of such sera with gametes or embryos must be further analysed before we can be certain which particular *H-2* product is expressed on the material studied.

HISTOCOMPATIBILITY-2 COMPLEX EXPRESSION IN GAMETES AND EMBRYOS

The high degree of polymorphism shown by *H-2* products implies that almost always in pregnancy the *genetic* potential exists for rejection of the conceptus as an allograft. However, rejection is prevented by many means, including antigenic silence of trophoblast and antigenic immaturity of the conceptus (Edidin 1972). In general, no products of the *H-2* complex have been detected in preimplantation embryos. Where *H-2* expression has been found, the particular region expressed is often in doubt, mainly because of the complexity of anti-H-2 sera, but also because of uncertainties as to genetic requirements for *H-2*-dependent cell-mediated graft destruction. Two designs used for all experiments probing *H-2* expression depend either on detection of bound antibody or on the appearance of cellular responses to *in vivo* grafts. The latter system uses a rough comparison of rates of rejection and lymphocytic infiltration when embryos are grafted to the kidney capsule of either unimmunized mice or mice immunized against *H-2*, only, of the embryo donor strain. This technique was originally used to show that cleavage embryos through 9-day stages bear some transplantation antigens. Embryo grafts to unimmunized recipients grew for some time and differentiated before being destroyed, while grafts to immune animals never increased in size or differentiated (Simmons & Russell 1966). A more sophisticated design was used by Patthey to detect only *H-2* complex products. Here, congenic-resistant strains, differing only at *H-2*, were used for donor and recipient. We monitored rejection histologically by counting round cells (lymphocytes and monocytes) per unit area in grafts sampled at intervals after placement (Patthey & Edidin 1973). Although 7- to 11-day embryo fragments provoked a moderate cell infiltrate within 48 hours of grafting (the minimum time required for a fully antigenic graft such as skin to bring up an infiltrate), 6-day embryos did not provoke an infiltrate until four days after grafting. This observation indicated that *H-2* complex products were not expressed on 6-day mouse embryos. Later work, using the same design, scoring for embryo survival and for speed of host response, showed that as expected the blastocyst too lacks *H-2* products provoking graft rejection (Searle *et al.* 1974).

Serological findings correlate well with *in vivo* findings, though we cannot tell whether this correlation means that products of *H-2* region genes are co-expressed or whether it indicates a requirement for some serologically detectable antigen in graft rejection.

Eggs and sperm appear to bear some products of the *H-2* complex, in that they may react with complex anti-H-2 sera in mixed absorption or complement-mediated lysis assays (Olds 1968; Johnson & Edidin 1972). However, the sera have never been thoroughly analysed, and the only indication of their specificity comes from more recent experiments suggesting that sperm bear Ia antigens (Hämmerling *et al.* 1975). In particular, the low titers of anti-H-2 sera against sperm may be entirely due to anti-Ia antibodies. This area remains open for further experimentation.

The studies of zygotes, cleavage embryos and later stages of development can be summarized more consistently. Palm *et al.* (1971) used indirect immuno-fluorescence to show the presence of H-3 and H-6 antigens, the products of two 'weak' histocompatibility loci on zygotes and cleavage eggs. Their techniques, adequate for detecting binding of low-titred anti-H-3 and H-6 antibodies, did not detect binding of anti-H-2 antibodies to these stages. Immunofluor-escence studies have been extended to blastocysts in culture (Heyner 1973). Blastocysts cultured for six days, whose trophoblast cells had migrated off the inner cell mass and onto the surrounding glass, reacted specifically, though weakly, with anti-H-2 sera. The positive embryos were judged by Heyner to be

TABLE 2

H-2 and other histocompatibility antigens in mouse gametes and embryos

Stage	Weak H-antigens	H-2
Egg	—	?
Sperm	?	Ia, ? D and K
Cleavage embryos	H-3,6 serologically; Others by transplantation	— serologically
Blastocysts	H-3,6 serologically; Others by transplantation	— serologically and by transplantation
Egg cylinder stages (6 days)	+ by transplantation; + by transplantation	— by transplantation; + serologically
7-day embryo	+ by transplantation	+ by transplantation and serologically

equivalent to approximately normal $6\frac{1}{2}$-day embryos, a stage judged H-2-positive by grafting. In another study, 8- and 9-day embryo cells specifically absorbed complex alloantisera that were primarily anti-H-2 (Edidin 1964).

The serological findings, like the results of grafting, indicate that products of the major histocompatibility complex, H-2, are absent from early embryos. The combined results are summarized in Table 2. However, all the findings are poorly resolved. We know that some parts of the H-2 gene complex are not expressed in early development, but we may have failed to detect products of other regions in the complex, in particular regions that do not produce surface antigen expression, but rather alter reactivity of the cell surface with other cells or with hormones (Iványi et al. 1972; Shreffler & David 1975; Meruelo & Edidin 1975).

TWO MODELS FOR THE STUDY OF THE DIFFERENTIATION OF CELL SURFACES OF EARLY MOUSE EMBRYOS

The natural history of H-2 in development, outlined above, suggests the possibility of experimental approaches to the molecular differentiation of cell surfaces. However, the relatively small number of cells to be obtained from normal embryos, and the difficulties of isolating single cells from embryos and maintaining them in culture, have led us and others to two systems that may serve as models of normal embryo surfaces. One model system, testicular teratoma, introduces several more surface features into our history and re-inforces our view that early embryo cells lack most products of the H-2 complex. The second model, cell lines derived from normal blastocysts, suggests that we are naive historians, and that expression of cell-surface features in development may be more complex than we might infer from a first reading of the story of their appearance.

Testicular teratoma

Mouse testicular teratomas occur spontaneously in some strains, notably 129, and may be induced by transplanting early embryos to the testis of adults in this and other strains (Damjanov & Solter 1974; Stevens 1967). These tumours are malignant, growing progressively to kill their hosts, but they are also capable of differentiating histologically normal tissues of many types (Pierce 1967). Many tissue culture lines have been established from teratomas initially propagated in animals (Kahan & Ephrussi 1970; Rosenthal *et al.* 1970; Evans 1972; Artzt *et al.* 1973). Some of these lines may differentiate, either under appropriate culture conditions or when returned to animals, while others have lost this potential and appear to be composed entirely of 'nullipotent' teratocarcinoma cells.

Antisera raised against both sorts of cultured teratoma lines appear to react with some stages in normal embryos, as well as with tumour cells. Two very different sera have been described recently. One of these, made by immunizing adult 129 mice with nullipotent F9 cells derived from tumour OTT6050, reacts with 2-cell and morula stages of normal embryos, though published work indicates no reaction with 1-cell zygotes or with unfertilized eggs (Artzt *et al.*

TABLE 3

Definition of teratoma-associated antigens by absorption of rabbit anti-402AX serum on various mouse tumours

Absorbing cell	Reacting cell[a]			
	Teratoma 402AX	Cl 1d	Melanoma B16	Hepatoma BW7756
Cl 1d	+	−	−	+
Melanoma	+	−	−	+
Hepatoma	+	−	−	−
Teratoma	−	−	−	−

Cl 1d and melanoma cells share a single antigenic reactivity which is also present on hepatoma and teratoma cells. Hepatoma cells bear an additional specificity shared with teratoma, but not with Cl 1d. Additionally, teratoma bears an antigen detected by anti-teratoma serum, but not present on any other cell tested.

[a] All reactivities were tested by indirect immunofluorescence. Positive cells were at least 60% positive. For details see Gooding & Edidin (1974).

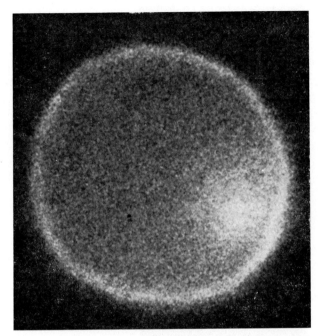

Fig. 1. Unfertilized egg treated with rabbit antibody to teratoma antigen I and further with fluorescent goat anti-rabbit IgG. × ~800

1973). The F9 antigens are also present on sperm, and absorption studies strongly suggest that the antiserum detects one of the products of a complex genetic locus linked to *H-2*, the *T* locus (Artzt *et al.* 1973).

A second anti-teratoma serum has been developed against cells of another strain 129 teratoma, the spontaneous tumour 402AX (Stevens 1958). This is a hetero-immune serum, made in rabbits, which reacts primarily with 402AX and other tumours of numerous mouse strains, as well as with cultured cell lines, but not with normal mouse tissues (Gooding & Edidin 1974). The serum detects at least three antigens, which have been defined by absorption studies, summarized in Table 3. Of these antigens, antigen III appears unique to teratoma 402AX and is not further considered here. Our attention has been chiefly focused on antigen I, which, at least in one cultured cell line, the L-cell-derived Cl 1d, co-caps with H-2, implying a physical association between the two antigens at the cell surface (Gooding & Edidin 1974). With this physical association in mind, it is interesting to examine normal embryos with anti-teratoma serum, paying particular attention to the cells and stages expressing antigen I, and to the temporal relation between antigen I and H-2 expression.

Sera used for the study were either whole anti-teratoma serum, reacting with

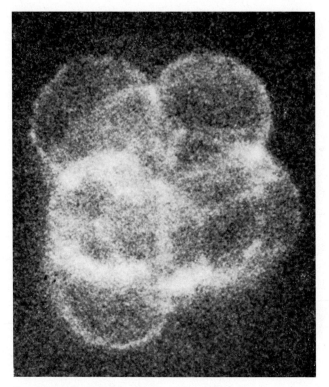

FIG. 2. Morula, treated as in Fig. 1. $\times \sim 800$

at least three teratoma-defined antigens, antiserum absorbed with C1 1d cells which is negative for antigen I but still reacts for antigens II and III, and anti-body eluted from an antigen I affinity column. (The latter was made by coupling Sepharose 100 000 $g \times 120$ min supernatant of melanoma cell lysate. This extract contains only antigen I, and the coupled extract removes anti-I, or operationally, anti-C1 1d antibodies, from the whole serum. The antibodies in turn could be eluted at low pH, and then they specifically stained C1 1d, melanoma and teratoma cells.)

Unfertilized ova, zygotes and preimplantation embryos were obtained after timed matings of superovulated mice. 'Implanted embryos' were studied after blastocysts had been cultured on collagen substrates for up to a week (Hsu 1973). The trophoblast surrounding the blastocysts migrates off them into the collagen; hence the inner cell mass, which continues to differentiate, is accessible to antibodies and may be observed by immunofluorescence.

An unfertilized egg and two representative embryos are shown in Figs. 1–3. The egg and the morula are stained with specific anti-I antibody and fluorescent-

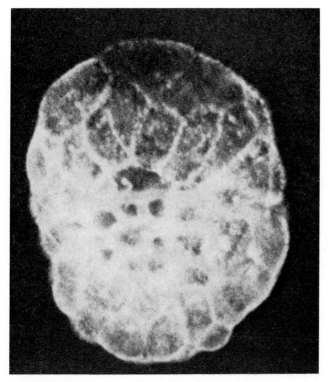

FIG. 3. Blastocyst treated with whole rabbit anti-teratoma serum and fluorescent goat anti-rabbit IgG. $\times \sim 800$

conjugated anti-globulin. All cells are outlined by fluorescence, indicating a surface stain (apparent internal stain is mainly due to overexposure in the slides from which these prints were made). The blastocyst shown is stained with whole anti-teratoma serum and fluorescent anti-globulin. Trophectoderm cells are again outlined by fluorescence. There is a consistent suggestion in all preparations that the inner cell mass end of the blastocyst is less reactive than other portions of the surface. When these stages are tested with whole anti-teratoma serum absorbed with C1 1d cells to remove reactivity with antigen I, the eggs are nearly negative, while cleavage embryos and portions of the unhatched blastocyst surface are entirely negative. The inner cell mass of post-implantation embryos reacts with both antigen I and with antigen II, a specificity defined by absorption on hepatoma cells. Trophoblast cells at this stage are negative when tested with whole anti-teratoma serum—this despite the fact that their precursors bear antigens I and II in preimplantation embryos.

The reactions of early embryos with anti-teratoma sera are summarized in

TABLE 4

Teratoma-defined antigens on early mouse embryos[a]

| Stage | — | Anti-serum absorbed on: | | Anti-antigen I antibody Unabsorbed |
		Cl 1d	Hepatoma	
Unfertilized egg	+	+/−	−	+
Cleavage stages (4–16 cells)	+	−	−	+
Early (unhatched) blastocyst trophectoderm	+	+[b]	−	nd
Hatched blastocyst trophoblast	+	+	−	−
Postimplantation inner cell mass	+	+	−	+
Trophoblast giant cells	−	−	−	−

[a] Embryos were reacted with 1/10 antiserum or equivalent amount of anti-I antibody.
[b] Cells overlying the inner cell mass were negative when tested with Cl 1d-adsorbed serum.
nd = not determined.

Table 4. The teratoma-defined antigen I, physically associated with H-2 when it appears in at least one cultured cell line, is present on stages of normal development that appear to lack any products of the *H-2* complex when tested either serologically or by transplantation. Teratoma antigen II is also present on cells of the inner cell mass of embryos equivalent to around six days of normal development. Both antigens persist to some extent on cells on $8\frac{1}{2}$-day embryos, but they then disappear altogether from cells of the embryo proper. Antigen II persists on yolk sac cells although, as noted above, neither antigen can be detected on trophoblast.

Teratoma-defined antigens observed in the embryo follow a time course which is the reciprocal of that for the expression of H-2. This reciprocal relationship for expression of the antigens tempts us to speculate on a precursor function for the teratoma-defined antigen, especially antigen I, in early development. Earlier, Bennett *et al.* (1972) suggested that products of the *T* locus might serve as such precursors. Our ignorance is at present so vast that there seems to be no need to reconcile the two speculations. Both teratoma-defined antigens are detected on early embryos; the fact that 402AX antigens appear to persist until H-2 has clearly expressed a number of its regions may merely be due to differences in sensitivity of assay methods used and of strength of the anti-teratoma sera, and both sets of antigens may well functionally precede H-2 in development. Indeed, the two teratomas which define the antigens that I have discussed share another property important for our argument: they lack serologically detectable H-2, either entirely, as F9 does (Artzt 1974), or in the main, as 402AX does. Also, 402AX and the parent of F9, OTT6050, are only feebly antigenic when tested for H-2 *in vivo*.

Our test took advantage of congenic-resistant mouse strains, bred to differ only by a chromosome segment containing the *H-2* complex. A pair of strains, B10.Br and B10, differ from one another in that B10.Br bears the *H-2^k* haplotype while B10 bears the *H-2^b* haplotype; the latter is the same as that of strain 129. To test for H-2^b antigens in teratomas, we immunized B10.Br adults either with teratoma cells or with graded doses of 129 adult lymphocytes, cells rich in H-2. Three days after immunization, the animals were challenged with B10 skin. While immunization with tumour of lymphocytes probably sensitized the B10.Br animals to many histocompatibility antigens, only *H-2* sensitization could affect the fate of B10 grafts since, aside from *H-2*, B10 shares all other histocompatibility loci with B10.Br. The rate of graft rejection in this case is a rough indication of the antigenicity of the cell inoculum given before grafting. The results of such experiments are shown in Table 5. Relatively small numbers of lymphocytes sensitize for accelerated rejection of B10 skin (compare groups 2 and 3 with group 1). One hundred and fifty to 300 times more tumour cells are needed to approximate the accelerated rejection effected by lymphocytes (groups 5 and 6). Indeed, when OTT6050 cells were given together with lymphocytes, no additive effect of the two doses could be seen (compare groups 3 and

TABLE 5

Survival of *H-2^b*, B10 skin on preimmunized *H-2^k* B10.Br recipients

Group	Preimmunization[a]	[b]	Mean percentage of epithelial survival of grafts on days:				
			7	9	10	11	12
					after grafting		
(1)	None	(9)	99	72	57	28	21
(2)	2×10^4 strain 129 lymphocytes	(5)	92	40	28	16	12
(3)	4×10^4 strain 129 lymphocytes	(4)	92	30	0	0	0
(4)	4×10^4 strain 129 lymphocytes plus 6×10^6 OTT6050 teratoma cells	(5)	90	15	0		
(5)	6×10^6 OTT6050 teratoma cells	(7)	96	43	18	10	10
(6)	6×10^6 402AX teratoma cells	(5)	91	20	12	4	0

[a] Animals were injected intraperitoneally 3 days before grafting.
[b] Number per group.

4), though of course larger experimental groups might have shown up some differences. The experiment presented is consistent with our observations on the reaction of 402AX cells with anti-H-2 sera, which imply that a small percentage cells are specifically positive for H-2 (Edidin *et al.* 1974), with the observation by Artzt (1974) that F9 cells derived from OTT6050 were incapable of absorbing out anti-H-2 sera, and with our observations (S. Rosenberg & M. Edidin, unpublished) that OTT6050 cells do not absorb anti-H-2 sera. Indeed, our result with OTT6050 may be due entirely to slight contamination of the cell population with peritoneal cells of the tumour hosts. The tumour cells used for immunization were cultured for 24 h to kill off passenger lymphocytes, and to allow any macrophages present to migrate off the embryoid bodies of the tumour and onto the culture dish.

The cells of both tumours seem to be negative for antigens of the *H-2* complex. This property appears to be shared only with normal embryo cells; no attempt to select *H-2* null cells from *H-2* homozygous cultured lines or from *in vivo* propagated tumour cells has ever succeeded (reviewed in ch. 13 of Klein 1975). At present we are attempting to activate *H-2* genes of the teratomas, and we hope to use these cells to monitor the early events in H-2 antigen expression as well as to study further precursor relationships between teratoma antigen I and H-2.

Blastocyst-derived cell lines

Recently a second model for the cell surface in early development has become available. This is a series of cell lines, the so-called MB lines, derived by culture of mouse blastocysts under conditions which do not maintain the integrity of the inner cell mass but rather promote migration of cells from the embryo (Sherman 1975). It is not clear whether cells of any of these lines are of embryonic origin. Biochemically, one line at least, MB4, seems to be yolk sac, while another, MB2, may be derived from distal endoderm. In collaboration with Dr Michael Sherman, Dr Suzanne Rosenberg in my laboratory has been examining the H-2 antigens of four MB lines and three tumours derived from them. Though our observations are still incomplete, it is obvious that these cells, which bear teratoma antigens I and II, express only part of the complement of H-2 antigens expected for them. The embryos from which the cell lines were derived were F1 hybrids between *H-2*^{a} and *H-2*^{s} haplotype strains. As I mentioned (p. 179), antigenic products of the D and K regions of any *H-2* complex bear a number of antigenic determinants or specificities, and by careful choice of strains for immunization one can prepare sera against individual specificities of the products of each region. Though these sera in turn often react with several antigenic specificities, they allow a finer look at H-2 antigen expression than generalized sera of the sort that might be made by immunizing animals of two congenic strains against one another's lymphocytes.

A summary of results with one cell line, MB2, and a tumour, MB2T1, derived from it by R. Miller of Yale University is given in Table 6. This lists sera detecting one or a few specificities by number, indicates the haplotype expected to produce these specificities (either the maternal H-2^q or the paternal H-2^s), and notes whether the specificities are 'public', being found in many haplotypes and probably families of cross-reacting antigens, or 'private' and found only in one or a few H-2 haplotypes. The reactions of sera were detected by direct, complement-mediated lysis of cultured target cells using a standard micro-test (Amos *et al.* 1969). Though we have not found a consistent pattern to the expression of H-2 in these cells, it appears that only some antigens coded for by a particular haplotype may be detected by cell lysis tests. This is despite the fact that all the test sera used lysed adult lymphocytes bearing appropriate specificities. We also include results on one Ia antigen, a product of the I region, which again could be detected on adult lymphocytes, but not on MB2 or MB2T1 cells. A second point to be made is that the antigenic phenotype is not stable. Tumour cells derived from MB2 have lost some H-2 specificities, while expressing others.

It has long been known that direct lytic assays for H-2 and HL-A antigens may fail to detect these antigens on some cells. Accordingly absorption studies have been done on a number of sera which fail to lyse MB2 and MB2T1 cells

TABLE 6

Lysis of MB2 and MB2T1 cells by paucispecific anti-H-2 sera and complement

Serum	Range	Haplotype	Lysis of	
			MB2	MB2T1
C3	Public	q, s	+	+
C3b	Public	q, s	±	−
C11	Public	q]	−	−
D11	Public and private	q	+	−
D11b	Public	q	±	−
D12	Private	s	+	−
D18	Public	s	−	−
D19	Private	s	−	−
D20	Public	s	−	−
D30	Private and public	q	+	+
D32			−	+
A.Th anti-A.TL	Ia	q	−	−

Lysis was at least 40% of target cells in tests where backgrounds were 10–15%.

TABLE 7

Absorption of paucispecific anti-H-2 sera by MB2 and MB2T1 cells

Serum	Absorption relative to lymphocyte standards[a] by	
	MB2	MB2T1
C3b	1/2	1/3
C11	1/1	1/5
D11	1/1.5	No absorption[b]
D11b	1/8	1/7
D12	5/1	No absorption[b]
D18	No absorption	No absorption
D19	1/4	1/3
D-20	1/4	No absorption[b]

[a] Absorptions were performed with graded numbers of MB cells or of lymphocytes. Ratios are relative to cell numbers, rather than to total surface area.
[b] Less than 1/20 as active as lymphocytes.

directly (Table 7). Again, we cannot find a consistent pattern, but rather can find three patterns. First, specificities that are undetectable by direct cytotoxicity testing appear to be richly present when MB cells and lymphocytes are compared by absorption (for example, C11). Second, some specificities are present in lower amounts on the average in the cell population than they are in a lymphocyte population (for example, those defined by D11b or by D19). Finally, some specificities are undetectable even by absorption (for example D18 and D20).

We are intrigued by the possibilities afforded by this system. We expect to find all antigenic sites on a single polypeptide accessible to antibody if the gene coding for this polypeptide is expressed at all. Since this is not seen, alternative models must be devised for control of gene expression at the cell surface. Putting aside synthesis of incomplete *H-2* chains as unlikely, we might consider two other possibilities: association of a second polypeptide with the *H-2* product, masking some specificities, or physical changes in membrane structure, hindering attachment of antibodies, and cross-linkage of antigen–antibody complexes leading to complement fixation.

A clear candidate for the blocking polypeptide would be teratoma-defined antigen I. If H-2 were to assemble physically linked to antigen I, with the earlier-appearing antigen as its guide through the membrane, we might find that antigen sites present in close association with antigen I were blocked from reacting with antibody. This postulate is readily tested, both by single serum studies on the C1 1d cultured cells previously shown to associate H-2 and antigen I, and by extraction and purification of H-2 from MB cells.

Physical changes in membrane structure which restrict mobility of membrane proteins in the plane of the fluid membrane (Singer & Nicolson 1972; Frye & Edidin 1970; Poo & Cone 1974) could decrease the reactivity of these proteins with antibodies, or with receptors or other cells. In the present case, we can think of the H-2 glycoproteins as flexible polypeptide chains, with little tertiary structure, extending out of the membrane bilayer into the surrounding aqueous medium. The antigenic specificities detected by our sera are probably associated with groups of amino acids along the polypeptide chain, though some might also be determined by the 10% or so of sugars on each chain. For complement to be fixed, two IgG antibody molecules must have their combining sites filled and have their Fc portions in close association (for review, see Eisen 1974, ch. 18). These requirements are most readily met in cells whose surface antigens are mobile in the plane of the membrane, so that small aggregates of antigen and antibody which are formed as simpler complexes collide with one another during diffusion in the plane of the membrane. When surface antigens are fixed in place, then unless they are present in very high local concentrations, aggregates cannot be formed and complement fixation is greatly hindered. If the H-2 antigens of the MB cells were greatly restricted in their capacity for diffusion, then perhaps only antibodies to determinants at the free ends of the molecules could bind in a manner leading to complement fixation and cell lysis. In that case, while the base of the H-2 molecule would remain fixed, the tips could flex enough to allow cross-linking of two separate H-2 molecules, and formation of small, temporary associations of Fc portions which could activate complement.

Antibodies to determinants on the middle portions of fixed H-2 molecules would be expected to bind to cells, perhaps by only one of their two combining sites, but would be unable to bridge the distance from one antigenic molecule to another. Finally, antibodies directed against determinants near the bilayer sites which are exposed only transiently during thermal motion of a molecule would be unable to bind at all if the H-2 antigens were fixed. Thus, anchoring of a surface antigen could affect the full expression of an antigenic phenotype.

The mechanism proposed here extends beyond the problem of full antigenic expression in MB cells. Recently, this approach to cell interactions in development has been used by Johnson (1975) in discussing changes in gamete membranes during maturation and up to fertilization. In later development, restriction of the motion of membrane proteins could have a role in protecting the cells of the embryo against attack by the maternal immune system, since cells with fixed antigens would be liable to both antibody-mediated and cell-mediated damage. Also, surface enzymes would function differently if they were fixed or mobile in the plane of the membrane. For example, surface glycosyl transferases which may have a role in cell interactions could, if fixed in position, interact only with receptors on neighbouring cells; if they were mobile they would be free to interact with receptors on a single cell surface. Such a differential between so-called *cis* and *trans* interactions has been observed in a series of cultured cell lines (Roth 1973).

Note added in proof: Antigens of the H-2 complex have now been detected on preimplantation blastocysts, using a highly sensitive peroxidase antibody technique (Searle *et al.* 1976).

ACKNOWLEDGEMENTS

I thank Ms Lisa Schwender for her work in skin grafting. Original work reported here was supported by grant number AM11202 from the National Institutes of Health. This is contribution number 846 from the Department of Biology, The Johns Hopkins University, Baltimore, Md.

References

ALTER, B.J., SCHENDEL, D.J., BACH, M.L., BACH, F.H., KLEIN, J. & STIMPFLING, J.H. (1973) Cell-mediated lympholysis: Importance of serologically defined *H-2* regions. *J. Exp. Med.* *137*, 1303–1309

AMOS, D.B., BASHIR, H., BOYLE, W., McQUEEN, M. & TIILIKANNEN, A. (1969) A simple microcytotoxicity test. *Transplantation (Baltimore)* 7, 220–223

ARTZT, K. (1974) Absence of serologically detectable *H-2* on primitive teratocarcinoma cells in culture. *Transplantation (Baltimore)* *17*, 632–634

ARTZT, K., DuBOIS, P., BENNETT, D., CONDAMINE, H., BABINET, C. & JACOB, F. (1973) Surface antigens common to mouse primitive teratocarcinoma cells in culture and cleavage embryos. *Proc. Natl. Acad. Sci. USA 70*, 2988–2992

BENACERRAF, B. & McDEVITT, H.O. (1972) Histocompatibility-linked immune response genes. *Science (Wash. D.C.) 175*, 273–279

BENNETT, D., BOYSE, E.A. & OLD, L.J. (1972) in *Cell Interactions* (Silvestri, L.G., ed.), pp. 258–261, North-Holland, Amsterdam

DAMJANOV, I. & SOLTER, D. (1974) Experimental teratoma. *Curr. Top. Pathol. 59*, 69–130

DAVID, C.S., STIMPFLING, J.H. & SHREFFLER, D.C. (1975) Identification of specificity *H-2.7* as an erythrocyte antigen: Control by an independent locus, *H-2G*, between the *S* and *D* regions. *Immunogenetics 2*, 131–139

DELOVITCH, T.L. & McDEVITT, H.O. (1975) Isolation and characterization of murine *Ia* antigens. *Immunogenetics 2*, 39–52

DÉMANT, P. (1973) *H-2* gene complex and its role in alloimmune reactions. *Transplant. Rev.* *15*, 162–200

EDIDIN, M. (1964) Transplantation antigen levels in the early mouse embryo. *Transplantation (Baltimore) 2*, 627–637

EDIDIN, M. (1972) in *Transplantation Antigens* (Kahan, B.D. & Reisfeld, R.A., eds.), pp. 75–114, Academic Press, New York

EDIDIN, M., GOODING, L.R. & JOHNSON, M.H. (1974) Surface antigens of normal early embryos and a tumor model system useful for their further study. *Acta Endocrinol. Suppl.* 78, 336–356

EISEN, H. (1974) *Immunology*, Harper & Row, New York

EVANS, M.J. (1972) The isolation and properties of a clonal tissue culture strain of pluripotent mouse teratoma cells. *J. Embryol. Exp. Morphol. 28*, 163–176

FRYE, L.D. & EDIDIN, M. (1970) The rapid intermixing of cell surface antigens after formation of mouse—human heterokaryons. *J. Cell Sci. 7*, 319–335

GOODING, L.R. & EDIDIN, M. (1974) Cell surface antigens of a mouse testicular teratoma. Identification of an antigen physically associated with *H-2* antigens. *J. Exp. Med. 140*, 61–78

GORER, P.A. (1938) The antigenic basis of tumor transplantation. *J. Pathol. Bacteriol. 47*, 231–252

GORER, P.A., LYMAN, S. & SNELL, G.D. (1948) Studies on the genetic and antigenic basis of tumor transplantation. Linkage between a histocompatibility gene and 'fused' in mice. *Proc. Roy. Soc. Lond. B Biol. Sci. 135*, 499–505

HÄMMERLING, G.J., MAUVE, G., GOLDBERG, E. & McDEVITT, H.O. (1975) Tissue distribution of *Ia* antigens: *Ia* on spermatozoa, macrophages and epidermal cells. *Immunogenetics 1*, 428–437

HEYNER, S. (1973) Detection of *H-2* antigens on cells of the early mouse embryo. *Transplantation (Baltimore) 16*, 675–678

HSU, Y.C. (1973) Differentiation *in vitro* of mouse embryos to the stage of early somite. *Dev. Biol. 33*, 403–411

IVÁNYI, P., GREGOREVÁ, S. & MICKOVÁ, M. (1972) Genetic differences in thymus, lymph node, testes and vesicular gland weights among inbred mouse strains. Association with the major histocompatibility (H-2) system. *Folia Biol. (Prague) 18*, 81–97

JOHNSON, M.H. (1975) The macromolecular organization of membranes and its bearing on the events leading up to fertilization. *J. Reprod. Fertil. 44*, 167–184

JOHNSON, M.H. & EDIDIN, M. (1972) *H-2* antigens on mouse spermatozoa. *Transplantation (Baltimore), 14*, 781–786

KAHAN, B.W. & EPHRUSSI, B. (1970) Developmental potentialities of clonal *in vitro* cultures of mouse testicular teratoma. *J. Natl. Cancer Inst. 44*, 1015–1036

KLEIN, J. (1975) *Biology of the Mouse Histocompatibility-2 complex*, Springer-Verlag, New York

KLEIN, J., BACH, F. H., FESTENSTEIN, H., McDEVITT, H. O., SHREFFLER, D. C., SNELL, G. D. & STIMPFLING, J.H. (1974) Genetic nomenclature for the *H-2* complex of the mouse. *Immunogenetics 1*, 184–188

KLEIN, J., HAUPTFELD, V. & HAUPTFELD, M. (1975) Evidence for a fifth (*G*) region in the *H-2* complex of the mouse. *Immunogenetics 2*, 141–150

MEDAWAR, P.B. (1958) The immunology of transplantation. *Harvey Lect. 52*, 144–176

MERUELO, D. & EDIDIN, M. (1975) Association of mouse liver adenosine 3′:5′-cyclic monophosphate (cyclic AMP) levels with Histocompatibility-2 genotype. *Proc. Natl. Acad. Sci. USA 72*, 2644–2648

NATHENSON, S.G. & CULLEN, S.E. (1974) Biochemical properties and immunochemical-genetic relationships of mouse *H-2* alloantigens. *Biochim. Biophys. Acta 344*, 1–25

OLDS, P.J. (1968) An attempt to detect *H-2* antigens on mouse eggs. *Transplantation (Baltimore) 6*, 478–479

PALM, J., HEYNER, S. & BRINSTER, R.L. (1971) Differential immunofluorescence of fertilized mouse eggs with *H-2* and non-*H-2* antibody. *J. Exp. Med. 133*, 1282–1293

PATTHEY, H.L. & EDIDIN, M. (1973) Evidence for the time of appearance of *H-2* antigens in mouse development. *Transplantation (Baltimore) 15*, 211–214

PIERCE, G.B. (1967) Teratocarcinoma model for a developmental concept of cancer. *Curr. Top. Dev. Biol. 2*, 223–246

POO, M.M. & CONE, R.A. (1974) Lateral diffusion of rhodopsin in the photoreceptor membrane. *Nature (Lond.) 247*, 438–441

ROSENTHAL, M.D., WISHNOW, R.M. & SATO, G.H. (1970) *In vitro* growth and differentiation of clonal populations of multipotential mouse cells derived from a transplantable testicular teratocarcinoma. *J. Natl. Cancer Inst. 44*, 1001–1014

ROTH, S. (1973) A molecular model for cell interactions. *Q. Rev. Biol. 48*, 541–563

SEARLE, R. F., JOHNSON, M. H., BILLINGTON, W. D., ELSON, J. & CLUTTERBUCK-JACKSON, S. (1974) Investigation of *H-2* and non-*H-2* antigens on the mouse blastocyst. *Transplantation (Baltimore) 18*, 136–141

SEARLE, R. F., SELLENS, M. H., ELSON, J., JENKINSON, E. J. & BILLINGTON, W. D. (1976) Detection of alloantigens during preimplantation development and early trophoblast differentiation in the mouse by immunoperoxidase labelling. *J. Exp. Med. 143*, 348–359

SHERMAN, M. I. (1975) Long term culture of cells derived from mouse blastocysts. *Differentiation 3*, 51–67

SHREFFLER, D. C. & DAVID, C. S. (1975) The *H-2* major histocompatibility complex and the *I* immune response region: Genetic variation, function and organization. *Adv. Immunol. 20*, 125–195

SIMMONS, R. L. & RUSSELL, P. S. (1966) The histocompatibility antigens of fertilized mouse eggs and trophoblast. *Ann. N.Y. Acad. Sci. 129*, 35–45

SINGER, S. J. & NICOLSON, G. (1972) The fluid mosaic model of the structure of cell membranes. *Science (Wash. D.C.) 175*, 720–731

SNELL, G. (1966) in *Biology of the Laboratory Mouse* (Green, E., ed.), 2nd ed., pp. 457–472, Blakiston, New York

STEVENS, L. C. (1958) Studies on transplantable testicular teratomas of strain 129 mice. *J. Natl. Cancer Inst. 20*, 1257–1270

STEVENS, L. C. (1967) The biology of teratomas. *Adv. Morphog. 6*, 1–31

Discussion

Graham: You saw a change in surface antigenicity between cell line MB2 and the tumour derived from it. Was this due to the selection of particular cells from the original MB2 population?

Edidin: My understanding is that the tumour is not clonally derived; rather there is selection for escape from growth control in the mouse. We may be seeing a subpopulation that was selected out of the main population.

Saxén: In your fusion experiments, can you exclude the possibility that the components you are demonstrating are synthesized in the heterokaryons?

Edidin: Yes; we can fix cells in paraformaldehyde and their surface antigens still mix. This is consistent with what we know about protein fixative effects on diffusion of, say, rhodopsin.

Newth: You told us that H-3 and H-6 could be demonstrated at the 2-cell stage. Is that equally true whether they are paternally or maternally derived?

Edidin: The experiment was done with homozygotes.

Gropp: If you are interested in studying the expression of the triplicated *H-2* locus in the delayed embryo, I would be glad to provide you with trisomy 17, which has triplication of the *H-2* locus.

Edidin: It would be interesting to grow those trisomic cells, though it is clear that we have enough problems with a single-locus MB2 haplotype.

McLaren: You mentioned cell locomotion. Aren't concanavalin A receptors concerned in some way with cell movement?

Edidin: The story of Con A receptors is a long one, in three chapters. First, if Con A binding sites are marked on the cell surface they seem to move away from the ruffled leading edge of the moving fibroblast and towards a perinuclear region, on the surface. The most consistent but not necessarily most correct theory is that, as part of cell locomotion, membrane components are continually swept away from the leading edge of the cell and this is what forms a cap (Abercrombie *et al.* 1972).

The second chapter is a set of observations on the binding of cells to fibres treated with Con A. The experiments seem to indicate that a fixed cell will not bind to the fibres, and it is suggested that this was due to restricted mobility of the Con A receptor after fixation (Rutishauser & Sachs 1974), though other interpretations are possible (see below).

The third chapter is the story that has been nicely worked out in G. Edelman's laboratory. That is that binding Con A to the surface in turn affects the mobility of other surface components, so that in some way blocking one set of receptors affects a second set of receptors. The data on Con A-mediated adhesion of cells to fibres and to other cells really seem to require mobility of surface components. It may be a very interesting system for analysing the requirements further. It also might turn out, though, that the adhesion has to occur via a microprocess that is thrown out and that the fixed cell cannot throw out that process. Indeed a recent paper indicates this (Gibson *et al.* 1975).

McLaren: Has the fourth chapter, on how Con A receptors come and go on a mouse embryo cell, been written?

Edidin: I understand that it is being done.

Graham: The amount of binding of concanavalin A is similar for unfertilized and fertilized eggs and for preimplantation stages of development (Pienkowski 1974). H. Alexandre (personal communication, 1975) from Brussels finds that the Con A binding sites in fixed blastocysts are exclusively in the inner cell mass.

Edidin: What stage of blastocyst?

Graham: I think around hatching.

Glucksohn-Waelsch: If cell surface proteins are required for cell locomotion, would you expect, in the course of differentiation, to find a quantitative increase during those stages where cells are known to undergo a lot of movement? You showed changes up to $7\frac{1}{2}$ days but if you were to break down the stages later on and make quantitative measurements, would you expect to find changes parallel to locomotion?

Edidin: There might be changes parallel to locomotion. I don't think H-2 antigens in cells can be claimed to take part in cell locomotion or cell adhesion, although we don't know. Someone in my laboratory has preliminary results showing that fibroblast adhesion is affected by *H-2* genotypes in the system where congenic fibroblasts stick to one another. There may be other genes in the *H-2* complex which are not expressed as surface antigens, but which affect surface functions. On the other hand if locomotion requires certain general physical properties of membranes, then I might expect that in parallel with the change in locomotion I might find a parallel change, say, in the ease of lysis of cells in antisera and complement. The later findings show that up to about 10 days, H-2 antigens reach about 10% of the adult levels and stop there. After 10 days, when organs form, one seems to get a history of cell traffic through them. For example, in the liver the content of H-2 antigens goes up and down during development and I think this affects haemopoietic cell traffic rather than changing parenchymal cell H-2.

Gluecksohn-Waelsch: So H-2 is still in search of a function.

Wolpert: I don't understand why you say these antigenic sites have anything whatsoever to do with locomotion.

Edidin: I only said that I think certain physical properties of membranes are required for locomotion. That is, the membranes in cells that are moving must allow free movement of the surface integral protein. The antigens we have got are simply a sample of one integral protein and should therefore reflect the general properties of all integral proteins.

Wolpert: I thought you were suggesting that the presence or absence or linking of these antigenic sites could have something to do with locomotion?

Edidin: No; I only think that the observations that they do or do not move freely in the bilayer reflect the more general properties of the cell surface that are required for locomotion. I didn't say that the antigens themselves are involved. I don't think that a cell that has all its surface proteins locked up, however that is done, is capable of moving.

Gardner: The whole trophectoderm of the early blastocyst is positive for antigen I, but when cells transform into giant cells you say they become negative?

Edidin: That is correct.

Gardner: What is the distribution of antigen within the embryo later on? For example, is it present on the small ectoplacental cone cells or in endoderm?

Edidin: We have no later observations. That probably ought to be examined on histological sections.

Newth: One of your theories was that the distance between antigenic components of the cell surface might be responsible for failures in lysis. When you do a cell fusion experiment at some time you presumably greatly increase the distance after redistribution has occurred. You could then test that particular hypothesis.

Edidin: No; on the average they are further apart but if the antigens are free to move then any antibody coming along acts as a sink and collects them together. The antigen distance notion is inferred from other models, notably the erythrocyte in which kinetic data indicate that two IgG molecules must be close together for complement to be fixed (Borsos & Rapp 1965).

Kelley: Would you comment on the structural nature of the anchoring elements of the inner leaflet of the lipid bilayer? And you indicated that the outermost components on the outer leaflet may be free to move not only within the plane of the membrane but also outside the plane of the membrane. I have difficulty in understanding that on a structural basis. Other materials are present in the cell coat. Wouldn't these hinder the motility of such polypeptide chains on this outer surface? And if they do not, why not?

Edidin: The anchoring systems are still problematic. Both colchicine and cytochalasin B go to a lot more places and do a lot more things than we would like. In some cells there seems to be a fibrillar cytoplasmic network which makes connections that have never been shown with membrane proteins.

I don't know how many molecules I would have to put in to build up the glycocalyx. Even then I wouldn't know if that would lead to a rather rigid ionically bonded shell around the membranes, which would upset that notion, or whether there would simply be more chains waving in the breeze. I don't think there would be any highly structured material there, unless there were cross-links of some sort.

References

ABERCROMBIE, M., HEAYSMAN, J.E.M. & PEGRUM, S.M. (1972) Locomotion of fibroblasts in culture V. Surface marking with concanavalin A. *Exp. Cell Res. 73*, 536–539

BORSOS, T. & RAPP, H.J. (1965) Complement fixation on cell surfaces by 19S and 7S antibodies. *Science (Wash. D.C.) 150*, 505–506

GIBSON, D.A., MARGUARDT, M.D. & GORDON, J.A. (1975) Cell rigidity: Effect on concanavalin A-mediated agglutinibility of fibroblasts after fixation. *Science (Wash. D.C.) 189*, 45–46

PIENKOWSKI, M. (1974) Study on the growth regulation of preimplantation mouse embryos using concanavalin A. *Proc. Soc. Exp. Biol. Med. 145*, 464–469

RUTISHAUSER, U. & SACHS, L. (1974) Receptor mobility and the mechanisms of cell-cell binding induced by concanavalin A. *Proc. Natl. Acad. Sci. USA 71*, 2456–2460

Electron microscopy of cell associations in *T*-locus mutants

MARTHA SPIEGELMAN

Department of Anatomy, Cornell University Medical College, New York

Abstract Observations on the fine structure of mouse embryo cells during chordamesoderm migration and differentiation support the contention that appropriate cellular interactions are essential to normal development, and, further, that the *T* locus may control cell-surface properties that are critical to morphogenesis.

Embryos homozygous for the *T* gene (Brachyury) and for the t^9 gene arrest in development with specific groups of cells affected in each of the lethal phenotypes. In both mutants deranged cellular interactions result in organizational defects of major tissues.

In *T* homozygotes at late 8-day to early 9-day stages (8 to 20 somites) the integrity of axial structures is impaired because neuroepithelial cells form close associations, including specialized contact zones, with neighbouring cells identified as notochord and somites. The basal lamina of the neuroepithelium is deficient where contacts between dissimilar cells are seen.

Presumptive mesodermal cells of early 8-day t^9 homozygotes neither establish typical cell contacts with one another nor form normal microfilament-containing filopodia. These structural defects may indicate paralysis of the cellular motility apparatus.

It is postulated that components of the cell surface that serve as devices for recognition or response during cell-cell interaction are disturbed by the mutant genes and result in abnormal types of cell associations.

The classical studies of embryology have established that normal development proceeds via the orderly unfolding of a sequence of appropriately timed cellular and tissue interactions. The fate of each particular circumscribed region in the early vertebrate embryo is interlocked with the fate of its neighbours. The precision of cell–cell recognition and response has been amply demonstrated by recombination experiments with embryonic tissue rudiments and by reaggregation studies of dissociated embryonic cells.

As a result of these and related observations, the concept has grown that cell surfaces mediate cell–cell interactions and thereby channel histogenesis (Weiss 1946; Townes & Holtfreter 1955; Grobstein 1967; Moscona 1973). This concept has been amplified to suggest that morphogenesis is guided by the presence on cells of specific, gene-determined, cell-surface components, or 'differentiation antigens' (Bennett *et al.* 1972*a*).

Observations of genetically abnormal phenotypes in a wide range of organisms indicate that so-called 'developmental genes' control normal embryogenesis. Single gene mutations that result in clear-cut developmental abnormalities can furthermore aid in the analysis of developmental mechanisms, especially since such mutations must initially act through a single aberrant gene product.

THE *T* LOCUS IN THE MOUSE

The *T* locus in the mouse provides exactly the needed tool in the search for information on the mechanisms of both normal and deviant development. This locus on chromosome 17 is identified by the dominant mutation Brachyury (*T*) which produces a short-tailed heterozygote (Dobrovolskaia-Zavadskaia 1927), and is an embryonic lethal in homozygous condition (Chesley 1935). A number of recessive alleles (*t*) also occur at the locus; each *t* allele interacts with *T* to produce tailless mice (*T/t*). Six of these *t* alleles are also lethal and, as in *T/T* embryos, each homozygote arrests at a specific time during development (for reviews see Dunn & Bennett 1964; Gluecksohn-Waelsch & Erickson 1970; Bennett 1975).

In each lethal homozygote a particular syndrome of aberrant organization occurs in defined groups of cells; these organizational defects are interpretable as a failure of cells to interact appropriately. The abnormalities appear principally as disturbances in the embryonic ectoderm or its derivatives, including neuroepithelium, primitive streak and chordamesoderm. The *T* locus is further interesting because of striking effects of the mutant genes on the production and function of sperm (Bennett & Dunn 1971; Dooher & Bennett 1974).

The importance of the *T* locus in uncovering the mechanisms of cellular and embryonic differentiation was recognized early, and observations on this complex chromosomal region have been carefully collected over many years, by L. C. Dunn, S. Gluecksohn-Waelsch, and D. Bennett among others. As a result of the continuity of these efforts, we are now in a position to accelerate the exploitation of the *T* locus in its dual role of experimental and teratological agent in the analysis of development.

Recently, specific cell-surface components determined by genes at the *T* locus have been detected serologically on sperm cells but not on other adult cells

(Bennett *et al.* 1972*b*; Yanagisawa *et al.* 1974). These findings, coupled with the fact that *t* alleles affect sperm production and function and also arrest embryonic development, suggest that the mutant genes may determine not only specific cell-surface components on sperm cells but also those on the affected cells in each of the arrested embryos. Since each of the mutant genes interrupts normal development at important determinative stages, it has been further postulated that the role of wild-type genes at the *T* locus is to control the sequential expression on specific cells of surface components necessary to successive differentiative steps (Bennett *et al.* 1972*a*). In fact, one such differentiation antigen has been recognized on blastomeres of normal cleavage and morula stage embryos; significantly, the gene determining this cell-surface antigen has been identified as the wild-type alternative to the t^{12} allele (Artzt *et al.* 1974), which in homozygotes arrests development at the morula stage.

MORPHOLOGICAL OBSERVATIONS

While further genetic and immunological studies of the *T* locus continue, it is essential also to arrive at a knowledge of cellular structure in the embryo, especially with respect to the cell surface and its appendages, and the organization of organelles in the sub-surface cytoplasm. The role of cell-surface differentiation antigens during embryogenesis cannot be interpreted without detailed morphological knowledge of cells affected by mutant genes and their normal counterparts.

Morphogenesis requires not only cell–cell recognition but also response, often in the form of changes in cell movement, cell adhesion, cell shape, and cell coat materials. Such elements as cell-surface appendages, sub-surface microfilaments, microtubules, cell junctions, cell coat, and external limiting laminae may all contribute to the cell movement and cellular interactions that lead to the development and maintenance of tissue structure; that is to say, these elements may constitute true morphogenetic machinery.

There are not many published observations on the fine structure of normal or genetically abnormal mammalian embryos at the important determinative stages of primitive streak, mesoderm formation, and axial organization. The *T* locus mutants that are particularly useful in this respect are t^9 and *T*. Homozygotes for these two genes show abnormalities in the primitive streak, neural tube, notochord, and mesoderm from early 8-day to early 9-day stages, the period when axial organization is under way in normal littermates. Fine structural observations of affected cells in each mutant support the contention that deranged cellular interactions account for the organizational defects seen.

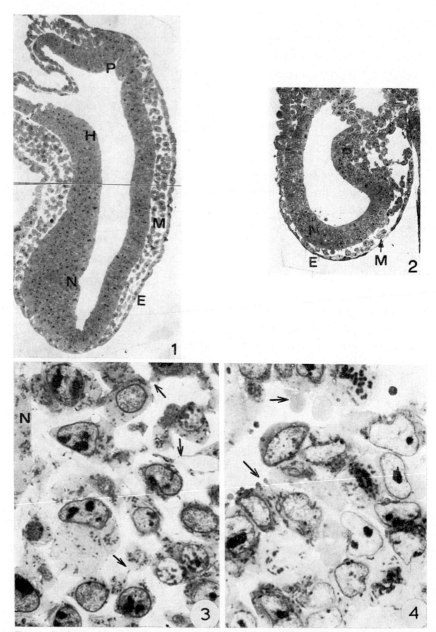

FIG. 1. Sagittal section through 8-day normal embryo. *H*, head-fold; *P*, primitive streak; N, neural ectoderm; *E*, endoderm; *M*, mesoderm. × 125.

FIG. 2. Sagittal section through 8-day t^9 mutant embryo. Primitive streak, *P*, is unusually large, no head-folds are present, and 'mesoderm', *M*, is deficient. Embryo is very retarded in size. *N*, neural ectoderm; *E*, endoderm. × 125.

The t^9 mutant embryo*

Early on day 8 of gestation normal embryos have head-folds, two to four pairs of somites, and are undergoing neural tube closure; t^9/t^9 littermates are characterized by their small size, retarded development of axial tissues and, especially, a greatly enlarged primitive streak (Bennett & Dunn 1960). The mutants die before day 10 probably because of circulatory defects resulting from the lack of mesodermal tissues (Artzt & Bennett 1972).

Histologically, it can be seen that the large primitive streak causes a bulge of tissue into the proamniotic cavity and that mesoderm is deficient (Figs. 1, 2). Furthermore, although normal mesodermal cells are stellate in outline and have many filiform cytoplasmic processes in contact with one another (Fig. 3), the mesoderm of the mutant appears as cohesive clusters of cells with large areas of apposing surfaces in contact (Fig. 4). The cells are more rounded than those of normal mesoderm and they have lobose pseudopods and dense surface blebs. Filiform processes are rarely encountered.

Normal mesodermal cells, in embryos of several species (Gustafson & Wolpert 1967; Trelstad *et al.* 1967; Johnson 1972) as well as various kinds of moving cells *in vitro* (Ingram 1969; Abercrombie *et al.* 1971; Allison 1973; Goldman *et al.* 1973), are arrayed in networks of stellate cells that contact one another or the substrate by means of fine pseudopods. Such cell shapes and contacts are usually interpreted as reflecting the motile activity of the cells. The mesodermal cells of the t^9 mutant, however, do not present this typical appearance of a population of motile cells.

We have explored these mutant embryos and their normal counterparts in the electron microscope (Spiegelman & Bennett 1974) and find that normal mesodermal cells are in contact with one another by means of junctions between the apposing plasma membranes of the filopodia (Fig. 5). The mutant mesodermal cells are also in contact but over large areas of apposed membrane rather than by slender cytoplasmic processes (Fig. 6).

---

* Lack of complementation between t^9 and t^{w18} (Van Valen 1966) and between t^9 and t^4 (Moser & Glueksohn-Waelsch 1967) shows that these alleles are indistinguishable.

←

FIG. 3. Mesoderm of normal embryo. Cells are stellate and have many finely tapering processes (*arrows*) which contact neighbouring cells. N, neural ectoderm. × 1000.

FIG. 4. 'Mesoderm' of t^9 mutant embryo. Cell aggregates have large areas of adjacent surfaces in contact. Fine cellular processes are not evident; several cells have lobose pseudopods (*arrows*). × 1000.

All tissue shown in Figs. 1–26 was fixed in glutaraldehyde and osmium, and embedded in Epon. Sections 1 μm-thick were stained with toluidine blue. Ultrathin sections were stained with uranyl acetate and lead citrate (for methods see Spiegelman & Bennett 1974).

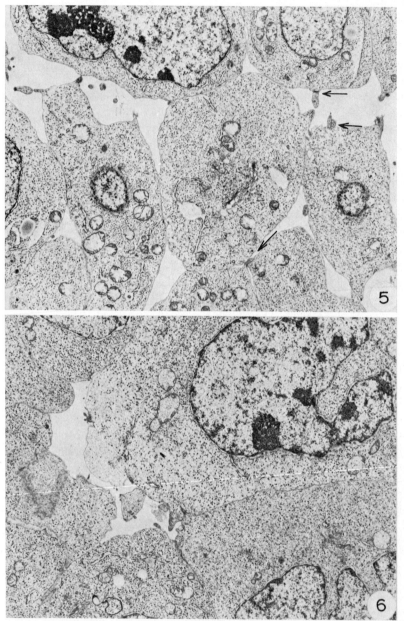

FIG. 5. Mesodermal cells bordering the primitive streak in 8-day normal embryo. A few cells still have large areas of surface in contact but there is space between most cells. Junctions are present between contacting filopodia (*arrows*). × 4000.

FIG. 6. Mesodermal cells of the 8-day t^9 mutant have extensive areas of apposed surface. There is little space between the aggregated cells. Few contacting filopodia are seen. × 4000.

These so-called mesodermal cells of the mutant in fact resemble the cells seen at the margin of the primitive streak in the normal 7-day embryo. The close association of the mesodermal cells in the t^9 mutant, coupled with the fact that the primitive streak remains abnormally large and mesoderm is deficient, suggests that these cells have not completed the transition to mesoderm, have not migrated into their appropriate location and, as clustered cells in an inappropriate location, have failed to differentiate normally. Probably as a result of the immobilization of primitive streak cells, other axial structures, such as neuroepithelium, notochord and somites, that are derived from or are dependent on morphogenetic properties of the primitive streak are defective.

It has been shown that a microfilament lattice is present in the sub-surface cytoplasm of lamellipodia of moving cells *in vitro* (Ingram 1969; Spooner *et al.* 1971; Heaysman 1973) and it is suggested that these lattices, together with external adhesive sites, function as a major element in cell motility and changes in cell shape (Abercrombie *et al.* 1971; Goldman *et al.* 1973; Ludueña & Wessells 1973; Spooner *et al.* 1973). In normal mesodermal cells of the mouse embryo, this kind of lattice is seen in tangential sections through filopodia (Figs. 7, 9, 10). Corresponding sections through lobopodia of the mutant cells rarely show more than a few microfilaments (Figs. 8, 11, 12). In addition, ribosomes penetrate completely to the sub-surface cytoplasm in lobopodia, whereas

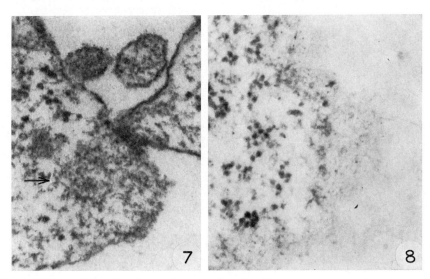

FIG. 7. Typical filopodia of normal mesodermal cells. The sub-surface cytoplasm is occupied by microfilaments (*arrow*). × 75 000.

FIG. 8. A somewhat tapering cytoplasmic process of t^9 mutant mesodermal cell. Ribosomes penetrate into sub-surface cytoplasm and microfilaments are few. × 75 000.

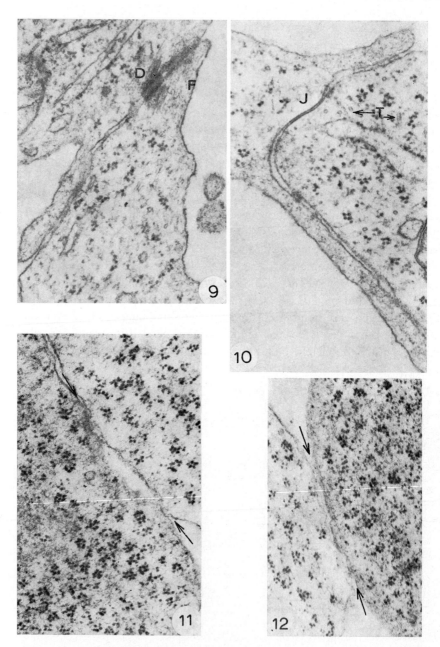

FIGS. 9, 10. Contacting mesodermal cells of normal embryo are joined by a desmosome, *D*, but more frequently by gap junctions, *J*. Microtubules, *T*, and microfilaments, *F*, are usual components of cytoplasm near zones of contact. Filopodia typically extend over the cell surface adjacent to the junction sites. × 46 000.

in filopodia this volume is largely occupied by microfilaments and microtubules. These observations suggest that these rather rigid cytostructural elements which impose form on the cell surface at the same time restrict the location of organelles. Conversely, the abundance of ribosomes near the plasma membrane of lobopodia is further evidence that microfilaments and microtubules are of low frequency here.

The lobose cell-surface appendages of the mutant mesodermal cells do not appear capable of generating the forces necessary for cellular translocation since it is likely that anastomosing microfilaments, having attachments at least part of the time to the inner face of the plasma membrane, must interact to effect cytoplasmic extension and retraction. Lack of such a network, as in most of the lobopodia, probably curtails wave-like movements of the cell surface.

Contact specializations shared by normal mesodermal cells are often seen as thickenings in the apposing plasma membranes that are accompanied by fibrillar zones in the sub-surface cytoplasm; junctions of this sort are probably transitory. Desmosomes are also found (Fig. 9) but are of low frequency, as might be expected in a population of motile cells. The most numerous contacts observed are gap junctions (Fig. 10) which are usually implicated in electrical coupling of cells (Staehelin 1974). Presumably, in embryonic cells gap junctions play a role in cell communication just as they do in other tissue types where they commonly occur.

Cellular junctions are not entirely absent in the mutant mesoderm but they occur as small membrane densities sparsely distributed along the extensive apposing cell surfaces of the cell aggregates rather than as the numerous and large junctions present on filopodia of normal mesodermal cells. Moreover, wherever junctions occur on the filopodia of normal cells, cytoplasmic processes containing a fine filamentous meshwork extend away from the contact site, and spread over the apposing cell surface (Figs. 9, 10) as if making further exploratory movements. The surfaces of mutant mesodermal cells do not appear to behave in the same way. In these abnormal cells filopodia are not often seen. Even where contacts occur between lobopodia, cytoplasmic processes do not extend out from the contacting site (Figs. 11, 12).

The morphological picture of mesodermal cells in the normal mouse embryo may be interpreted in the same way as similar views of other moving cells: that is, force is generated by intracellular contractile (actin-like) filaments in the sub-surface cytoplasm at the site of adhesion between cells or between cell and

←

Figs. 11, 12. Apposed surfaces of t^9 mutant mesodermal cells appear to be in contact at some places (*arrows*), but typical junctions do not often form. Microfilaments and microtubules are rarely seen; ribosomes occupy the sub-surface cytoplasm and filopodia do not develop. × 46 000.

substrate (Behnke *et al.* 1971; Allison 1973; Ludueña & Wessells 1973; Spooner *et al.* 1973; Durham 1974). Presumably, with cytoplasmic flow away from the adhesive site, new bonds form as former ones disengage.

In some respects, the aberrant mesoderm of t^9 mutants is not unlike the mesenchyme seen in the limb bud of *talpid³*-mutant chick embryos (Ede *et al.* 1974). Mesenchyme cells in these limbs are rounded and have fewer tapering cytoplasmic processes than normal; there are few contacts with the basal lamina of the overlying apical ectodermal ridge. These slowly moving cells often aggregate. Like mesenchymal cells of the *talpid³* limb bud, mesodermal cells of the t^9 homozygote form extensive areas of contact with one another and seem to remain in contact too long. Conceivably, in both mutants the cell surface and possibly sub-surface structures are not organized normally and therefore appropriate cell–cell or cell–substrate interactions cannot take place.

In the t^9 mutant, some functional aspect of the cell surface is clearly defective. It may be that the outer faces of the plasma membranes of adjacent cells do not interact and so fail to generate appropriate contact specializations. On the other hand, the inner face of the plasma membrane may not permit stable insertions of microfilaments. It is not possible at the moment to discriminate between the two alternatives, and in fact the two may well be coupled. In any case, it is proposed that a 'mesodermal cell surface' does not develop in the presence of the t^9-homozygous genotype; thus the motile apparatus of presumptive mesodermal cells is impaired and one of the fundamental early differentiative events, cell migration, is inhibited.

The T mutant embryo

Normal embryos in the middle of day 8 of gestation have about six pairs of somites, the neural tube is closed at the mid-trunk level, the primitive streak has regressed to a small region at the caudal end, and an allantois is present. By day 9, the embryo has a notochord and 12 or more pairs of somites, the neural tube is closed except at the most anterior and posterior levels, and both pairs of limb buds are present (Snell & Stevens 1966; Theiler 1972).

In contrast, the *T* homozygote in the middle of day 8 is characterized by its foreshortened trunk, large primitive streak, somewhat irregular neural tube, and the presence of transparent dorsal blisters; these blebs disappear by 9 days and are of unknown significance (Chesley 1935). At 9 days, the embryo is still more abnormal; the trunk terminates in a mass of disorganized tissue without forming posterior structures such as hindlimb buds and allantois. The neural tube is sinuous and somites are diffuse in outline. The embryo dies before 11 days because of its failure to establish contact with the maternal circulation (Gluecksohn-Schoenheimer 1944).

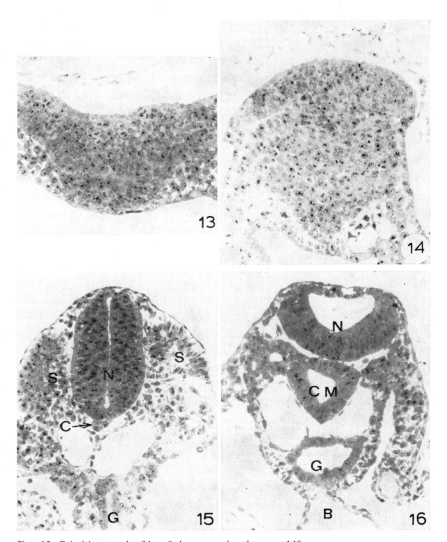

FIG. 13. Primitive streak of late 8-day normal embryo. × 140.

FIG. 14. Arrested primitive streak of late 8-day T mutant. × 140.

FIG. 15. Early 9-day normal embryo at the level of the posterior intestinal portal. N, neural tube; C, notochord; S, somites; G, gut. × 140.

FIG. 16. Early 9-day T mutant at the level of the closed hind-gut. Arrested chordamesoderm has organized into tubular epithelia, CM, in the position normally occupied by notochord and somites. Neural tube, N, nevertheless appears to have a fairly normal form. Pycnotic cells are present in both the neural tube and chordamesoderm tubules. G, gut; B, blood vessel. × 140.

(Figs. 13–16: Light micrographs of transverse sections.)

The histological picture of these mutants is complicated and the events occurring between 8 and 9 days are incompletely known. At early stages of development (8 days) T mutants are not distinguishable from normal littermates; they have a notochord and up to four pairs of somites. Later, however, axial structures begin to degenerate; the notochord disappears, somites become irregular, and both neural tube and chordamesoderm become abnormal (Chesley 1935). The degree of disorganization and necrosis in the neuroepithelium and chordamesoderm varies along an anterior–posterior gradient and is always more severe at the posterior end of the embryo.

Observations on T/T embryos suggest that the proliferation and differentiation of chordamesoderm from the primitive streak is interrupted. In the normal mid-8th day embryo, the primitive streak has regressed to a small zone at the posterior extreme of the trunk. In T homozygotes, however, a large mass of presumptive chordamesoderm persists through the posterior third of the trunk (Figs. 13, 14). Although this apparently arrested primitive streak never forms normal chordamesoderm derivatives, by 9 days the remaining cells begin to form extensive tubular epithelial structures in the position normally occupied by notochord and somites (Figs. 15, 16). Although these unusual tubules apparently develop from chordamesoderm cells, their tissue configuration is not typical of notochord or somites and they are much larger. Because these tubules are located ventral and lateral to the neural tube and follow the longitudinal body axis, however, this tissue may be construed as being an aberrant kind of notochord and somite construction. Anterior to this region, the notochord and somites which had formed earlier have by this time begun to lose their integrity; their cells either disperse unrecognizably or form atypical associations with neighbouring tissues, especially the neural tube.

There is no structural continuity between the degenerating axial tissues in the anterior region of the mutant embryo and the abnormal tubules in the posterior. The interface between the two regions occurs at the mid-trunk level where the tubular epithelia end blindly, posterior to the open mid-gut. In normal embryos of this stage, the neural tube is closed, somites have a typical rosette arrangement of cells, and a notochord is present, usually as a separate entity but sometimes still intercalated into the roof of the gut (Fig. 17). At this body level in the mutant, the neural tube is often still open, somites usually appear as small clumps of cells, and there is no discrete notochord although some cells are loosely arrayed in the notochord position (Fig. 18).

In normal embryos from the late 8th to early 9th days, the neural tube is very regular in form and has a sharply delimited boundary, except in the extreme posterior body level where primitive streak and neuroepithelium are contiguous. Even where neural tube and notochord come into close relation, the two struc-

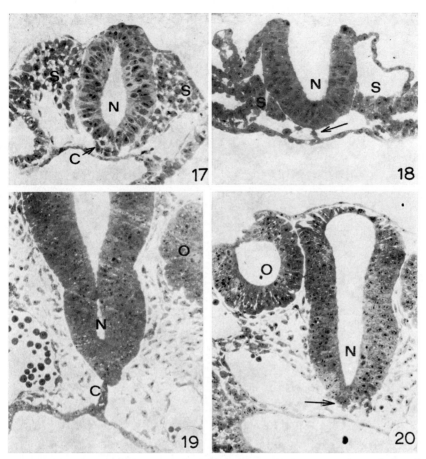

FIG. 17. Normal embryo at open mid-gut level. Discrete axial structures are distinct from one another. *N*, neural tube; *C*, notochord; *S*, somites. × 140.

FIG. 18. *T* mutant at open mid-gut level. Neural tube, *N*, is not closed. Somites, *S*, appear as small clumps of cells. Notochord is lacking but a few cells are in its position (*arrow*). × 140.

FIG. 19. Normal embryo at foregut and otocyst (*O*) level. Neural tube, *N*, and notochord, *C*, have sharp boundaries even though they are in close proximity. × 140.

FIG. 20. *T* mutant at foregut and otocyst (*O*) level. Neural tube, *N*, is irregular at the ventral margin and its cells appear to mingle with cells in the notochordal location, (*arrow*). × 140. (Figs. 17–20: Light micrographs of transverse sections.)

tures remain sharply demarcated and separated from each other (Fig. 19) (Huber 1918; Jurand 1974). The neural tube is always outlined by a continuous, narrow basal lamina and the notochord, which consists of a compact group of cells, is likewise bound by a basal lamina. The two tissues are always separated by these interposed external laminae and their cells do not contact one another (Fig. 21),

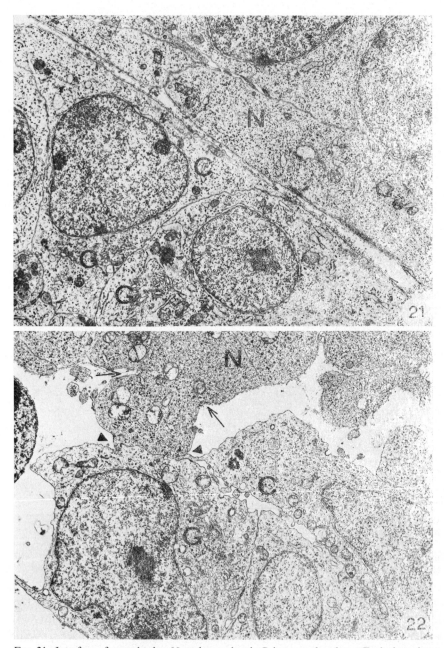

FIG. 21. Interface of neural tube, *N*, and notochord, *C*, in normal embryo. Each tissue has a compact epithelial construction and they are always separated from each other by a small space and a narrow basal lamina (*arrows*) on the surface of each. Notochordal cells typically have a conspicuous Golgi complex, *G*. × 10 000.

On the other hand, in the mutant at these stages the neural tube is ragged in outline at several body levels and seems to be in contact with cells loosely arrayed in the notochord position (Fig. 20). The basal lamina of the neural tube is interrupted at the ventral margin and at several places the basal portions of neural cells protrude beyond the neural tube boundary into the mesodermal space (Figs. 22, 23). These neural cells, no longer enclosed in an external lamina, are frequently in contact with cells of the mesoderm or notochord; in such cases the plasma membranes of the two closely apposed cells of the two tissues are often no more than 20 nm apart, the same distance usually seen between cells *within* a tissue. It is even more remarkable that such cells sometimes form contact specializations resembling the junctions seen between cohering cells comprising a single tissue (Figs. 23, 24).

The tissue arrangement and fine structure of some of the cells associated with neuroepithelium suggest that they are notochordal in origin. As in the normal notochord, the cells follow one another's contours closely to compose an epithelium; moreover, the cells contain a prominent Golgi complex bordered by abundant vesicles, a picture typical of notochord but unlike mesoderm at this stage. Some of these cells have small amounts of basal lamina material clinging to their surfaces, which is also typical of notochord but not of individual mesodermal cells.

The unusual association of neuroepithelium and notochord suggests that both tissues may be incompletely differentiated and may retain or resume cell-surface contacts shared by their precursor cell populations. At earlier stages in the primitive streak, for example, neuroepithelium and presumptive chordamesoderm are mingled. Likewise, the prechordal plate is at first tightly wedged between the neural tube and endoderm and appears to be in contact with these tissues for a time (Jurand 1974). This view is in accord with the contention that contacts between neuroepithelium and notochord are too long maintained or are established anew and with the idea of abnormal notochordal 'stickiness' (Grüneberg 1958).

The fact that notochord cells disperse or become incorporated into other tissues may account for somite dissociation. It has been found in chick embryos that the notochord is not necessary initially for somite formation but that the caudad movement of Hensen's node is necessary; the *maintenance* of somites

---

←

FIG. 22. Interface of neural tube, *N*, and cells ventral to it, possibly notochordal cells, *C*, in the *T* mutant. Like normal notochord, the cells have an epithelial arrangement and a prominent Golgi complex, *G*. A basal lamina, however, is not conspicuous on the surface of this cell group. Basal lamina of the neural tube is interrupted at several places (*arrows*), and basal portions of cells protrude beyond the tissue boundary, forming close associations with the putative notochordal cells (*arrowheads*). × 10 000.

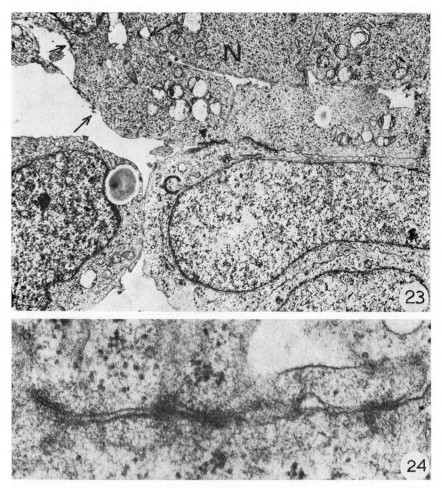

FIG. 23. Another view of unusually close association between cells of neural tube, *N*, and putative notochord, *C*, with neural cell extending far beyond neural tube boundary. Basal lamina shows a number of interruptions (*arrows*), and the boundary of the neural tube is quite ragged. Cellular junctions (*arrowhead*) are apparently present at contacts between neural cell and notochordal cell. × 8000.

FIG. 24. Higher magnification than Fig. 23 of extensive cellular junction between dissimilar cells, showing that the junction has typical structure with membrane thickenings, apposition as close as 5 nm, and densely fibrillar sub-surface cytoplasm. × 75 000.

depends, however, on some notochordal 'stabilizing factors', presumably cell coat or extracellular materials (Lipton & Jacobson 1974; Kosher & Lash 1975). Somites from anterior body levels of *T*/*T* embryos are incapable of chondro-genesis *in vitro* (Bennett 1958), perhaps because, without the presence of normal notochord in the mutant embryo, the somites could not achieve the proper level of competence to continue further differentiation.

Electron microscopic images reveal that the posterior chordamesoderm tubules have a structural organization similar to that of the neural tube; their cavities, however, do not become continuous. In both epithelia the apical cell surfaces are rounded with occasional villous projections (Figs. 25, 26). The apical–lateral margins of adjacent cells are joined by tight junctions and desmosomes; a web of filaments is situated in the sub-surface cytoplasm. Ciliary basal bodies are often seen at the apical surfaces of cells of both tissues. Rough endoplasmic reticulum and abundant polysomes are present in cells of both tubules. A Golgi complex is conspicuous and microtubules are oriented parallel to the long axis of the columnar cells. As in other epithelia at this time, a basal lamina encloses each of these tubular tissues.

These observations on T/T embryos suggest that a block arises *after* the transition of some, but not all, primitive streak cells into fully differentiated derivatives. Interruption of the morphogenetic activities of the primitive streak could account for the presence of the two distinct defects in axial structures seen in these mutants: disruption of notochord and somites in the anterior trunk, and accumulation of tubules of chordamesoderm in the posterior trunk.

After an early brief period in epithelial form, cells of normal somites become stellate and then reorganize into the final rosette pattern of definitive somites. It is likely that this reorganization will be halted, however, with primitive streak arrest, since further proliferation and differentiation of mesodermal cells as they continue to migrate from the primitive streak is necessary if this process is to occur. Likewise, without continued emergence of additional notochordal cells from the primitive streak, it is possible that the already-formed anterior notochord may revert to a prenotochordal state when associations with adjacent tissues are of normal occurrence.

At the same time, the later-developing chordamesoderm of the posterior trunk may not become fully competent to form normal notochord and somites. Cells remain trapped in the primitive streak; here they organize into tubular epithelia which resemble the neuroepithelium. Perhaps these incompletely determined chordamesoderm cells have assumed the most stable form attainable in these circumstances. Thus, *apparent* hyperplasia of neuroepithelium occurs at posterior levels of the mutant embryo. These abnormal tissues, however, are unable to differentiate further and they eventually degenerate.

Comparable but less drastic effects are seen in both tailless (T/t) and short-tailed ($T/+$) mouse embryos. Both lack a normal notochord in the tail rudiment and, at the most posterior part of the trunk, cells which may be notochordal in origin are attached to the neural tube or the gut. In the tail-bud of some short-

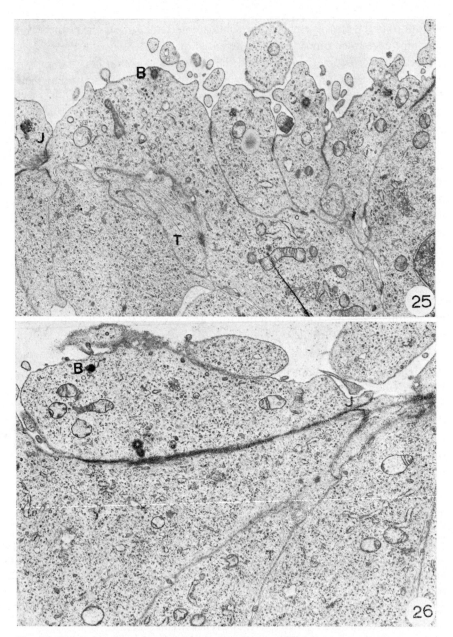

FIG. 25. Luminal surface of neural tube in *T* mutant. × 8000.

FIG. 26. Luminal surface of chordamesoderm tubule in *T* mutant. Although apparently developing from two different precursor populations and assembling in different ways, the two tissues appear very similar, that is, like neuroepithelium. In both, junctional complexes, *J*, occur at the apical–lateral margins of adjacent cells, ciliary basal bodies, *B*, are present,

tailed embryos, a tubular epithelium resembling that seen in the arrested chordamesoderm of T/T embryos has been designated as notochord. It appears that similar defects of the primitive streak are restricted to later stages and more posterior body levels in these genotypes as compared to T/T (Gluecksohn-Schoenheimer 1938; Grüneberg 1958).

It is interesting that the neural tube seems to undergo essentially normal morphogenesis throughout the mutant embryo during the period from the late 8th to early 9th days. Even though normal primitive streak derivatives are absent in T/T embryos, one essential activity, the induction of neural tube, persists.

SUMMARY AND CONCLUSIONS

Morphological observations on cell shape and cell contacts in both t^9 and T homozygous embryos are compatible with the view that mutant genes at the T locus alter cell-surface components so that normal morphogenetic movements and cellular interactions are impaired.

The lethal genes t^9 and T are an interesting pair, since it appears that t^9 defines the first differentiative hurdle in the determination of the neuroepithelium and mesoderm from the primitive streak and T defines a subsequent hurdle, the organization of axial structures from these same cells.

In both mutant embryos, incomplete determination of primitive streak derivatives seems to occur. Extensive translocation of mesodermal cells from the primitive streak is impeded and arrested mesodermal cells form unusually close associations with one another. Cells trapped in the primitive streak of the T mutant, however, are capable of constructing a tissue, although it is atypical; defective mesoderm of the t^9 mutant does not form any stable tissue. This difference may mean that mesoderm of the t^9 homozygote is 'less differentiated'.

The morphological abnormalities of both mutants may result from derangements in cell-surface antigens such as have already been recognized on sperm cells carrying T locus genes. A search for antigenic products of T locus genes on embryonic cells is under way in our laboratory. In normal embryos one might expect antigens determined by the $+t^9$ gene to appear on presumptive mesodermal cells in embryos at the primitive streak stage, and to decline during axial organization as products of the $+^T$ gene appear on cells of the neural tube, notochord and somites. The implication is that gene products, determined by $+t^9$ and $+^T$, are sequentially expressed on the surface of these cells as they

---

←

microtubules, T, are oriented parallel to the long axis of the columnar cells, and polysomes and rough endoplasmic reticulum occupy most of the cell. × 8000.

differentiate. Likewise, the same cellular specificities and sequence would be predicted for products of the corresponding mutant genes in the appropriate homozygous embryos.

It is intriguing to speculate that the gene products on normal embryonic cells may be surface carbohydrates or complementary glycosyltransferases such as those demonstrated in cell–cell interactions in chick embryos during early morphogenetic events before the appearance of more specific differentiation products (such as chondroitin sulphate, myosin and so on) (Roth 1973).

In the normal mouse embryo the *T* locus may control a battery of cell-surface modifications which permits early tissue segregation and morphogenesis. Definitive cellular and tissue differentiation may be initiated by sequential expression on cell surfaces of molecules that control cell–cell recognition and response.

ACKNOWLEDGEMENTS

I am grateful to Mrs Joyce Dieckmann for expert technical assistance and to Professor Dorothea Bennett for critically reading the manuscript. This work was supported by National Science Foundation (USA) grant GB 33804X.

References

ABERCROMBIE, M., HEAYSMANN, J. E. M. & PEGRUM, S. M. (1971) The locomotion of fibroblasts in culture, IV. Electron microscopy of the leading lamella. *Exp. Cell Res. 67*, 359–367

ALLISON, A. C. (1973) in *Locomotion of Tissue Cells (Ciba Found. Symp. 14)*, pp. 109–148, Associated Scientific Publishers, Amsterdam

ARTZT, K. & BENNETT, D. (1972) A genetically caused embryonal ectodermal tumor in the mouse. *J. Natl. Cancer Inst. 48*, 141–158

ARTZT, K., BENNETT, D. & JACOB, F. (1974) Primitive teratocarcinoma cells express a differentiation antigen specified by a gene at the *T*-locus in the mouse. *Proc. Natl. Acad. Sci. USA 71*, 811–814

BEHNKE, O., KRISTENSEN, B. I. & NIELSEN, L. E. (1971) Electron microscopical observations on actinoid and myosinoid filaments in blood platelets. *J. Ultrastruct. Res. 37*, 351–369

BENNETT, D. (1958) *In vitro* study of cartilage induction in *T/T* mice. *Nature (Lond.), 181*, 1286

BENNETT, D. (1975) The *T*-locus in the mouse: a review. *Cell 6*, 441–454

BENNETT, D. & DUNN, L. C. (1960) A lethal mutant (t^{w18}) in the house mouse showing partial duplications. *J. Exp. Zool. 143*, 203–219

BENNETT, D. & DUNN, L. C. (1971) Transmission ratio distorting genes on chromosome IX and their interactions, in *Proc. Symp. Immunogenetics of the H-2 System (Liblice-Prague, 1970)*, pp. 90–103, Karger, Basel

BENNETT, D., BOYSE, E. A. & OLD, L. J. (1972a) Cell surface immunogenetics in the study of morphogenesis, in *Cell Interactions* (Silvestri, L., ed.) *(Lepetit Coll. Biol. Med. 3)*, pp. 247–263, North-Holland, Amsterdam

BENNETT, D., GOLDBERG, E., DUNN, L. C. & BOYSE, E. A. (1972b) Serological detection of a cell-surface antigen specified by the *T* (Brachyury) mutant gene in the house mouse. *Proc. Natl. Acad. Sci. USA 69*, 2076–2080

CHESLEY, P. (1935) Development of the short-tailed mutant in the house mouse. *J. Exp. Zool. 70*, 429–459

DOBROVOLSKAIA-ZAVADSKAIA, N. (1927) Sur la mortification spontanée de la queue chez le souris nouveau-née et sur l'existence d'un charactère (facteur) héréditaire 'non viable'. *C.R. Séances Soc. Biol. Fil. 97*, 114–116

DOOHER, G.B. & BENNETT, D. (1974) Abnormal microtubular systems in mouse spermatids associated with a mutant gene at the *T*-locus. *J. Embryol. Exp. Morphol. 32*, 749–761

DUNN, L.C. & BENNETT, D. (1964) Abnormalities associated with a chromosome region in the mouse. *Science (Wash. D.C.) 144*, 260–267

DURHAM, A.C.H. (1974) A unified theory of the control of actin and myosin in nonmuscle movements. *Cell 2*, 123–136

EDE, D.A., BELLAIRS, R. & BANCROFT, M. (1974) A scanning electron microscope study of the early limb-bud in normal and talpid[3] mutant chick embryo. *J. Embryol. Exp. Morphol. 31*, 761–785

GLUECKSOHN-SCHOENHEIMER, S. (1938) The development of two tailless mutants in the house mouse. *Genetics, 23*, 573–584

GLUECKSOHN-SCHOENHEIMER, S. (1944) The development of normal and homozygous Brachy (*T/T*) mouse embryos in the extraembryonic coelom of the chick. *Proc. Natl. Acad. Sci. USA 30*, 134–140

GLUECKSOHN-WAELSCH, S. & ERICKSON, R.P. (1970) The *T*-locus of the mouse: Implications for mechanisms of development. *Curr. Top. Dev. Biol. 5*, 281–316

GOLDMAN, R.D., BERG, G., BUSHNELL, A., CHANG, C.-M., DICKERMAN, L., HOPKINS, N., MILLER, M.L., POLLACK, R. & WANG, E. (1973) in *Locomotion of Tissue Cells (Ciba Found. Symp. 14)*, pp. 83–107, Associated Scientific Publishers, Amsterdam

GROBSTEIN, C. (1967) Mechanism of organogenetic tissue interaction. *Natl. Cancer Inst. Monogr. 26*, 279–299

GRÜNEBERG, H. (1958) Genetical studies on the skeleton of the mouse. XXIII. The development of Brachyury and Anury. *J. Embryol. Exp. Morphol. 6*, 424–443

GUSTAFSON, T. & WOLPERT, L. (1967) Cellular movement and contact in sea urchin morphogenesis. *Biol. Rev. 42*, 442–498

HEAYSMAN, J.E.M. (1973) in *Locomotion of Tissue Cells (Ciba Found. Symp. 14)*, pp. 185–194, Associated Scientific Publishers, Amsterdam

HUBER, G.C. (1918) On the anlage and morphogenesis of the chorda dorsalis in Mammalia, in particular in the guinea pig *(Cavia cobaya) Anat. Rec. 14*, 217–264

INGRAM, V.M. (1969) A side view of moving fibroblasts. *Nature (Lond.) 222*, 641–644

JOHNSON, K.E. (1972) The extent of cell contact and the relative frequency of small and large gaps between presumptive mesodermal cells in normal gastrulae of *Rana pipiens* and the arrested gastrulae of the *Rana pipiens* ♀ × *Rana catesbiana* ♂ hybrid. *J. Exp. Zool. 179*, 227–238

JURAND, A. (1974) Some aspects of the development of the notochord in mouse embryos. *J. Embryol. Exp. Morphol. 32*, 1–33

KOSHER, R.A. & LASH, J.W. (1975) Notochordal stimulation of *in vitro* somite chondrogenesis before and after enzymatic removal of perinotochordal materials. *Dev. Biol. 42*, 362–378

LIPTON, B.H. & JACOBSON, A.G. (1974) Experimental analysis of the mechanisms of somite morphogenesis. *Dev. Biol. 38*, 91–103

LUDUEÑA, M.A. & WESSELLS, N.K. (1973) Cell locomotion, nerve elongation, and microfilaments. *Dev. Biol. 30*, 427–440

MOSCONA, A.A. (1973) in *Cell Biology in Medicine* (Bittar, E.E., ed.), pp. 571–591, Wiley, New York

MOSER, G. & GLUECKSOHN-WAELSCH, S. (1967) Developmental genetics of a recessive allele at the complex *T*-locus in the mouse. *Dev. Biol. 16*, 564–576

ROTH, S. (1973) A molecular model for cell interactions. *Q. Rev. Biol. 48*, 541–563

SNELL, G.D. & STEVENS, L.C. (1966) in *Biology of the Laboratory Mouse* (Green, E.L., ed.), 2nd edn., pp. 205–245. McGraw-Hill, New York

SPIEGELMAN, M. & BENNETT, D. (1974) Fine structural study of cell migration in the early mesoderm of normal and mutant mouse embryos (T-locus: t^9/t^9). *J. Embryol. Exp. Morphol. 32*, 723–738

SPOONER, B. S., YAMADA, K. M. & WESSELLS, N. K. (1971) Microfilaments and cell locomotion. *J. Cell Biol. 49*, 595–613

SPOONER, B. S., ASH, J. F., WRENN, J. T., FRATER, R. B. & WESSELS, N. K. (1973) Heavy meromysin binding to microfilaments involved in cell and morphogenetic movements. *Tissue Cell 5*, 37–46

STAEHELIN, L. A. (1974) Structure and function of intercellular junctions. *Int. Rev. Cytol. 39*, 191–283

THEILER, K. (1972) *The House Mouse*, Springer-Verlag, New York

TOWNES, P. L. & HOLTFRETER, J. (1955) Directed movements and selective adhesion of embryonic amphibian cells. *J. Exp. Zool. 128*, 53–120

TRELSTAD, R. L., HAY, E. D. & REVEL, J. P. (1967) Cell contact during early morphogenesis in the chick embryo. *Dev. Biol. 16*, 78–106

VAN VALEN, P. (1966) *A Genetical and Embryological Comparison of Two Similar Lethal Alleles at the T-Locus in the House Mouse*, Ph.D. dissertation, Columbia University, New York

WEISS, P. (1946) The problem of specificity in growth and development. *Yale J. Biol. Med. 19*, 235–278

YANAGISAWA, K., BENNETT, D., BOYSE, E. A., DUNN, L. C. & DIMEO, A. (1974) Serological identification of sperm antigens specified by lethal t-alleles in the mouse. *Immunogenetics 1*, 57–67

Discussion

Škreb: In the normal embryo mesodermal cells migrate from the ectoderm. Is there any difference between normal and t^9 ectoderm?

Spiegelman: We haven't looked at this stage yet. The earliest that we have been able to detect a homozygote class of embryo when we are dissecting embryos from the uterus is early on the 8th day, when the mesoderm has already formed in normal littermates. We could perhaps look for that difference by examining sections of the whole litter of embryos at 7 days. There are a number of good experiments that can be done. These genes have pronounced effects on sperm as well and they produce specific cell components on the surface of sperm cells. This is true for sperm but for no other kind of adult cell. The mutant embryos are arrested at specific times during development; specific groups of cells are affected in each case, and each case is different. It is therefore postulated that the same kind of specific cell-surface components could be present on affected cells of these mutants. That test on t^9 or on T homozygotes has not been done. Olivier Bernard in our laboratory is trying to find methods with which some sort of cell-surface difference could be detected serologically on the affected cells before the morphologically obvious defect is seen.

Bennett: We have antisera against t^9, against T, and against several other antigens produced on sperm. We have not been able to get a method for detecting these antigens on tissue sections of embryos. This appears to be a technical difficulty associated with the use of mouse anti-mouse alloantisera. For example, even with potent anti-H-2 antiserum, we have not been able to demonstrate that H-2 was present on tissue sections of 11-day mouse embryos. Until we can do that, we are in no position to look for these *T*-locus antigens in serological systems that are much weaker than H-2.

McLaren: It will be very exciting when you can.

Saxén: You showed abnormal homotypic relations between the mesenchymal cells of the t^9 embryos. Wouldn't this also affect heterotypic cell relations between ectoderm and mesoderm?

Spiegelman: I have no pictures of that. In the primitive streak, where there is no clear demarcation between presumptive ectoderm and presumptive mesoderm, the picture is not the same as in the more anterior locations where we are looking at mesoderm–ectoderm relationships. If we look at that posterior zone randomly, we would assume that some of the cells are presumptive ectoderm, such as neuroepithelium and some presumptive mesoderm. But at that point we can't identify them and they are not demarcated by the presence of a basal lamina.

Gluecksohn-Waelsch: When we studied t^9 homozygotes some years ago (Moser & Gluecksohn-Waelsch 1967) we obtained clear evidence that the balance between ectoderm and mesoderm was disturbed. We compared the whole normal embryo with the t^9 homozygote at around 8 days. In the t^9 homozygote two-thirds of the embryo is taken up by the head-folds, and the

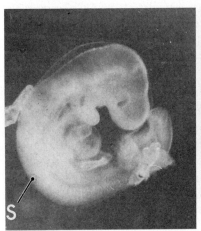
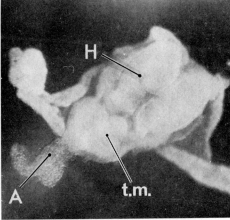

FIG. 1. (Gluecksohn-Waelsch). *Left:* Side view of normal 9-day-old embryo. S: somites. × 12. *Right:* Dorsal view of homozygous mutant 9-day-old embryo. Note irregular overgrown head-folds (H), lack of somites, and unattached duplicated allantois (A); t.m., trunk mesoderm. × 22 (From Moser & Gluecksohn-Waelsch 1967).

trunk mesoderm is totally undifferentiated (Fig. 1). We concluded at the time that the mutation caused failure of normal regulation of the pattern of ecto-dermal and mesodermal differentiation. We never looked at the ultrastructure of these embryos. If your t^9 allele is still the same recessive t allele as ours, the ultrastructural abnormalities that you showed might be responsible for the ab-normal balance between ectoderm and mesoderm, and for the excess of dif-ferentiation of ectodermal neural structures in the mutant homozygotes, at the expense of mesodermal structures which totally fail to differentiate.

Spiegelman: Do you think some of the mesenchyme in the head region might originate from neural crest?

Gluecksohn-Waelsch: Quite possibly, because it was specifically trunk meso-derm that we found to be deficient in the t^9 homozygote. As to T homozygous embryos, we were able to identify these earlier than had been possible before, by the appearance of the posterior embryonic region: the allantois is short and tuberous rather than being expanded as in the normal embryo.

Spiegelman: The posterior trunk never really forms. It is very abnormal in T/T.

Gurdon: Do you think that these defects arise because the primary genetic defect affects the surface component? People studying amphibians know that specific tissue derangements can be seen in early development, and a tissue will appear quite abnormal for totally unspecific reasons. For example, if genes are made to operate abnormally at certain stages of development, the endoderm typically will become abnormal. The cells lose their associations with each other and this can often be described as a characteristic defect. Would you resist the suggestion that genes are in some general way made to be abnormal here and that these surface derangements are entirely a secondary consequence of that? Or do you prefer the idea that the surface abnormalities are in some way pri-mary defects?

Spiegelman: My prejudice is that the surface defect is the primary defect and the other abnormalities are secondary. We are thinking along those lines because there may be specific cell surface components detectable as on the surface of sperm cells. There are several abnormalities in each of these embryos but, at least in some of them, only one group of cells is affected initially.

Gurdon: Yes, I understand that argument, and also that you can't test this directly. If you created a lot of minor chromosome abnormalities would you never get aberrations of that type? That is, is it possible somehow to collect minor chromosomal deletions and so on, and then simply see whether you could get defects of that general nature, for these obviously unspecific reasons?

Spiegelman: One could do that, but the question one wants to ask is, what is happening in this particular case?

Snow: It might be worth looking a little deeper into the cell than the cell membrane. It is fairly well established, in a whole range of cell types during the normal process of division, that at the end of G_2 just before mitosis the cell cortex becomes extremely labile and the cell surface blisters. Normally this is a transitory condition, exactly like the blisters that you have shown on these cells, Dr Spiegelman, and like those that Dr Pedersen showed in his yellow mutants. In the 2-cell mouse egg at the transition between G_2 and prophase this blistering effect can be grossly enhanced if the eggs are treated with cytochalasin B. The general impression one gets is that the lability and transitory loss of organization of the cell cortex produces the blistering and an inability to retain cell shape and so on. What you described could be entirely due to the cell losing its ability to organize its cortical regions. So when the cell wants to put out a process in a specific direction and make a contact it just doesn't have the necessary rigidity.

Bennett: What do you mean by 'blister'?

Snow: The blunt protuberances which Dr Spiegelman seemed to be correlating with the rather more filamentous processes seen in the normal mesoderm. But those blunt protuberances might just be accidental, reflecting the fact that the cortical layers of the cell are not under control. This means that if the cell wants to move it doesn't have the control and rigidity it needs in its cortical layers if it is to progress in any particular direction. Its cell membrane and its contacts are telling it to do the normal thing but it cannot do it.

Spiegelman: I think that those filamentous structures in the sub-surface cytoplasm of normal cells are probably at least partly responsible for the rather rigid form or filiform appearance of these pseudopods in normal mesodermal cells. These structures are probably, at least part of the time, attached to the cell surface or cell membrane. Otherwise they wouldn't be involved in motility and in changes in cell shape. You may be thinking that only the filaments themselves and not necessarily the surface affect the cell shape.

Gropp: Blistering or formation of pseudopods is often seen, for instance under the influence of colchicine. Could the changes you observed therefore be induced by an exogenous agent of that kind, at the cellular level?

Spiegelman: Possibly, but I don't really know how to do that without harming the mother.

Pedersen: In time-lapse films that I have made of the division from one to two cells it seems that there is a gross distortion of the membrane for 15 minutes or so just after division and the egg surface is quite contorted. This apparent destabilization occurs to a lesser extent during later cleavage, perhaps because the blastomeres are getting smaller. I believe that this phenomenon is distinct from the formation of pseudopodia at the time of blastocyst attachment and trophoblast outgrowth, when the blunt protrusions of the A^y homozygote can be recognized. Perhaps these latter processes have something to do with attachment and migration of the trophoblast cells.

McLaren: The microvilli around the cleavage furrows are one site that has been suggested for formation of new surface membrane. Maybe there is a link there too.

Snow: The formation of surface processes seems to be inextricably linked with microfilaments and filamentous processes of various sorts in the cell cortex. The fineness of the point of the pseudopods you showed, Dr Spiegelman, may well be a function of some of those filaments. If they are disrupted in any way, or have to form up in smaller or larger units, perhaps there can only be a round-ended structure, not a point.

Spiegelman: That is one of the observations. The filaments are not there in the lobose pseudopods. In the t^9 the cellular defect may involve the microfilaments, or the attachment of the microfilaments to the cell surface, or both together.

Snow: Terms like pseudopods, lobopseudopods, filopods, etc. are to me inextricably associated with cell movement as a result of their use in reference to protozoans. They are used in describing locomotion in many cell types. I feel that they should be confined to that use and not employed to describe morphologically similar but peculiar and maybe unintentional processes put out of cells under duress. If the 'blisters' put out by t^9 mesoderm cells are shown to be associated with locomotion then by all means they could certainly be re-named 'pseudopods', but perhaps we should wait until that association is established.

Gardner: Are there any indications in these mutants of the abnormalities in lipid metabolism and aerobic metabolism that Nina Hillman (1975) found in t^{w32}, t^{12} and t^6.

Spiegelman: I haven't noticed it in t^9 mutants but in the T mutant I have seen what I would call excess lipid droplets or inclusions in cells in the mesoderm.

Gardner: Would it not be possible to turn the story round and say that if there was an abnormality in synthesis of membrane lipid, the antigen that you find might be due to exposure of different determinants on a protein or other membrane-bound macromolecule that was structurally identical in both wild-type and mutant? In other words, the mutant may affect the conformation or distribution of a macromolecule rather than alter its primary structure.

Spiegelman: I think that is possible.

Glucksohn-Waelsch: The lipid droplets Dr Hillman and others saw in these mutants may actually be secondary and the result of cell degeneration or degradation of metabolic products.

Bennett: The difficulty is that Dr Hillman finds them as early as the 2-cell stage in mutants homozygous for genes like t^{w32} and t^{12}.

Spiegelman: The excess lipid cannot be due to *in vitro* conditions alone because then the normal cells, also cultured, should show similar inclusions.

Kelley: There seemed to be many more polyribosomes in some t^9/t^9 cells than in others.

Spiegelman: I think that is simply because polyribosomes are restricted from that part of the cell, a pseudopod, shown in the field.

Bennett: Dr Gardner's comment is perfectly reasonable, but one thing that argues against it is that on sperm we can detect a number of different specificities associated with each individual *t* mutation. These lethal *t* alleles frequently mutate to other forms. Sometimes they mutate to forms which as far as we can see are completely normal with respect to sperm function, embryonic development and so on, except that they continue to interact with the dominant gene to give a tailless phenotype, which defines them as *t* alleles. When a lethal *t* allele mutates to that kind of viable *t* variant, the variant maintains at least some of the abnormal specificities that were associated with the lethal *t* allele. Since the sperm, for example, don't seem to have any gross abnormalities of any kind, it is unlikely that the additional antigens or inappropriate antigens revealed by the cell result from abnormal membrane.

Edidin: Couldn't one say that the mutation to normal phenotype partly restores normal membrane metabolism? The key thing is that some of the abnormal specificities are still present. The antisera are made against the abnormal mutant sperm and presumably all these antigens are exposed. The altered phenotype of back mutation might still have some specificities available for antibody, although the revertant might not be as fully antigenic or immunogenic as the original mutant.

Cooke: In this series of genes there is obviously a degree of paralysis of whatever part of the cell's apparatus is used in normal contact and migration behaviour. This can set in at various times and thus, because of the sequential nature of the morphogenetic movements, can affect various levels in the whole head-to-tail pattern of differentiation. Development is brought to a stop in the same way, but at different times.

In amphibian embryos we have been looking at the parts of morphogenesis equivalent to those that go wrong here. We can measure the numbers of cells that get involved by a given time in the new behaviour that generates notochord and somites, as the wavefront of morphogenesis of these structures passes sequentially down the body pattern from front to back. There is an intrinsic graded difference whereby the rate of recruitment of the cells into these new activities slows down systematically, going down the future body pattern from head to tail. The numbers of cells involved, plotted against time in development, form a curve that falls off to zero as the animal finishes forming its body. There must therefore be some intrinsic, quantitative variation in a property of the cells, according to position in the body pattern. If each of the present series of genes or pseudoalleles is paralysing the cells in the same way but to a different degree, their effects would be expected, roughly as is observed, to halt the activity of morphogenesis at different parts of the pattern.

Dr Spiegelman spoke of this genetic locus as if it were hypermutable, but is that so in a molecular way?

Gluecksohn-Waelsch: The mode of origin of new *t* alleles is unequal crossing over.

Cooke: So quite a considerable length of chromosome, in genetic terms, is involved?

Spiegelman: Rather than just one gene, the *T* locus is probably a string of genes.

References

HILLMAN, N. (1975) Studies of the t-locus, in *The Early Development of Mammals (2nd Symp. Br. Soc. Dev. Biol.)* (Balls, M. & Wild, A.E., eds.), pp. 189–206, Cambridge University Press, London

MOSER, G.C. & GLUECKSOHN-WAELSCH, S. (1967) Developmental genetics of a recessive allele at the complex T-locus in the mouse. *Dev. Biol. 16*, 564–576

General discussion II

CULTURE SYSTEM FOR EMBRYOS

Hensleigh: To define an optimum culture system based on the initial work of Hsu (1971, 1972), we compared the growth and development of mouse blastocysts in several different culture media and sera (McLaren & Hensleigh 1975). In our hands, minimum essential medium (Eagle's salts) with 10 to 20% fetal calf serum gave the highest degree of development of the inner cell mass. The extent of development of the inner cell mass varied with different batches of fetal calf serum. The inner cell mass showed more extensive development in fetal calf serum than in adult bovine serum and in fetal mouse serum than in adult mouse serum. The use of reconstituted rat tail collagen as a substrate for attachment was not necessary with fetal calf serum. In this series of cultures using fetal calf serum, about 45% of the blastocysts attached to the culture dish with outgrowth of the trophoblast cells and development of the inner cell mass cells; in 18% of these outgrowths the inner cell mass closely resembles the early egg-cylinder stage. Solter *et al.* (1974) observe little difference ultra-structurally between such *in vitro* egg cylinders and *in vivo* egg cylinders. Virtually all the *in vitro* egg cylinders develop fluid-filled cavities after 120 h in culture, and over longer periods one cavity continues to enlarge. Histologically, these vesicles resemble visceral yolk sac with large vesiculated endoderm-like cells on the exterior surface and mesothelial-like cells lining the interior surface.

I am now studying the synthesis of extra-embryonic fluid and fetal plasma proteins by these yolk sac vesicles. In both amniotic fluid and fetal plasma there are three main groups of proteins: three transferrins (Tr 1 to 3), five α-feto-proteins (1 to 5), and albumin. Tr 1, 2 and 3 and α-fetoproteins 4 and 5 have been shown to be of fetal origin and not of maternal origin (Gustine & Zimmerman 1972; Renfree & McLaren 1974). Fluid was collected from yolk sac vesicles after 12 days in culture from the blastocyst stage and electrophoresis was done on 7% polyacrylamide gels. The fluid contains Tr 1 and α-fetoproteins 1, 2 and 3; the electrophoretic mobility of these proteins was the same as in samples of amniotic fluid and fetal plasma collected on the 13th day of pregnancy, whereas samples of the culture medium containing human cord serum had no bands of similar electrophoretic mobility. These findings provide evidence for the fetal origin of these proteins and suggest that the early site of synthesis is the visceral yolk sac. Interestingly, the vesicle fluid did not contain human cord serum proteins from the culture medium in detectable amounts and the fluid did not contain murine albumin. I plan to examine fluid from yolk sac vesicles at later stages to see if they are also capable of synthesizing Tr 2 and 3 and α-fetoproteins 4 and 5.

McLaren: Dr Pedersen, you mentioned that some of your embryos developed to beating-heart stage. Do you get differentiation of haemoglobin?

Pedersen: I believe so; we can definitely see that the blood islands are red.

McLaren: Hsu commented that he had to put a supplementary source of iron into the medium before he got visible haemoglobin. Do you do that?

Pedersen: We did not initially add iron, but the human cord serum samples frequently contain a small amount of haemolysed blood that may be a source of iron. To evaluate the iron requirement one would need an iron-free serum source.

Škreb: Are these vesicles floating or sticking to the dish?

Hensleigh: Some of them remain attached to the culture dish. Others detach and become free-floating.

Škreb: Once they detach, you are never going to get differentiation into embryonic structures.

Hensleigh: Many of the embryos developing into egg cylinders tend to round up as the fluid-filled cavities form and detach from the culture dish.

Graham: How do you draw that conclusion about the synthesis of α-fetoprotein? α-Fetoprotein often tends to stick to cells. It is possible that the yolk sac could accumulate these molecules from the culture medium. Did you use some method to distinguish the putative transferrin 1 and α-fetoproteins 1, 2 and 3 of mouse from those of human cord serum?

Hensleigh: To avoid cellular contamination we took samples from inside the vesicles with a micropipette and centrifuged the samples. The murine transferrin 1 and α-fetoproteins can easily be distinguished from the proteins present in human cord serum by their different electrophoretic mobility.

Pedersen: We also frequently observe hollow vesicles when we maintain cultures beyond the fifth post-blastocyst day. Even when we add 20% human cord serum most of the surviving growing embryos are these vesicle types.

Only a small number, perhaps 5%, seem to maintain structures other than the extra-embryonic portion. Earlier (pp. 32–33) we heard that the primary ectoderm may give rise to all of the embryonic shield structures. The specific problem of *in vitro* culture, then, is how to stimulate the primary ectoderm to grow, or to keep it alive. Sometimes in our cultures, about the seventh post-blastocyst day, there is a small amount of necrosis in the ectoderm of the portion of the elongated egg cylinder that is distal from the trophoblast. Something seems to be deficient or deleterious in the culture environment so that it is inadequate for maintaining the development of that primary ectoderm.

Gluecksohn-Waelsch: Has anyone tried to use hormones in the medium?

Hensleigh: It has been suggested that differences between different batches of fetal calf sera or between fetal and adult serum could be due to different levels of steroid hormones. However, Salomon & Sherman (1975) have found no difference in embryonic development in fetal calf serum after removal of steroids with dextran-coated Norit.

McLaren: In these cultures there seems to be an inverse relationship between inner cell mass and trophoblast development. Do different environmental factors favour one versus the other, or is there any direct antagonism? One gets the same impression of an inverse relationship in the growths that develop from blastocysts transferred to ectopic sites.

Gardner: Could the inverse relationship be more apparent than real, in the sense that in ectopic sites when people talk about extensive trophoblast growth what may well be happening is an enlargement of cells by endoreduplication, without any further proliferation? So when trophoblast is not very prominent it is nevertheless proliferating more and developing more normally than when there appears to be a vast outgrowth in an ectopic site or *in vitro*. Only by counting numbers of giant cells and/or apparently diploid cells will one be able to see whether this is an illusion or not.

Snow: One can certainly be horribly confused by the enormous size of some of these cells. But *in vivo*, although the measurements haven't actually been done, it seems clear that between implantation at $4\frac{1}{2}$ days and 6 days the tissue that proliferates fastest is the extra-embryonic ectoderm and the developing ectoplacental cone. It is only later that the embryonic derivatives, the inner cell mass derivatives, really take over and start to proliferate much more rapidly than the trophectoderm derivatives. So the conditions which favour these two types of growth may well be different. *In vitro* there may be a situation which will favour inner cell mass growth but won't favour trophoblast. This is what one appears to see. It would be worth doing outgrowths first in a culture condition which favours trophoblast proliferation, which is what happens *in vivo*, and then, once one has managed to get the embryo away from whatever it is that is holding it back, switch to the other culture medium favouring growth of the inner cell mass.

Rutter: Research in this area would benefit from specific markers for each of the cell types. Has anyone used the two-dimensional isoelectric focusing SDS gel system of O'Farrell (1975), which resolves a great many proteins and has great sensitivity, to attempt to find membrane components? It might then be possible to follow the relative enrichment of one cell type versus another quantitatively.

Gardner: I think markers are beginning to emerge. Mike Sherman finds that progesterone synthesis is a property of giant trophoblast cells. The only complication is that it is quite stage-specific. In other words the cells have to be in culture for a certain time before they produce much of it (Sherman 1975). That seems to be a feature of giant cells and it is beginning to look as if α-feto-protein is an endodermal gene product. One can't say this definitely at the moment because there is mesoderm in the visceral yolk sac. I agree that we need more markers.

GENE MUTATIONS IN EARLY MAMMALIAN DEVELOPMENT

McLaren: Another question that we should consider is the type of gene mutation acting at this early stage.

Gurdon: In thinking of the gene mutants which affect early mammalian development, I have always found it useful to distinguish the cell-type-specific gene effects from gene effects seen in all cell types. Similarly it is useful to distinguish postzygotically acting genes from prezygotically acting ones. Genes in the latter category are commonly referred to as maternal effect mutants. Maternal effect mutants have been found extensively in certain amphibian species and in *Drosophila*, species in which gene activity is not thought to take place immediately after fertilization. Maternal effect gene mutants are particularly likely to be found in such circumstances. Since the mammalian genome appears to be active very soon or immediately after fertilization, one might predict that nothing has been found, or will be found, which falls into the category of a prezygotic or maternal effect mutant. Is it true that, within that category, no one so far has found a maternal effect cell-type-specific gene mutation, which would be the most interesting kind?

Within the category of postzygotic or postfertilization egg-acting mutants, which mutants are thought most likely to be cell-type-specific, in that their expression occurs in some types of early cells and not in others? For example, I think Dr Chapman's mutant (p. 117) would clearly be a non-cell-type-specific gene. I don't know how the agouti yellow would fit in there. I would welcome some general agreement about these gene effects in early development.

McLaren: Does a 'maternal-effect mutant' imply a maternal effect mediated through the cytoplasm? The complication in mammals is that maternal effects may often be mediated through the uterus later in gestation.

Gurdon: These mutants have usually been found in mothers homozygous in respect of the mutation, so that irrespective of what male fertilizes her eggs, the effect is still shown. That is the clearest test of such a mutant.

McLaren: As far as I know, the only convincing example of a cytoplasmic effect in mammals is that described by Wakasugi (1973, 1974). It involves a strain difference, but the breeding results suggest that the effect is due to a single gene. When females of the DDK inbred mouse strain are mated to males of another strain, not DDK, most of the embryos die at around the time of implantation. The effect is still seen when DDK ovaries are transplanted to females of another strain, which implicates the cytoplasm of the egg rather than the environment of the reproductive tract. It does not appear to be cell-type-specific.

Glueksohn-Waelsch: I would like to cite an example here of a maternal effect where the genotype of the mother prevents embryonic development of any zygotes beyond midgestation, independent of the embryo's own genotype. Such mothers are complementers for two different radiation-induced lethal albino alleles. It is not known at what stage the maternal effect is expressed: the eggs of such mothers may be defective from the beginning, although hormonal or later maternal influences are not excluded (S. Lewis, unpublished observations).

Gurdon: Does the genotype of the father affect the development of the eggs?

Glueksohn-Waelsch: This particular effect is independent of the father.

Bennett: Another gene with some form of maternal effect is a dominant gene at the *T*-locus, known as hairpintail (T^{Hp}). Females heterozygous for this gene produce no viable offspring carrying the gene, whereas the same females can give birth to viable offspring carrying the T^{Hp} gene coming through sperm.

McLaren: But for all we know this may be a uterine effect?

Bennett: Presumably not, because the T^{Hp} heterozygous female seems incapable of carrying to term only eggs that carry her own T^{Hp} gene, whereas she can successfully carry eggs carrying paternally derived T^{Hp} genes. So you would have to propose some very special uterine effect with very fine discrimination.

The oocyte is effectively tetraploid until the first meiotic division is completed, which in mammals only occurs just before ovulation. This means that all eggs from heterozygous females, for example, carry the same functioning genome until this time.

Gardner: I am not aware of a mutant gene that acts in specific types of cell in the early stages of development. The critical analysis has not been done.

There is a very dependent relationship between extra-embryonic and embryonic structures. Many of the mutants have been studied histologically or ultra-structurally but it is impossible by these means alone to say where the primary defect lies. For example defective development of the trophectoderm could well depend on some anomaly of the inner cell mass. Slightly later on in development embryonic ectoderm anomalies could be a consequence of failure of yolk sac transport or a failure of trophoblast giant cells to carry out an embryo-trophic role. Only by generating chimeric situations, and preferably chimeric situations where specific cell types go in, so that one can say with certainty that normal endoderm or normal embryonic ectoderm or normal trophectoderm have been put into the system, will it be possible to begin to define the primary site of action of such mutant genes.

Pedersen: Based on the gross morphology of A^y/A^y embryos during and after trophoblast outgrowth (Pedersen 1974), I am inclined to believe that this is a cell lethal. Dr Gardner's experiments on transfer of the homozygous yellow inner cell mass suggest, however, that it may be an embryonic lethal, and I think it has to be studied further with a linked recessive marker before any surviving homozygous A^y cells can be decisively identified.

Gardner: As I mentioned earlier (p. 150), homozygous yellow lethal (A^y/A^y) embryos appear to form normal blastocysts in our inbred balanced lethal stock. We have transplanted inner cell masses isolated from blastocysts obtained from

TABLE 1 (Gardner)

Investigation of the developmental potential of homozygous yellow (A^y/A^y) inner cell mass and trophectoderm by transplanting inner cell masses between blastocysts* (V. E. Papaioannou & R. L. Gardner, unpublished work)

Derivation of blastocysts		Implantation rate		No. of decidua containing embryonic tissues		No. of normal embryos	
Inner cell mass donors	Host blastocysts	Overall	Pregnant recipients only	Chimeric	Total	Chimeric	Total
$A^y/a^e \times A^y/a^e$ CFLP		54/94	54/67	44	53	41	50
$a^e/a^e \times A^y/a^e$ CFLP		27/42	27/35	22	26	19	22
$A^y/a^e \times a^e/a^e$ CFLP		43/56	43/45	42	43	37	38
CFLP	$A^y/a^e \times A^y/a^e$	26/53	26/33	22	23	17	17
CFLP	$a^e/a^e \times A^y/a^e$	24/52	24/30	22	24	18	19

* Uterine fostermothers were of the same Gp^i-1 genotype as host blastocysts, and were killed at $10\frac{1}{2}$ days p.c.

matings between yellow heterozygotes into blastocysts of the random-bred CFLP strain, and vice versa. Reciprocal transfers of inner cell masses between CFLP blastocysts and those obtained from $A^y/a^e \times a^e/a^e$ and/or $a^e/a^e \times A^y/a^e$ matings served as controls. Host and donor embryos differ in $Gp^i - 1$ genotype in all combinations used, those of the CFLP strain being $Gp^i - 1^a/Gp^i - 1^a$ and those of the balanced lethal strain $Gp^i - 1^b/Gp^i - 1^b$.

The results we have obtained so far are summarized in Table 1. The proportions of chimeras found in the $(A^y/a^e \times A^y/a^e) \rightarrow$ CFLP experiments differ moderately significantly by χ^2 test from three-quarters of the proportion expected on the basis of the control data $(0.05 > P > 0.02)$. The results of the reciprocal experiments are more marginal $(0.1 > P > 0.05)$. Hence, although it is essential to obtain more data, available results suggest that yellow lethal inner mass and trophectoderm cells survive at least four days beyond their normal time of death in chimeric combination with normal embryonic tissues.

Snow: Isn't it possible that it is not a cell-specific effect? It is quite apparent that the trophoblast doesn't behave like normal trophoblast, so one could presume that those cells are abnormal. One can alternatively presume that the inner cell mass is abnormal but that in your chimeras you are getting metabolic cooperation between the inner cell mass and trophectoderm which is allowing the yellow trophectoderm to survive.

Gardner: But we don't know at the moment whether the survival is only in certain inner cell mass derivatives or whether it depends just on an appropriate distribution of cells.

Gluecksohn-Waelsch: Dr Gurdon, when you say cell-specific, do you restrict yourself to early stages where ectoderm differentiates into mesoderm, or do you mean any stage of cell differentiation, including that of organs which usually differentiate rather late?

Gurdon: The first category is the more interesting.

Gluecksohn-Waelsch: There exist definite examples of the second category.

Graham: What is the evidence against the view that most of the early-acting embryonic lethal genes in the mouse are cell lethals which happen to kill different cell types at various stages of embryogenesis? It would be possible to show that they were not cell lethals in three ways: they might be rescued in a chimera, they might be maintained as a teratocarcinoma, or they might be maintained in cell culture. Is there really any evidence which would convince a sceptic that these are not cell lethals?

Gluecksohn-Waelsch: I think such evidence exists for T homozygotes in the work of Ephrussi (1935) who explanted tissues from T lethal homozygotes and succeeded in keeping them alive *in vitro*. They grew and differentiated into all the structures that the embryo itself never forms because it fails to survive, lacking connection by umbilical vessels to the maternal placenta. Ephrussi concluded that the T mutation was not a cell lethal.

Graham: The kind of mutations I am thinking of are early-acting lethals, for instance those that cause death *in utero* by the 7th day of development.

Bennett: You are asking for evidence against a cell lethal?

Graham: Yes.

McLaren: Not too many genes are known to act before 7 days. I don't know of any published evidence for any of them not being cell lethals.

Bennett: Dr Spiegelman and I have studied another dominant T mutation that may be relevant here (Bennett *et al.* 1975). Of course it has not been subjected to Dr Gardner's criteria. The homozygous embryo forms an early egg cylinder with embryonic and extra-embryonic mesoderm, endoderm and yolk sac. Subsequently the embryonic ectoderm becomes pycnotic and dies. By doing mitotic counts, we were able to ascertain that for the next day or day and a half the proximal endoderm, distal endoderm and ectoplacental cone continue their division essentially normally in the absence of the embryonic ectoderm. We didn't follow it very closely after that, and the rest of the embryo dies. It looks like a very specific effect, on morphological grounds.

Graham: Some tissues certainly die before others in most of these mutants. When I say that I would like someone to show that it is not a cell lethal, I really mean that it should be grown for up to two months so that there is no possible carry-over effect.

Gurdon: If these cells divide, as I think you said they do, and if that goes on for a few divisions, then it is unreasonable for you to say that there was so much left that just those cells were keeping going on inherited molecules whereas the others weren't.

McLaren: The embryonic part of the egg cylinder is also affected by ploidy. Specifically there is the triploid syndrome described by Dr Tarkowski's colleague Wróblewska (1971), in which the extra-embryonic tissues develop, but little or no embryonic tissue is seen. In the tetraploids that you have studied, Dr Tarkowski, I believe that the extra-embryonic tissue was remarkably unaffected (unpublished work).

Tarkowski: Yes, only the embryonic part of the egg cylinder is affected. In some embryos there is no embryonic mesoderm at all, while in others formation of mesoderm is initiated but continues only on a small scale and for a short time.

McLaren: In a case like that, how long would the extra-embryonic membranes continue to be viable, and how long would cell division continue without the presence of the embryo?

Tarkowski: At least until the 10th day, but I don't know whether cell divisions continue after that.

Gluecksohn-Waelsch: In an embryo with the cell and tissue interactions characteristic of vertebrates, including mammals, one would not really expect to find restriction of mutant effects to one cell type. Whenever one cell type is abnormal, the interaction of different cell types would immediately affect further differentiation of the 'normal' cell type, even though it may not express the particular mutation itself.

Gurdon: Yes, but where it looks as though one cell type is affected much earlier or more than another, then I think it is appropriate to do the chimeric graft experiment to find out whether in fact only one cell type *is* affected. But there is little incentive to do that if every indication is that all cells are affected equally.

Gluecksohn-Waelsch: When the methods are available that should indeed be done. We are still suffering from a scarcity of experimental approaches. The production of chimeras, particularly with Dr Gardner's methods, should answer many of these questions which we cannot answer from descriptive studies.

Gardner: Perhaps it is not so much a shortage of techniques as of pairs of hands!

Pedersen: When does the OY embryo die?

McLaren: Morris (1968) claims that it dies at the first cleavage division, but the evidence is still very circumstantial.

DEVELOPMENT OF BILATERAL SYMMETRY

McLaren: On the question of the development of bilateral symmetry, one can distinguish two different but possibly related processes, one being axis formation, that is the transformation of radial to bilateral symmetry, and the other polarity, that is the appearance of the head and tail. They may be simultaneous—that is, they may be the same process—or alternatively axis formation may occur first and polarity subsequently. Remarkably little has been done on this. About 20 years ago Ancel & Reyss-Brion (1956) looked at the direction of the embryonic axis in the uterus and found that it was usually perpendicular to the uterine axis, or nearly so. The first obvious non-radial symmetry appears at the primitive streak stage. Does anyone who has looked at large numbers of embryos any earlier know when asymmetry develops?

Snow: Jean Smith (personal communication) has checked the orientation of the embryonic axis with respect to the uterine axis. She first looked at transverse sections of $7\frac{1}{2}$-day embryos to see where the presumptive head end lies and where the primitive streak is located. She confirmed what Dr McLaren has just said: the axis of the embryo is indeed essentially transverse to the uterus, within a fairly narrow tilting range. The primitive streak may be located at either end of this transverse axis.

Jean Smith then looked to see how early other forms of asymmetry can be seen in the implanting embryo. In longitudinal sections of $4\frac{1}{2}$- and 5-day embryos she has found that the actual attachment to the endometrium usually occurs on one side first. It is very seldom that the $5\frac{1}{2}$-day egg cylinder is attached uniformly. When she analysed embryos in transverse sections she found that the initial attachment, where polar trophectoderm proliferates and the ecto-placental cone begins to form, takes place eccentrically. The orientation of this attachment point bears a striking resemblance to the picture that she gets from the primitive streak stage. She has not yet looked at the top end of the embryo, at the ectoplacental cone, to see whether the asymmetry seen at $5\frac{1}{2}$ days has persisted, and whether there is more growth of ectoplacental cone on one side. It is possible that this attachment point, whichever side it occurs, could be positively correlated with one end or the other, or one side or the other.

Gardner: The problem with conventional histology when one is looking at blastocyst orientation, for example, is that penetration by conventional fixatives leads to distortion, separation, and possibly rotation of the embryo. Could that be happening in those preparations, so that the cells stick to one part?

McLaren: I am sure that is so, but of course the very fact that there is an artifact may reveal an underlying asymmetry which would not have been seen had it remained tightly closed. So this asymmetry may not be random.

Newth: Even if the correlation is 100%, you still don't know which is cause and which is effect, do you? Is it the head that is going in first, or does the part that goes in first become the head?

Snow: Nobody can argue about that, but at least it tells us that the signals occur somewhat earlier than previously imagined.

Tarkowski: The rat, like the mouse or any other species showing inversion of the germ layers, is not a very convenient species in which to study this problem. Could anyone tell us about the position of the embryonic axis in relation to the uterine axes in the rabbit embryo, which has a flat embryonic shield like that of the chick?

Gluecksohn-Waelsch: Brambell (1948) describes the implantation of rabbit blastocysts which are oriented in the uterine lumen with the embryonic shield towards the mesometrium.

Eguchi: Amphibian embryos are of course different from both mammalian and avian embryos, but I think they can provide some useful information which is also relevant to development in higher animals. In amphibian embryos bilateral symmetry of the head organs anterior to the eye is established rather late in development. The removal of prechordal mesoderm from the newt embryos of neural plate stage results in cyclopia. The cyclopean embryo has a single eye located where the mouth is in the normal embryo. The presumptive eye anlage is localized in the mid-anterior end of the neural plate; it is not separated bilaterally but is in a single area (field) in the neural plate. The removal of the underlying prechordal mesoderm suppresses the bilateral growth of the median part of the eye anlage and a single cyclopean eye is formed as a result of development of the eye field as a whole (Eguchi 1957; Sato & Eguchi 1960). This does not mean that two eye rudiments fuse but that the process of separation of the presumptive eye anlage fails and there is no bilateral growth. This interaction between the prechordal mesoderm and the eye anlage may perhaps be established within less than 15 minutes.

McLaren: This raises the whole question of the position of the primitive streak. At the symposium here 10 years ago Dr Tarkowski told us that in chimeric embryos two primitive streaks sometimes formed, which suggests that there may be an effect of tissue mass or cell number on the induction of the primitive streak. Have any more of these been observed since?

Tarkowski: What I said then was that very rarely in chimeric conceptuses are two egg cylinders formed (Tarkowski 1965). To my knowledge there is no evidence for two primitive streaks being formed in single chimeric egg cylinders.

McLaren: The armadillo normally has monozygotic quadruplets, with four primitive streaks forming on a single embryonic shield. With human monozygotic twinning, one has very little idea of the stage at which the twinning occurs.

Gardner: Was there any evidence that the orientation of primitive streaks was the same in both embryos in the single conceptus, Dr Tarkowski?

Tarkowski: I cannot answer that because those few cases of chimeric 'twins' which I have come across were examined either at the early egg-cylinder stage or at the beginning of the second half of pregnancy, after the embryos have already turned and when the position of the embryo has probably no relation to the original orientation of the primitive streak.

Gardner: When we injected a large series of inner cell masses into genetically dissimilar host blastocysts, about 5% of the resulting day 10 conceptuses contained twin embryos within a single trophoblastic shell (V.E. Papaioannou & R.L. Gardner, unpublished work). At this stage, it was unfortunately too late to check for orientation of the primitive streaks. If donor and host inner cell masses are deliberately kept apart, it should be possible to increase the frequency of twinning. The interesting point to establish would be whether the primitive streaks of such twins are always similarly oriented. Lack of cor-

Fig. 1 (Gluecksohn-Waelsch). Schematized outline drawings of abnormal and normal mouse embryo 7 days old (egg-cylinder stage). At the left abnormal *Ki/Ki* embryo with two embryonic axes (EI and EII). At the right, normal egg cylinder (E). (From Gluecksohn-Schoenheimer 1949.)

respondence would suggest that determination of bilateral symmetry is a property of the inner cell mass, and the reverse that it depends on the trophoblast or uterus.

Snow: In Edinburgh, with our random-bred Q strain mice we must have looked at hundreds of egg cylinders. In five years there I don't remember seeing two egg cylinders forming in a single deciduum. But since we began working in London a year ago I must have seen a dozen.

Gluecksohn-Waelsch: We have described a mutation in the mouse, near the *T* locus where in homozygotes two egg cylinders may form in one deciduum. This is the Kinky mutation, Fu^{Ki} (Gluecksohn-Schoenheimer 1949) (cf. Fig. 1).

References

ANCEL, P. & REYSS-BRION, M. (1956) Sur les relations entre le grand axe de l'utérus et le plan de symétrie bilatérale chez l'embryon de souris. *C.R. Hebd. Séances Acad. Sci. 243,* 932–935

BENNETT, D., DUNN, L.C., SPIEGELMAN, M., ARTZT, K., COOKINGHAM, J. & SCHERMERHORN, E. (1975) Observations on a set of radiation-induced dominant *T*-like mutations in the mouse. *Genet. Res. 26,* 95–108.

BRAMBELL, F.W.R. (1948) Prenatal mortality in mammals. *Biol. Rev. 23,* 370–407

EGUCHI, G. (1957) Formation of a single eye in cyclopean embryos of the newt, *Triturus pyrrhogaster. Zool. Mag. (Tokyo), 66,* 48 [in Japanese]

EPHRUSSI, B. (1935) The behavior *in vitro* of tissues from lethal embryos. *J. Exp. Zool. 70,* 197–204

GLUECKSOHN-SCHOENHEIMER, S. (1949) The effects of a lethal mutation responsible for duplications and twinning in mouse embryos. *J. Exp. Zool. 110,* 47–73

GUSTINE, D.L. & ZIMMERMAN, E.F. (1972) Amniotic fluid proteins: evidence for the presence of fetal plasma glycoproteins in mouse amniotic fluid. *Am. J. Obstet. Gynecol. 114,* 553–560

Hsu, Y. (1971) Post-blastocyst differentiation *in vitro. Nature (Lond.) 231*, 100–102

Hsu, Y. (1972) Differentiation *in vitro* of mouse embryos beyond the implantation stage. *Nature (Lond.) 239*, 200–202

McLaren, A. & Hensleigh, H.C. (1975) Culture of mammalian embryos over the implantation period, in *The Early Development of Mammals (2nd Symp. Br. Soc. Dev. Biol.)* (Balls, M. & Wild, A.E., eds.), pp. 45–60, Cambridge University Press, London

Morris, T. (1968) The XO and OY chromosome constitutions in the mouse. *Genet. Res. 12*, 125–137

O'Farrell, P. (1975) High resolution two-dimensional electrophoresis of proteins. *J. Biol. Chem. 250*, 4007

Pedersen, R.A. (1974) Development of lethal yellow (A^y/A^y) mouse embryos *in vitro. J. Exp. Zool. 188*, 307–319

Renfree, M. & McLaren, A. (1974) Fetal origin of transferrin in mouse amniotic fluid. *Nature (Lond.) 252*, 159–160

Sato, T. & Eguchi, G. (1960) Über Linsenregeneration bei Zyklopenlarven von *Triturus pyrrhogaster. Wilhelm Roux' Arch. Entwicklungsmech. Org. 152*, 373–397

Sherman, M.I. (1975) The role of cell-cell interaction during early mouse embryogenesis, in *The Early Development of Mammals (2nd Symp. Br. Soc. Dev. Biol.)* (Balls, M. & Wild, A.E., eds.), pp. 145–165, Cambridge University Press, London

Salomon, D. & Sherman, M. (1975) Implantation and invasiveness of mouse blastocysts on uterine monolayers. *Exp. Cell Res. 90*, 261–268

Solter, D., Biczysko, W., Pienkowski, M. & Koprowski, H. (1974) Ultrastructure of mouse egg cylinders developed *in vitro. Anat. Rec. 180*, 263–268

Tarkowski, A.K. (1965) Embryonic and postnatal development of mouse chimeras, in *Preimplantation Stages of Pregnancy (Ciba Found. Symp.)* pp. 183–193, Churchill, London

Wakasugi, N. (1973) Studies on fertility of DDK mice: Reciprocal crosses between DDK and C57BL/6J strains and experimental transplantation of the ovary. *J. Reprod. Fertil. 33*, 283–291

Wakasugi, N. (1974) A genetically determined incompatibility system between spermatozoa and eggs, leading to embryonic death in mice. *J. Reprod. Fertil. 41*, 85–96

Wróblewska, J. (1971) Developmental anomaly in the mouse associated with triploidy. *Cytogenetics (Basel) 10*, 199–207

'Transdifferentiation' of vertebrate cells in cell culture

GORO EGUCHI

Laboratory for Cell Differentiation and Morphogenesis, Institute of Biophysics, Faculty of Science, University of Kyoto

Abstract　Pigment epithelial cells of eyes of some avian and urodelan species transdifferentiated into lens cells after vigorous cell growth in prolonged cell culture. This type of 'transdifferentiation' or 'foreign' differentiation has been confirmed in the pigment epithelium of the iris and retina of adult newts and 8–9-day-old chick and quail embryos. A refined technique of clonal cell culture proved that the transdifferentiation occurred after a long lag of more than 120 days in chick pigment cells and after a rather short lag period of 30 days in newt pigment epithelial cells. Several factors affecting transdifferentiation are discussed with particular reference to cell growth and to lens regeneration *in situ* in amphibians.

The regeneration of certain eye tissues has long been studied as an exceptionally clear example of metaplasia, in which previously specialized tissues change into other types. The lens is differentiated from the 'foreign' tissue, the iris epithelium, after lentectomy in urodelan amphibians, in a few species of teleost, and also in very early chick embryos (for review see Scheib 1965). After removal of the neural retina, the retinal pigment epithelium changes to the neural retina in amphibians (for review see Reyer 1962) and early chick embryos (Coulombre & Coulombre 1965). This tissue can also differentiate into lens in certain experimental conditions (Sato 1951; Lopashov & Sologub 1972). However, all these studies were of *in situ* experimental systems or *in vitro* organ or tissue culture systems. Cell culture analyses under well-controlled conditions starting from dissociated cells should lead to a much deeper understanding of the mechanisms at cellular level.

　Recently, it has become possible to observe pigment epithelial cells changing into lens cells in cultures of cells from the adult newt (Eguchi *et al.* 1974) and from avian embryos at late stages in development when they are unable to regenerate lens *in situ* (Eguchi & Okada 1973). The term *'transdifferentiation'* has been introduced to denote a switch of previously differentiated cells into other types of cells (cf. Selman & Kafatos 1974). We prefer to avoid using 'transformation' for this process, since this term has been widely used to denote the change of normal cells into malignant cells in vertebrate tissues.

TRANSDIFFERENTIATION OF LENS IN AVIAN RETINAL PIGMENT CELLS

Cultures at high density

The retinal pigment cells of 8–9-day-old chick embryos were cultured in humidified condition, 95% air–5% CO_2 at 37°C, in Eagle's minimum essential medium (MEM) supplemented with 6% of fetal calf serum (Eguchi & Okada 1973). Pigment cells inoculated at a population density of 1.0×10^5 cells per 3.5-cm dish (Falcon Plastic) proliferated vigorously without losing pigment granules, and formed a black epithelial monolayer sheet within three weeks. In the third generation of culture, about 50 days after inoculation, depigmented cells appeared and their number increased thereafter. Then, at 60–90 days, usually at the terminal period after several passages, transparent piles of elon-

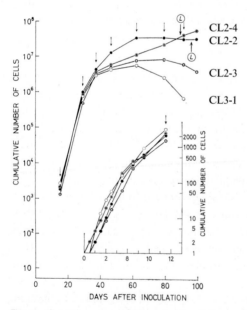

FIG. 1. Growth curves of four clonal cell lines of retinal pigment cells of chick embryos. Growth of early phase is shown in insert, lower right. *Arrows* indicate stages of subculturing: except for the first subculturing, about 1×10^5 cells were sown into each 3.5-cm dish. Stages at which lentoid bodies appeared are indicated by *L*. (After Eguchi & Okada 1973.)

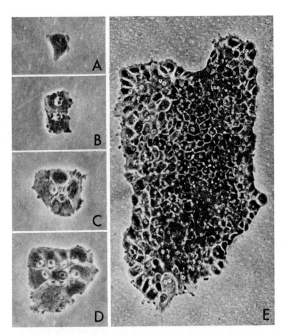

FIG. 2. An example of clonal outgrowth of a singly plated pigment cell that originated from the pigmented focus appeared in the secondary culture of retinal pigment cells of chick embryos. (A) 1 day after inoculation; (B) 2 days; (C) 3 days; (D) 4 days; (E) 10 days. A–D, × 400; E, × 200.

gated cells were differentiated in these non-pigmented epithelial foci. The piles had the same characteristics as the structures differentiated in cultures of dissociated cells of the lens epithelium of 1-day-old chicks (Okada *et al.* 1971, 1973). We identified the piles obtained in cultures of dissociated retinal pigment cells as 'lentoid bodies' by means of fluorescent-antibody staining with fluorescein-isothiocyanate-conjugated antibodies against chick lens-crystallins and also by electron microscopy.

Culture at low density

The crucial procedure of clonal cell culture was attempted so that we could rule out the possibility that the 'lentoid bodies' originated from lens cells or cell types other than pigment cells adventitiously contained in the initial culture inocula (Eguchi & Okada 1973). Pigmented cells taken out of the very black foci of secondary mass cultures of retinal pigment cells were isolated for this purpose. Two of eight clonal lines started from single pigment cells survived for more than 100 days (Fig. 1), and differentiation of lentoid bodies was observed in both these lines. In the initial phase, pigment cells actively proliferated with pigment granules to form clonal colonies consisting of cohesive sheets of heavily pigmented cells of single cell origin (Fig. 2); these colonies could be maintained as the clonal culture line for several subculture generations. When the rate of cell growth began to decline after about 50 days' culturing, the proportion of non-pigmented cells gradually increased. Eventually, these cells formed compact epithelial islands from which a number of lentoid bodies differentiated during the terminal period of culturing, more than 120 days after the culture was initiated (Figs. 1 and 3).

Stability in differentiation of avian pigment cells

These results provide substantial evidence that one well-defined vertebrate cell type can change into another, i.e. can transdifferentiate, in cell culture. According to classical embryology the cells of retinal pigment epithelium used in the present culture should already be determined and be incapable of regenerating lens *in situ* (cf. van Deth 1940; Scheib 1965). Pioneer work on clonal culture by Cahn & Cahn (1966) revealed that the retinal pigment cells from chick embryos maintained the heritability of their differentiation in a stable fashion for more than 50 cell generations. What mechanisms underlie a switch of such stable pigment cells into lens cells? In our cultures the same type of cells as Cahn & Cahn (1966) used changed at the end of unusually prolonged periods of cultivation. Repeated replication of DNA seems to be one of the prerequisites

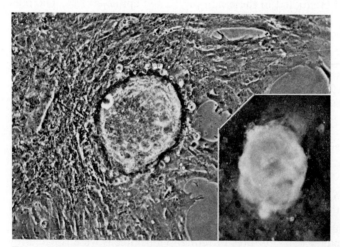

FIG. 3. Lentoid body developed in culture of a clonal line originating from a single pigment cell of chick embryo. The result of fluorescein-isothiocyanate conjugated antibody staining is shown in the insert. × 75.

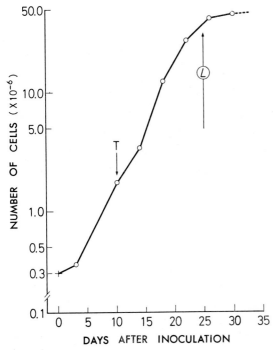

FIG. 4. Growth curve of quail retinal pigment cells from embryos 8–9 days old. T: The stage of subculturing. L: The stage of first appearance of lentoid bodies.

for such transdifferentiation. However, we have found recently that the switch in differentiation was accelerated by an inhibitor of melanin pigmentation. When dissociated retinal pigment cells were cultured in the presence of 0.5 mM-phenylthiourea lentoid bodies differentiated, even in the primary cultures, within 25 days of culturing. This result makes it possible to speculate that regulation at translational level is the key mechanism of the phenomenon, although the activation of dormant genes for a cell-specific product—lens-crystallins in the present cases—during repeated replication of DNA should not be excluded as a possible mechanism.

The results obtained with chick retinal pigment cells have been confirmed by our experiments with embryos of Japanese quail (*Coturnix coturnix japonica*). Transdifferentiation in the quail cells, however, is a somewhat different process from that in the chick cells. Quail pigment cells transdifferentiated to lens cells much faster than chick cells did, with lentoid bodies being observed at about 25 days after inoculation, and with perhaps many fewer repeats of DNA replication than are needed in the chick cells (Fig. 4). The retinal pigment cells of quail embryos seem to maintain their heritability of differentiation less stably than the chick cells.

It should be emphasized that the pigment cells of both chick and quail embryos are able to switch their differentiation in one direction in cell culture —always into lens cells. This suggests that there is a sequence of differentiation in cell culture, starting from pigment cells and ending in the differentiation of lens fibres via lens epithelial cells (Okada *et al.* 1975). The lens epithelial cells were generally short-lived in cell culture, and after several cell replications they differentiated into mature lens fibres which could no longer replicate, and without any sign of transdifferentiation into other cell types (Okada *et al.* 1971, 1973).

TRANSDIFFERENTIATION OF LENS IN AMPHIBIAN PIGMENT CELLS

Transdifferentiation from iris epithelial cells

A pure population of pigment cells was obtained by dissociating iris epithelia isolated from eyes of adult newts, *Cynops pyrrhogaster*. Dissociated pigment cells were cultured in humidified air at 24–25 °C using 60% Leibovitz L-15 medium supplemented with 10% fetal calf serum (Eguchi *et al.* 1974). The cells freshly inoculated at a population density of $1-5 \times 10^4$ cells per 3.5-cm dish (Falcon Plastic) grew actively after a long lag period of about two weeks. The actively growing cells gradually lost their pigment granules and formed non-pigmented monolayer islands of polygonal epithelial cells. In some of these epithelial islands repigmentation occurred, while in many of them cells continued to grow without synthesis of pigment granules, eventually forming transparent piles of various sizes 35 to 40 days after culturing (Fig. 5). Such piles, which were apparently similar to the 'lentoid bodies' seen in cultures of chick cells, were formed in all culture plates of all culture lines. The lens specificity of these structures was substantiated by means of fluorescent-antibody staining as well as by immunodiffusion testing of homogenates of cultures, using rabbit antisera against purified newt α-, β-, and γ-crystallins (Fig. 6). Electron microscope studies showed that these piles were assemblies of elongated cells comparable to lens fibres *in situ*.

In this experiment, the epithelial cells of the dorsal and ventral halves of the iris were separately isolated and cultured to see whether the dorsal predominance of lens-forming potency that exists in the newt iris *in situ* also exists in cell culture. Unexpectedly, there was no difference between the dorsal and ventral cells in their ability to differentiate in cell culture (Figs. 5, 6). Cells from the ventral iris, which were incapable of lens regeneration *in situ*, were able to transdifferentiate into lens cells in the same way as the dorsal cells.

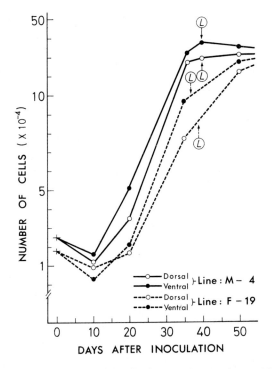

FIG. 5. Growth curves of primary cultures of newt iris epithelial cells. Parallel cultures of dorsal and ventral iris epithelial cells. Lentoid bodies first appeared at the point indicated by L in each curve. (After Eguchi et al. 1974).

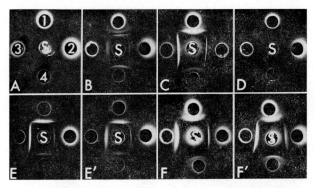

FIG. 6. Results of immunodiffusion test. Iris epithelium (A); lens regenerant in vivo 25 days after lens removal (B); normal full-grown lens (C); cells from dorsal iris cultured for 30 days (D); cells cultured for 40 days (E: dorsal and E′: ventral); cells cultured for 50 days (F: dorsal and F′: ventral). S: test antigen, 1: antiserum against whole lens extract, 2: anti-α-crystallin, 3: anti-β-crystallin, 4: anti-γ-crystallin. The arrangement of antisera is the same in all tests. No positive reactions were detected in A and D against any antisera. (After Eguchi et al. 1974).

Clusters consisting purely of 50 to 100 pigment cells were carefully marked immediately after the inoculated cells attached to the substrate, and the fate of these clusters was followed (Fig. 7). In 37 of 85 marked clusters of pigment cells, 'lentoid bodies' appeared about 40 days after culturing (Fig. 7B, C). These results indicate that the lens cells were actually derived from pigment epithelial cells of adult newts, not from inadvertent contamination by non-pigmented cells.

Successful cultivation of dissociated epithelial cells of the newt iris has recently been reported (Horstman & Zalik 1974), though no lens-like structures were observed. The inductive influence of the neural retina has been emphasized in a number of experiments on lens regeneration *in situ* (Reyer 1954, 1962; Scheib 1965), and this has been confirmed in tissue- or organ-culture studies in which the integrity of the tissue fragments was preserved throughout the culture period (Eguchi 1967; Connelly *et al.* 1973; Yamada *et al.* 1973; Yamada & McDevitt 1974). The present observations of autonomous lens differentiation stand in sharp contrast to these reports. Differences in culture methods and variations in batches of fetal calf serum incorporated into the culture media may explain these differences.

Transdifferentiation from retinal pigment cells

Pieces of retinal pigment epithelium of newts, when grafted into the eye chamber, have been shown to differentiate into lens (Reyer 1962). It was therefore interesting to test whether pigment cells of the retina can transdifferentiate into lens in our cell culture conditions, just as the pigment cells of the iris epithelium did. Some results from unpublished experiments will be briefly described.

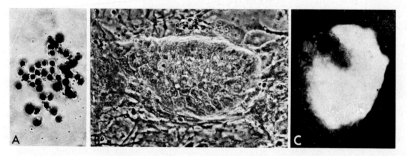

Fig. 7. A: Cluster of pigment cells of newts. B: A lentoid body differentiated from cell clusters such as shown in A. C: The result of antibody staining of the lentoid body using fluorescein-isothiocyanate-conjugated rabbit antiserum against whole lens-crystallins of newt. × 100.

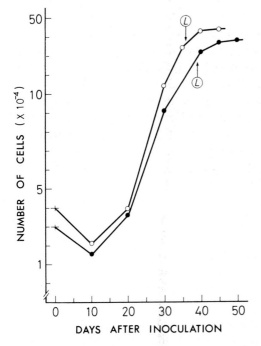

FIG. 8. Growth curves of retinal pigment cells of adult newts. Lentoid bodies first appeared at the point indicated by *L*.

(*a*) *Culture at high density.* The neural retinal layer was removed from the posterior three-quarters of the eyeballs of the adult newt after they had been incubated in Ca^{2+}- and Mg^{2+}-free balanced salt solution (CMF). The pure pigment epithelium of the retina was then carefully stripped off the choroidal tissue after further treatment with EDTA. Dissociated pigment cells were obtained by the same procedures as adopted for iris cells (Eguchi *et al.* 1974) and were cultured in L-15 medium as described for iris cells. Usually $2–5 \times 10^4$ cells were inoculated in a 3.5-cm dish with 1.8 ml of diluted Leibovitz L-15 medium. The dissociated retinal pigment cells grew actively after a long lag of about two weeks (Fig. 8). Most of the growing cells lost pigment granules gradually and transdifferentiated a number of lentoid bodies within 40 days, in the same manner as observed in cultures of iris cells. The lens specificity of the lentoid bodies was confirmed by the fluorescent-antibody technique. We attempted clonal culture of the cells of the retinal pigment epithelium so that we could know directly the relationship between growth and expression of foreign differentiation, as well as know how many cells of the pigment retina have the potential of lens differentiation.

(b) *Culture at low density.* Usually 10^3 cells were inoculated in Falcon plastic Petri dishes of 6 cm diameter. Single dissociated cells attached to the substrate within 24 hours of inoculation. Singly-plated cells were each marked on the fourth day of culture and the further growth and differentiation of each marked cell were followed daily. About 50% of the marked cells started to divide on the 11th day of culturing, and further outgrowth continued with a generation time of about 44 h for the formation of clonal colonies of cohesive epithelial cells. Most cells lost pigment granules rapidly during the period of repeated mitosis (Fig. 9A). In some cases the cells continued to differentiate and synthesize pigment in a stable way, forming colonies of very cohesive sheets of pigmented cells (Fig. 9B). When the number of cells in each colony reached 300–1000, at about 30 days after inoculation, lentoid bodies appeared in many non-pigmented colonies (Fig. 10). Staining with fluorescein-isothiocyanate-conjugated antibodies against newt lens-crystallins revealed that all the lentoid bodies possessed lens specificity (Fig. 10). Thus, we can say that the retinal pigment cells of adult newts can transdifferentiate into lens cells.

The results of clonal cultures are summarized in Table 1. Clonal efficiency (number of colonies grown compared to number of inoculated cells) was between 3.10 and 4.80%. Differentiation of the lentoid body was observed in 28.4% of clonal colonies consisting of more than 100 cells, while pigmented

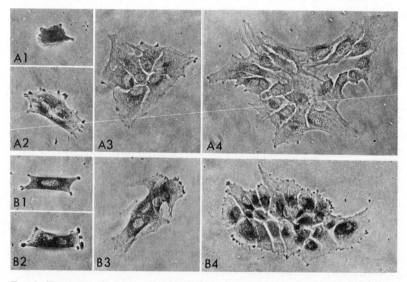

FIG. 9. Examples of clonal outgrowth of a singly-plated retinal pigment cell of the newt. A: A clonal line which became a non-pigmented colony, 4 days (A1), 15 days (A2), 17 days (A3), and 20 days (A4) after inoculation. B: A clonal line which became a pigmented colony, 4 days (B1), 11 days (B2), 13 days (B3), and 20 days (B4) after inoculation. × 100.

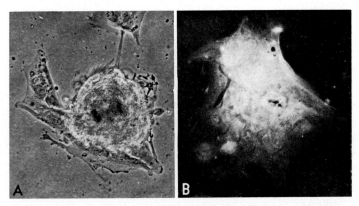

FIG. 10. A: A lentoid body differentiated from the clonal colony 30 days after inoculation of cell. B: Staining with the fluorescent antibody of a clonal colony which begins to form a lentoid body 30 days after inoculation of cell. × 50.

TABLE 1

Colony formation and lens differentiation in low-density cultures (6 plates inoculated with 10^3 cells) of retinal pigment cells of adult newts[a]

Culture plate	Total No. of colonies (over 100 cells)	Differentiated colonies		Unidentifiable colonies
		Lentoid body	Pigmentation	
1	48	14	11	23
2	35	10	9	16
3	41	14	12	15
4	38	11	7	20
5	31	8	5	18
6	32	7	9	16
	225	64	53	108
	(100)[b]	(28.4)	(23.6)	(48.0)

[a] All the plates were fixed 30 days after inoculation and the results were scored under low power magnification.
[b] % of total no. of colonies examined.

colonies occurred in 23.6%. The differentiation characteristics of the rest were unidentifiable. Most such colonies consisted of elongated cells of fibroblast-like morphology. In this group three colonies consisted of cells with morphological characteristics similar to differentiating neural cells *in vitro*. These cells, which certainly originated from single retinal pigment cells, had long axon-like cytoplasmic processes which stained positively with Bodian's method. This preliminary observation may suggest the possibility of neural cells transdifferentiating from retinal pigment cells *in vitro*.

Factors affecting transdifferentiation in amphibian pigment cells

In the regeneration of lens *in situ*, DNA replication of iris epithelial cells always precedes the expression of lens specificity (Yamada 1967, 1972; Eisenberg & Yamada 1966; Reyer 1971; Eguchi & Shingai 1971). In cultures of dissociated newt cells, the cells grew actively and then differentiated lens structures rather synchronously 35 to 40 days after culturing. Lens differentiated from iris epithelial cells *in vitro* more slowly than it did *in situ*. Possibly the absence of other cells that could interact with iris cells may cause such a delay *in vitro*. Observations on retinal pigment epithelium cells in clonal cultures are highly important to any discussion of how much cell division is needed before 'foreign' differentiation can occur. About one-third of the colonies examined switched synchronously into lens when the number of cells per colony reached 300–1000, that is after seven to ten cell generations. At this stage many colonies still remained which could maintain their own differentiation as pigment cells. Thus, these facts suggest that the pigment epithelium of the newt may contain quite a large number of cells which have the ability to switch easily to lens cells after several passages of DNA replication. The lens potency of the pigment epithelium of the newt *in situ* may be due to the presence of a large number of such cell populations. In contrast, the retinal pigment epithelium of chick embryos at late stages in development contains a very low percentage of cells with that potential (Eguchi & Okada 1973); most cells maintain the heritability of differentiation in cell culture after repeated replication (Cahn & Cahn 1966). In this respect, the situation in the pigment retina of the late embryos of quails is of interest.

In newt eyes *in situ* the ability of pigment epithelium to generate lens is strictly limited in the dorsal half of the eye (Sato 1951; for review see Reyer 1954, 1962; Scheib 1965). In our cell cultures of newt pigment cells, however, lentoid bodies were invariably differentiated from cells of both the dorsal and the ventral iris epithelium. On this point, it should be noted that cell association 'loosens' in the dorsal marginal iris after lentectomy, whereas the characteristic tissue architecture of the ventral iris is well maintained (Eguchi 1963; Yamada 1972; Dumont & Yamada 1972). A potent carcinogen (and mutagen), *N*-methyl-*N'*-nitro-*N*-nitrosoguanidine, evoked the regeneration of lens from the ventral iris *in situ*, presumably by disturbing the original tissue architecture of the ventral iris epithelium (Eguchi & Watanabe 1973). An old report suggested that mechanical disturbance resulted in lens regeneration from the ventral iris (Ciaccio 1933). In the cell cultures I have described, the cells of both dorsal and ventral iris were treated with trypsin, which must drastically change the surface properties of the cells. We may speculate, therefore, that changes in the properties of the cell surface provide the signal for the expression of lens potentials in cells of the ventral iris.

ACKNOWLEDGEMENTS

This work was supported in part by a grant for basic cancer research from the Ministry of Education, Japan. I wish to thank Professor T.S. Okada for his help in preparing the manuscript and Mr M. Araki for helping to prepare the material for cell culture. The work reviewed here represents joint research done with Professor T.S. Okada, Mr Shin-ichi Abe and Mr Kenji Watanabe.

References

CAHN, R.D. & CAHN, M.B. (1966) *Proc. Natl. Acad. Sci. USA 55*, 104–114
CIACCIO, G. (1933) *Arch. Biol. (Paris) 44*, 179–249
CONNELLY, T.G., ORTIZ, J.R. & YAMADA, T. (1973) *Dev. Biol. 31*, 301–315
COULOMBRE, J.C. & COULOMBRE, A.J. (1965) *Dev. Biol. 12*, 79–92
DUMONT, J.N. & YAMADA, T. (1972) *Dev. Biol. 31*, 385–401
EGUCHI, G. (1963) *Embryologia 8*, 47–62
EGUCHI, G. (1967) *Embryologia 9*, 246–266
EGUCHI, G. & OKADA, T.S. (1973) *Proc. Natl. Acad. Sci. USA 70*, 1495–1499
EGUCHI, G. & SHINGAI, R. (1971) *Dev. Growth Differ. 13*, 337–349
EGUCHI, G. & WATANABE, K. (1973) *J. Embryol. Exp. Morphol. 30*, 63–71
EGUCHI, G., ABE, S. & WATANABE, K. (1974) *Proc. Natl. Acad. Sci. USA 71*, 5052–5056
EISENBERG, S. & YAMADA, T. (1966) *J. Exp. Zool. 162*, 353–368
HORSTMAN, L.P. & ZALIK, S.E. (1974) *Exp. Cell Res. 84*, 1–14
LOPASHOV, O.G. & SOLOGUB, A.A. (1972) *J. Embryol. Exp. Morphol. 28*, 521–546
OKADA, T.S., EGUCHI, G. & TAKEICHI, M. (1971) *Dev. Growth Differ. 13*, 323–336
OKADA, T.S., EGUCHI, G. & TAKEICHI, M. (1973) *Dev. Biol. 34*, 321–333
OKADA, T.S., ITOH, Y., WATANABE, K. & EGUCHI, G. (1975) *Dev. Biol. 45*, 318–329
REYER, R.W. (1954) *Q. Rev. Biol. 29*, 1–46
REYER, R.W. (1962) in *Regeneration* (Rudnick, D., ed.), pp. 211–261, Ronald Press, New York
REYER, R.W. (1971) *Dev. Biol. 24*, 233–258
SATO, T. (1951) *Embryologia 1*, 21–58
SCHEIB, D. (1965) *Ergeb. Anat. Entwicklungsgesch. 38*, 46–114
SELMAN, K. & KAFATOS, F.C. (1974) *Cell Differ. 3*, 81–94
VAN DETH, J.H.M.G. (1940) *Acta Neerl.-Scand. Morphol. 3*, 151–169
YAMADA, T. (1967) *Curr. Top. Dev. Biol. 2*, 247–283
YAMADA, T. (1972) in *Cell Differentiation (Proc. 1st Int. Conf. Cell Differentiation)* (Harris, P., Allin, P. & Viza, D., eds.) pp. 56–60, Munksgaard, Copenhagen
YAMADA, T. & MCDEVITT, D.S. (1974) *Dev. Biol. 38*, 104–118
YAMADA, T., REESE, D.H. & MCDEVITT, D.S. (1973) *Differentiation 1*, 65–82

Discussion

Newth: In the chick you can culture the cells in conditioned medium. Have you tried using lens epithelium instead of the retina to condition the medium?
Eguchi: We tested briefly lens-conditioned medium and did not find any

obvious inhibitory effect, but it hardly enhanced cell growth and differentiation.

Newth: In the mass cultures where you may get a large number of lentoid bodies or lenses in one culture is their spatial distribution random?

Eguchi: In our cultures it is usually random.

Newth: So you sometimes get two lenses very close together?

Eguchi: Yes.

Gluecksohn-Waelsch: Sato worked on Wolffian lens regeneration a long time ago (1930). The difference between your present results in culture and his early results seems to be that you get the ventral rim of the iris to transdifferentiate into lens. You ascribed that to the fact that the dorsal cells dissociate when the lens is removed and the ventral cells do not. But you seemed to have a significantly lower percentage of transdifferentiation in the ventral cells than in the dorsal. Is that correct?

Eguchi: The lens regeneration *in vivo* occurs always only from dorsal iris, not from ventral. In our cultures, however, cells from both dorsal and ventral iris can invariably transdifferentiate to lens cells. Actually, the number of cultured cells which show lens specificity is a little larger in the dorsal cells than in the ventral. However, I don't think that this difference is significant, because the numbers observed do not reflect the size of the potential cell population in the original iris epithelium *in situ*.

Gluecksohn-Waelsch: As far as the dorsal rim of the iris is concerned your findings seem to confirm the regeneration results *in situ*.

Saxén: Do you ever see both melanin and crystallin synthesis in the same cells? Or is crystallin synthesis always preceded by depigmentation?

Eguchi: We have often observed that cells containing pigment granules showed obvious lens specificity. However, we did not test the biosynthesis of melanin in these cells. We consider that it is very important to know whether cells with synthetic activity of melanin can synthesize crystallins at the same time or not.

Rutter: Would it be possible to dissociate a group of cells which had crystallin in them, start culturing them again and get pigmented cells? That is, once the process you described has started, do the cells stop growing and are they determined to form lentoid bodies?

Eguchi: I don't think that you can get pigment cells again from cells that have switched to lens cells, which are fixed towards lentoid body formation.

Gurdon: Have you given any other kind of specialized cells the same quite extensive trypsin treatment in the same medium and found whether they perform any other kind of transdifferentiation?

Eguchi: Neural retinal cells of chick embryos after 11 days' incubation will switch to either pigment cells or lens cells.

Gurdon: Have you tried using cornea?

Eguchi: No, not yet.

Wolpert: Did you say that the lentoid cells only started appearing after about 60 cell divisions?

Eguchi: In clonal cultures of the newt pigment cell they appeared after seven to ten cell generations. In the chick cell they appeared after probably more than 50 cell generations.

Wolpert: When you start getting lentoid bodies can you subculture again those pigment cells that do not become lentoid bodies?

Eguchi: In the newt when the clonal cells differentiate into lentoid body, all cells constituting a colony form a single lentoid body; perhaps they can grow no longer. In the chick cells the situation is a little different.

Wolpert: What happens if you subculture those cells?

Eguchi: We once tried subclonal culture of a clonal line derived from a single pigment cell of chick and differentiated lentoid bodies. Some subclonal colonies differentiated lentoid bodies again, and some were pigmented; however, many subclonal colonies consisted of cells that were something like fibroblastic cells in morphology. We found no subclonal colonies which had pigment cells and lentoid bodies at the same time (Eguchi & Okada 1973).

Wolpert: In other words, in the chick the probability of a cell becoming a lentoid body becomes greater and greater as the lentoid bodies start to form, and eventually other odd cells appear. But in the newt it seems that they all become lentoid bodies. Is that right?

Eguchi: Yes.

Gropp: In histological sections, were the lentoid bodies composed entirely of lens-type cells or did you find transitional cells between the lens cells and pigment-type cells?

Eguchi: Most lentoid bodies consisted of fully differentiated lens cells. Sometimes a small number of pigment cells were contained in the lentoid bodies which developed in mass culture of pigment epithelial cells; I think these pigment cells have been incorporated during lentoid body formation. It is difficult to distinguish transitional cells between lens cells and pigment cells.

Gluecksohn-Waelsch: Is that the same as found in the *in vivo* regeneration work?

Eguchi: Yes, I think so.

Gluecksohn-Waelsch: Has anyone tried to obtain clones of limb-regenerating cells for the purpose of testing their differentiating potentials? As far as I know the lens is the only other system, at least in the newt, that is able to regenerate.

Eguchi: I am not sure in limb regeneration; probably nobody has tried yet.

However, it is quite possible to analyse the differentiative potentials of limb-regenerating cells by such a clonal analysis.

Gardner: In Table 1 you showed percentages for the different type of clones —28.4% lens, 23.6% pigmented and 48% undetermined. Is it possible that these undetermined colonies have jumped to some other state but that your culture conditions don't allow the expression of their differentiated phenotype? Have you tried recloning those cells?

Eguchi: No, not yet. The colonies without any definite differentiation were listed as unidentifiable colonies in Table 1. Subclonal analysis of those colonies is a possible approach to analysing their differentiative capacities.

Polani: If you clone the cells which have lost the pigment and which are lens-positive what do you get?

Eguchi: I think most cells which have already switched to lens cells do not grow, particularly the newt cells.

Newth: If they can't grow they must presumably be able to move or you would never get a lentoid body. You showed us some pictures of fluorescent-labelled cultures in which individual cells were lens-positive. How do the lentoid bodies grow if these cells cannot divide?

Eguchi: In the newt clonal cultures, in the fluorescence studies the cells just turn off. From this state the cells cease growing and come to the centre of the colony and pile up. Then they form a single three-dimensional structure as a lentoid body.

Rutter: If fresh pigmented cells are mixed with a colony of cells in which most of the cells are obviously producing crystallins, can this process be in-hibited? Or do some of the cells which are mixed into the system then become incorporated into the lentoid bodies?

Eguchi: We have done such an experiment, where lens cells from day-old chicks were cultured together with pigment cells from chick embryos. Usually they sorted each other out. When the population of pigment cells mixed with lens cells is not too excessive, growth of lens cells and lentoid formation is not inhibited. From this result, I am able to suggest that, in newt cells, a colony of cells producing crystallins may not be inhibited by additional pigment cells.

Kelley: Are there any conditions where you see no directional movement towards lentoid body formation? In other words, among the variety of culture media or culture conditions that could be used are there any that do not move in this direction?

Eguchi: I don't know of one.

Morriss: Does the pigment just disappear from the cells during differentiation, or is it segregated into one or two dorsal cells at division? In other words, is it one of the binary decision situations that we were talking about earlier?

Eguchi: There is no substantial evidence on this. However, from my observations there are two possible ways for depigmentation to occur: one is dilution of pigment granules by cell division and the other is their active discharge into the medium by pigment cells themselves.

Gropp: Is there any advantage in talking about 'transdifferentiation' rather than metaplasia?

Eguchi: 'Metaplasia' is, of course, a possible term. However, we preferred 'transdifferentiation' because it distinguishes more explicitly the phenomenon at the cellular level which we have demonstrated from the phenomena of transformation and transdetermination.

Wolpert: If it really is transdifferentiation then it may be useful to keep the term because it may be related to transdetermination as seen in *Drosophila*.

Gluecksohn-Waelsch: Transdifferentiation is related to regeneration, which is not the case with transdetermination.

Wolpert: Not necessarily. It is too early to say. The work on *Drosophila* shows that certain regions are like a developmental sink. If a lot of different tissues all ended up as lentoid bodies we might draw an analogy with the so-called developmental sinks in *Drosophila*.

Gluecksohn-Waelsch: Transdifferentiation is more closely related to the *in vivo* phenomenon to which Dr Eguchi referred, namely the regeneration of a lens when the latter is extirpated, as shown first in studies at the turn of the century. But transdetermination has a totally different mechanism.

Wolpert: Why do you think it is a different mechanism?

Gluecksohn-Waelsch: In transdetermination it is assumed that, in the cells originally determined to differentiate into particular tissue types, the rest of the genome is turned off, so to speak. As the result of the action of the (as yet unknown) mechanism of transdetermination, parts of this repressed genome become derepressed, apparently in a particular sequence. In transdifferentiation, a variety of already fully differentiated tissues respond to the specific demands of the environment—in this case that for a lens—possibly by passing first through a dedifferentiated state, in analogy with amphibian limb regeneration.

Gardner: I don't think one can definitely conclude that transdetermination is really different on the grounds that you give. One still wants to know what those so-called undetermined cells are. They may represent other cell types and the right conditions may not be present to allow you to identify the nature of the 48% of so-called undetermined clones that are neither lens nor pigment.

Eguchi: Among the undetermined clonal colonies in the newt pigment cells were three colonies resembling neural cells in morphology. These cells were positive to a silver stain method but we are still doubtful about this result because the method is not specific enough to nerve cells. However, this type of transdifferentiation from pigment epithelial cells is quite possible; when neural retina is removed from the newt eye *in vivo*, neural retina is again regenerated completely from the remaining pigment epithelium.

References

EGUCHI, G. & OKADA, T.S. (1973) Differentiation of lens tissue from the progeny of chick retinal pigment cells cultured *in vitro*: A demonstration of a switch of cell types in clonal culture. *Proc. Natl. Acad. Sci. USA 70*, 1495–1499

SATO, T. (1930) Beiträge zur Analyse der Wolffschen Linsenregeneration I, II, III. *Wilhelm Roux' Arch. Entwicklungsmech. Org. 122*, 451–493; *130*, 19–78; *133*, 323–348

Hormone-like factor(s) in mesenchymal epithelial interactions during embryonic development

WILLIAM J. RUTTER and RAYMOND L. PICTET

Department of Biochemistry and Biophysics, University of California, San Francisco

Abstract   The mesenchymal tissue which is required for the development of the pancreas can be replaced by a factor (MF), extracted from embryonic tissues, which stimulates DNA synthesis and cell proliferation. This activity has some of the characteristics of polypeptidic hormones. Purified MF covalently bound to the surface of Sepharose beads is fully capable of stimulating DNA synthesis and of supporting differentiation. Thus, its action is apparently exerted at the surface of the cells. In addition, the DNA synthetic activity of this factor involves cyclic AMP. The stimulation of DNA synthesis by MF is inactivated by oxidation with periodate. Such inactivated factor is fully active in the presence of cyclic AMP derivatives but is not influenced by cyclic GMP derivatives or cyclic GMP itself. These results suggest that MF contains two functional components.

The conformational changes of the epithelial tissue in contact with the MF bound to Sepharose also suggest that morphogenesis of the organ may in part be determined by the site of action of MF.

The pancreas is a suitable paradigm for studies of organogenesis. The mature gland contains predominantly the acinar and duct cells of the exocrine pancreas. In addition, endocrine A, B and D cells form clusters of cells, the islets, which are interspersed throughout the exocrine gland. The differentiation of the acinar and endocrine cells involves the selective production of large quantities of specific proteins which are packaged within secretory vesicles for export. The acinar cells are characterized by a well-developed endoplasmic reticulum and the presence of zymogen granules containing the digestive enzymes (zymogens). The endocrine A and B cells contain glucagon and insulin respectively, in characteristic secretory granules. The duct cells secrete fluid with no known major protein product. They are not readily distinguished from earlier pancreatic embryonic cells. All of these functional cells are apparently derived from the pancreatic epithelium which develops from the gut epithelium (Pictet *et al.* 1976).

The normal growth and development of the pancreas is dependent on an interaction of the epithelium with mesenchymal cells (Grobstein 1967; Wolf 1968). This mesenchymal-epithelial interaction regulates cell proliferation (Ronzio & Rutter 1973; Pictet *et al.* 1975*a*) and in addition influences the final proportion of endocrine and exocrine cells (Pictet *et al.* 1975*b*).

The studies on the pancreas have contributed to our understanding of the mechanisms of cell–cell interaction. It is well known that cellular interactions play a crucial role in development and that epithelial–mesenchymal interactions are involved in organogenesis. The mechanisms of the cellular interaction have remained conjectural. Various alternatives have been entertained. One of these is the specific transfer of genetic information. Experiments purporting to show such transfer of RNA or DNA have occasionally been communicated; the results, however, are not convincing. Transfer of genetic material itself is not demanded since the interacting cells have an identical genome. A second possibility is a specific molecular signal such as a hormone. However, the usual hormones are not likely to be involved since there is reason to believe that such cellular interactions occur only over a short range and, with the exception of glucagon (Rall *et al.* 1973), none has been detected at this early embryonic stage. A third possibility is tissue complementation, via the production of either required metabolites or other cellular components which allow the normal expression of a programmed differentiative response.

Of the above possibilities, the second has substantial experimental precedence. There are many known cases of specific hormones or factors which influence the proliferation and/or differentiation of a given cell type. These factors appear to be entirely analogous to hormones in the sense that they are produced by certain tissues and act on other more or less distant target cells. In many cell–cell interactions, including epithelial–mesenchymal interactions, proximity of the two tissues appears a requisite for biological activity. Our studies with the pancreas show that this interaction may be mediated by a new class of interacting molecules that are insoluble under normal physiological conditions. This focalized regulation is tantamount to contact regulation. The experiments of Golosow & Grobstein (1962) and Kallman & Grobstein (1964) some years ago demonstrated that proximity of the epithelial and mesenchymal components was required, but that contact between the cells was not needed. These studies suggested that a molecular messenger was the basis of the communication between the cells and that direct transfusion of cellular constituents (e.g. through a gap junction) was not involved. Instead we have shown that translocation of molecules produced by the mesenchyme to the epithelial receptor cells was the functional basis of the interactive process. The factor activity (MF) is detected only in mesenchymal, not epithelial, cells (Rutter *et al.* 1964). Furthermore, it is assayable only in embryonic, not adult, mesenchymal tissues, and was not replaced by any known hormones or a variety of other proteins tested (Rutter *et al.* 1964). The mesenchymal factor seems to be selectively active on pancreatic epithelial cells. There is also a significant effect, however, on the pituitary epithelium. These responses are in agreement with the less specific requirement of these two tissues for their own mesenchyme. The properties of this factor differ substantially from those of other known hormones. In particular, MF activity is very low or absent from embryonic fluids and extracts, and is found selectively in membrane-rich fractions. Solubilization requires extraction with high salt concentrations (Ronzio & Rutter 1973). Treatment of such 'soluble' fractions in low salt concentrations with physiological levels of calcium ion precipitated the activity; in fact, this property is used in the purification procedure. This property emphasizes the limited solubility of this material and, therefore, the limited range of its action under physiological circumstances.

The material appears to be proteinaceous, since its activity was destroyed by relatively low concentrations of trypsin; furthermore a carbohydrate moiety appears to be required, since treatment with periodate, under the mild conditions usually employed for the oxidation of vicinal hydroxyl groups found in carbohydrates, destroys the activity. In contrast, the activity is completely resistant to deoxyribonuclease I (EC 3.1.4.5) and ribonuclease I (EC 3.4.1.22).

The biological effects of the mesenchymal factor mimic those of the mesenchymal tissue. It was initially observed that pancreatic epithelia do not proliferate in the absence of mesenchyme (Golosow & Grobstein 1962). Thus, an effect on cellular proliferation was inferred. *In vitro* experiments involving addition of MF to isolated pancreatic epithelia in culture showed a decisive action of this material on the incorporation of precursors into DNA and on cellular proliferation as evidenced by growth of the epithelium in the presence of MF (Ronzio & Rutter 1973; Pictet *et al.* 1975*a*). In fact, these processes appeared entirely dependent on the addition of MF or mesenchymal cells. Thus, the proliferative activity of the epithelial cells appears to be controlled by the mesenchymal cells via MF.

Another major effect of mesenchymal tissues on the development of the pancreas was discovered during an ultrastructural analysis of development *in vitro*. In the absence of mesenchymal tissue and of added MF there was little if any growth of the rudiment. Nevertheless it differentiated into an endocrine-rich tissue. The normal adult pancreas contains about 1 % endocrine A and B cells. Pancreatic epithelia cultivated in a defined medium containing only nutrients in crystallized albumin differentiated mostly into endocrine cells (A predominantly); very few acinar cells containing zymogen granules were detected. Under these conditions, however, there was significant sloughing off of cells and the mass and DNA content of the differentiated epithelium was less than that of the primitive tissue before cultivation. When periodate-inactivated MF was used in similar experiments, cell proliferation was restricted (compared with un-treated MF preparations, inactivated MF preparations stimulate less than 5% incorporation of precursors into DNA). These rudiments, however, withstand the culture conditions much more successfully and there is little if any cell loss during the culture period. In such experiments there was still a preponderance of endocrine cells (largely A cells) and a restricted number of acinar cells (Pictet *et al.* 1974) (Table 1). Thus, active mesenchymal factor appears necessary for the development of a high proportion of the acinar cells characteristic of the normal pancreas.

TABLE 1

MF affects cell proliferation and the proportion of differentiated cells in the developing pancreatic epithelia

Days in culture	Medium	DNA	Undifferen-tiated (duct) cells (%)	B Cells		A Cells		Acinar Cells	
				%	ng insulin/ μg DNA	%	ng glucagon/ μg DNA	%	μU amylase activity/μg DNA
0	—	0.03	94	0	0.17	6	4.6	0	0.05
7	MF	0.4	13	6	64	1	0.5	80	180
7	Inactivated MF	0.03[a]	15	5	43	60	17.6	20	32

[a] Low levels of DNA synthesis can be detected by autoradiography.

MF ACTS AT THE MEMBRANE OF THE EPITHELIAL CELLS

A molecule which regulates genetic expression so dramatically might, on *a priori* grounds, be expected to interact directly with its target, the cell nucleus. However, the biological effects appear to be mediated by a specific action on the cell membrane. It is unlikely that a molecule with these properties could ef-fectively penetrate the cell membrane. A direct demonstration of action at the cell surface, however, has come from experiments demonstrating that MF covalently linked to the surface of Sepharose beads is competent to exert its biological effects (Levine *et al.* 1973; Pictet *et al.* 1975a). In these experiments, a purified mesenchymal factor was bound by cyanogen bromide to Sepharose beads, which are much larger in diameter than a pancreatic epithelial cell. Beads treated in this way were then shown to have the competence to stimulate the

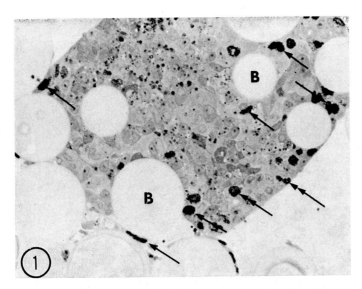

FIG. 1. The primary action of MF is on the cell surface. Day 12 pancreatic epithelia were isolated with trypsin. They were then incubated with MF covalently bound to Sepharose beads as previously described (Levine *et al.* 1973). The MF–Sepharose beads (B) are in close association with only two regions of the tissue. The cells of the part of the epithelium free of beads did not incorporate the [³H]thymidine as expected from the immobilization of MF. The small dots present in these cells are lysosomal structures, a feature already observed in these cells in the absence of MF (Levine *et al.* 1973). Many of the labelled cells are in contact with beads which are in the plane of the section (arrows). The other cells (double-headed arrows) could be in contact with beads above or below the plane of section or correspond to the few cells which incorporate [³H]thymidine in albumin medium. × 300. (From Pictet *et al.* 1975*a*.)

incorporation of labelled precursors into DNA (Fig. 1) and also to support acinar differentiation (Levine *et al.* 1973). A number of experimental controls have convinced us that these biological effects are in fact due to an interaction of the MF with the membrane of the epithelial cells. Binding of the epithelia to the Sepharose beads is specifically dependent on the covalently linked MF. Sepharose beads by themselves, or beads incubated only with MF before being washed, are incompetent to bind epithelium. Moreover, beads coated with other proteins such as albumin are ineffective in promoting DNA synthesis. MF-coated beads always bind to the basal surface of the cell, which *in vivo* is the site of the interaction with the mesenchymal cells. Thus, the epithelial cells appear to migrate over the surfaces of the Sepharose beads in such a way as to maximize contact. This movement of the cells on the beads' surface seems to involve microtubules and microfilaments (Fig. 2). The result is a single layer of epithelial cells in which the microvilli of the apical surface face outwards. Thus, the pancreatic bud is everted and its morphology is distorted by the binding of the

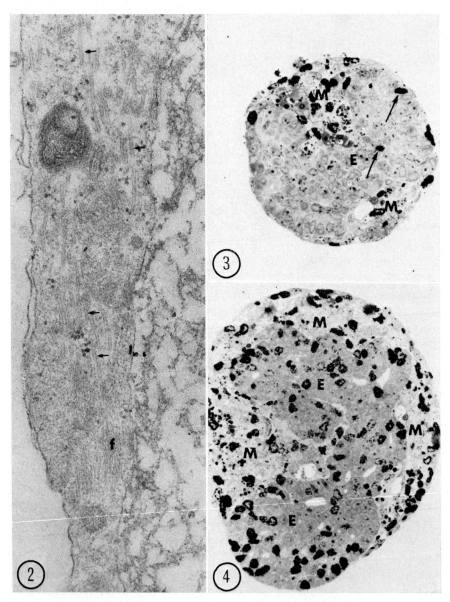

Fig. 2. Electron micrograph of a tip of an epithelial cell spreading onto the surface of a MF–Sepharose bead. The isolation and incubation of the tissue was done as in Fig. 1. During the first 24 h, the cells attach to the beads at their basal surface and move on their surface. The tips of these cells contain microfilaments (f) and microtubules (arrows) which are distributed parallel to the surface of the bead.

Figs. 3 and 4. Incorporation of [³H]thymidine in the presence of MF corresponds to the labelling of the epithelial cells. Day 12 pancreatic epithelia were isolated by dissection, and cultured in the absence (Fig. 3) and presence (Fig. 4) of MF for 24 h. For the last 6 h 10 μCi [³H]thymidine was added. The cells were harvested, fixed and prepared for autoradiography

MF–Sepharose beads, but the basic epithelial sheet in which the cells are linked by junctional complexes remains.

Fig. 1 shows that DNA synthesis as measured by autoradiography occurs largely in cells which are in direct contact with MF–Sepharose. Cells in the region between the Sepharose beads are rarely labelled, thus specific contact appears to be required. It is also evident from this figure that the binding of the cells to MF–Sepharose is very strong, since some of the epithelial cells are disrupted, perhaps by jostling of the beads during changing of the medium. Several other experimental results reinforce the conclusion that this specific binding is coincident with the biological effects of MF: extensively washed beads are still active; MF activity apparently does not leach off the beads significantly; and there is no detectable MF activity in the fluid bathing MF–Sepharose. Indeed, a stimulation of DNA synthesis is observed with amounts of Sepharose-bound MF which in solution in the volume of culture medium used would be insufficient to promote DNA synthesis. Since pancreatic epithelia are isolated by using trypsin, the stimulation of DNA synthesis resulting from the addition of MF may simply be due to the replacement of vital cell surface material removed by the trypsin. The non-trivial effect of MF is shown in Figs. 3 and 4. MF is active on epithelia whose surrounding mesenchyme was removed by dissection. In the absence of MF such epithelia do not undergo significant DNA synthesis. The addition of MF stimulates DNA synthesis to the same extent as in trypsinized epithelia (Pictet *et al.* 1975a).

Long-term cultivation of epithelial cells bound to MF–Sepharose is difficult primarily, we believe, because of the instability of the MF–Sepharose activity during the long culture period. Nevertheless full development of pancreatic epithelia into acinar structures has been observed as shown in Fig. 5. The results of these experiments therefore lead us to conclude that the biological effects of these mesenchymal factor preparations are mediated by an interaction with the surface of the epithelial cells.

MF CONTAINS TWO ACTIVITIES, ONE OF WHICH IS REPLACEABLE BY CYCLIC AMP DERIVATIVES

The evidence indicating that MF exerts its action at the cellular membrane

---

←

by light microscopy. In the absence of MF, the labelled cells are mostly restricted to the mesenchyme left by the dissection. Only a few epithelial cells are labelled (arrows) (Fig. 3). In the presence of MF, in addition to the mesenchymal cells, most of the epithelial cells incorporate the [³H]thymidine (Fig. 4). The difference in size between the two epithelia reflects in part the growth due to the presence of MF and in part the fact that the sections are in different planes. Mesenchyme (M); epithelium (E). × 300. (From Pictet *et al.* 1975a.)

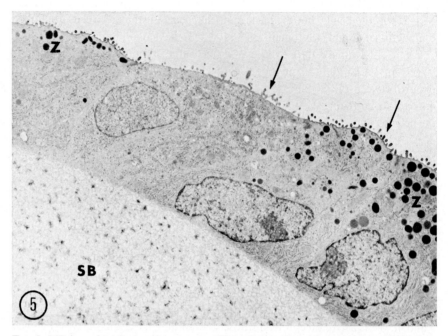

Fig. 5. MF bound to Sepharose supports differentiation. Day 12 pancreatic epithelia were cultured for 7 days in the presence of MF covalently bound to Sepharose beads. The normal acinar configuration of the tissue was lost and most of the cells formed a monolayer around the beads. The typical polarization of the cells was, however, maintained. The basal side of the epithelial cells faces the MF-Sepharose beads (SB) and the apical surface covered by microvilli (arrows) faces the outside. The cells shown are typically differentiated acinar cells containing well-developed rough endoplasmic reticulum as well as zymogen granules (Z). × 3400. (From Levine *et al.* 1973.)

raises the question whether the dramatic effects on nuclear functions are mediated by specific secondary messengers such as cyclic AMP, cyclic GMP, calcium ions, etc. Experiments to test these possibilities led to the discovery that the mesenchymal factor preparations contained two components or activities, one of which was replaceable by cyclic AMP analogues such as dibutyryl cyclic AMP (db-cyclic AMP) and 8-hydroxy-cyclic AMP which can pass the membrane barrier, and another activity which cannot be replaced by cyclic AMP or GMP derivatives or by calcium ionophores (Filosa *et al.* 1975; Pictet *et al.* 1975*a*). This second component is required for the action of cyclic AMP derivatives. The observations which led to these conclusions derive from experiments testing the effects of cyclic AMP and cyclic GMP and their analogues on the cultures in the presence and absence of MF. It was found that MF was not replaced by cyclic AMP, cyclic GMP or any of their analogues. The lack of an inhibitory effect on cyclic AMP was of some interest because of the negative correlation of cyclic AMP levels with proliferative activity in a number of tissue culture cells. This led to a more thorough investigation of the effects of the cyclic nucleotide analogues on periodate-treated MF preparations. These preparations can be fully 'activated' by db-cyclic AMP or 8-OH-cyclic AMP but not by cyclic GMP or any of its derivatives (Filosa *et al.* 1975) (Table 2). Both the cyclic AMP derivatives and the periodate-inactivated MF preparation in this instance are required for activity. This clear-cut result implies the presence of two functions in the MF preparations. One of these is apparently inactivated readily by periodate. This activity is replaced by db-cyclic AMP or 8-OH-cyclic AMP and we therefore term the activity $MF_{(cAMP)}$. The other function is not replaced by cyclic GMP derivatives under any of the experimental conditions tried (Filosa *et al.* 1975). Thus, we do not know the molecule that mediates its action and we term this function $MF_{(X)}$. Of course we have not ruled out the possibility that $MF_{(cAMP)}$ and $MF_{(X)}$ are part of the same molecule.

The fact that at least part of the activity of MF can be replaced by increasing cyclic AMP levels is fully consistent with an action of $MF_{(cAMP)}$ at the cell surface. Many protein hormones are thought to exert their action on the cell surface by modulating the internal cyclic AMP levels. The positive action of cyclic AMP on cell proliferation, however, clearly contrasts with the negative control by cyclic AMP in most other cells. This may imply that the regulation of cell proliferation via the cyclic nucleotides may vary in different cell types or, alter-

TABLE 2

Inactivated MF stimulates DNA synthesis in the presence of cyclic AMP but not cyclic GMP

	8-OH-cyclic AMP(10^{-3} M)	8-Br-cyclic GMP (10^{-4} M)	[^3H]Thymidine incorporated into DNA (c.p.m. per epithelium per 6 h)	n
Active MF	−	−	7330 (5200/9800)	8
	+	−	8680 (5660/13 100)	6
	−	+	7495 (6700/10 000)	10
Inactivated MF	−	−	290 (97/420)	6
	+	−	6500 (3300/8020)	8
	−	+	264 (180/405)	10

Pancreatic epithelia were isolated from rat embryos on the 12th day of gestation (about 35 somites). Individual epithelia were cultured for 18 h in the presence of MF or periodate-treated MF and of the various nucleotides at the indicated concentrations. The epithelia were further incubated for 6 h in fresh identical culture medium containing [^3H]thymidine (10 μCi/ml). The epithelia were then harvested and [^3H]thymidine incorporation into DNA was measured. Results are expressed as c.p.m. ^3H incorporated per epithelium during the 6-h incubation in the presence of [^3H]thymidine. (From Filosa *et al.* 1975).

natively, that there is a complex interplay between $MF_{(cAMP)}$ and $MF_{(X)}$. Clearly the mechanism of this positive effect of cyclic AMP on cell proliferation deserves further experimentation. However, it is not a unique observation: there are other instances in which intracellular cyclic AMP is positively correlated with cell proliferation. What appears most intriguing is the interplay between $MF_{(X)}$ and $MF_{(cAMP)}$ that sets in progress the complicated series of reactions leading to cell proliferation and cytodifferentiation as seen in this system. There are two basic mechanistic alternatives. The first involves a cooperative action between $MF_{(cAMP)}$ and $MF_{(X)}$ such that processes independently activated by these two components are required for the effect. Alternatively, pretreatment with one factor may sensitize the tissue to the second factor which is the regulator of the differentiative programme.

Whatever the specific details, these experimental results suggest a generalized mechanism for epithelial–mesenchymal and other cell–cell interactions during development. This hypothesis involves the production by the effector cell of specific components which act on the receptor cell surface. This leads to altered macromolecular synthesis and to the production of cell types with altered properties, including new cell-surface determinants. This generalized mechanism can be incorporated into a cascade model of differentiation in which the cell–cell interactions are permissive regulators of an intrinsic differentiative programme. The relatively tight coupling observed here between cell proliferation and differentiation may be frequently encountered during terminal differentiation but may not occur always during the intermediate stages of development when various cell lineages may develop without decisive regulation of cell number. However, the desirability of both cell proliferation and the process of differentiation being regulated concordantly throughout the developmental process is obvious. It seems mechanistically economical for the regulation to be coordinated via the same molecules.

DOES MF REGULATE MORPHOGENESIS?

The developing pancreatic epithelium consists of a sheet of epithelial cells, each joined by junctional complexes and polarized so that the basal end of the cells covered by a lamina faces the interior portion of the embryo while the apical portion covered with microvilli faces the lumen. During development the formation of the initial acinus and the continued development of the acinar tree occurs in such a way as to maintain the continuous epithelial sheet. The islets apparently arise by 'escaping' this epithelial matrix (Pictet & Rutter 1972). In these structures the endocrine cells are loosely packed with a few junctional complexes and no articulated structural pattern. When the endocrine cells have escaped the epithelial matrix, they rarely divide; thus they may be largely derived from stem cells existing within the exocrine matrix. Addition of MF to the primitive pancreatic epithelium stimulates DNA synthesis, with retention of the epithelial structures (Fig. 2). Since cultivation in the absence of MF leads to the formation of endocrine tissue, it is conceivable that this agent acts at least in part by perpetuating the epithelial sheet and maintaining the capacity for the formation of the junctional complexes between the cells. Thus, MF may be a determinative component in this aspect of structure. On the other hand, a strong alteration in morphology observed in the Sepharose bead experiments provides the basis for a hypothesis about the development of the typical acinar structure of the pancreas. The results of the experiments described above suggested that each individual cell must interact with MF as a requisite for DNA synthesis. If MF were produced in particular regions along the epithelial structures, selective proliferation and development of new acinar structures would be facilitated. The strong interaction between MF and the epithelial cells in the vicinity would thus lead to selective short-range stimulation. The pattern of production of MF would then determine the structure of the epithelium.

This hypothetical model could be extended to many other similar structures such as those found in the salivary gland and lung. The typical and distinctive branching pattern observed in each of these tissues would then be determined by the manner in which factors analogous to MF are produced in the mesenchymal cells. The means by which MF might be produced locally is by no means clear yet; however, it is deserving of an experimental test. The development of appropriate assay procedures for $MF_{(cAMP)}$ and $MF_{(X)}$ may expedite the isolation of pure molecules and subsequent testing of the loci of their production.

ACKNOWLEDGEMENTS

This work was supported by grants from the National Science Foundation, No. BMS 72-02222 (to W.J.R.), and The National Foundation—March of Dimes (to R.P.). R.P. is a recipient of a Career Development Award from the National Institutes of Health.

References

FILOSA, S., PICTET, R. & RUTTER, W.J. (1975) Positive control of cyclic AMP on mesenchymal factor controlled DNA synthesis in embryonic pancreas. *Nature (Lond.)* 257, 702–705

GOLOSOW, N. & GROBSTEIN, C. (1962) Epitheliomesenchymal interaction in pancreatic morphogenesis. *Dev. Biol.* 4, 242–255

GROBSTEIN, C. (1967) Mechanisms of organogenetic tissue interaction. *Natl. Cancer Inst. Monogr.* 26, 279–299

KALLMAN, F. & GROBSTEIN, C. (1964) Fine structure of differentiating mouse pancreatic exocrine cells in transfilter culture. *J. Cell Biol. 20*, 399–413

LEVINE, S., PICTET, R. & RUTTER, W. J. (1973) Control of cell proliferation and cytodifferentiation by a factor reacting with the cell surface. *Nat. New Biol. 246*, 49–52

PICTET, R. & RUTTER, W. J. (1972) Development of the embryonic endocrine pancreas, in *Handb. Physiol.*, Sect. 7: *Endocrinology*, vol. 1 (Steiner, D. F. & Freinkel, N., eds.), pp. 25–66, Williams & Wilkins, Baltimore

PICTET, R., LEVINE, S., FILOSA, S., PHELPS, P. & RUTTER, W. J. (1974) Control of cell proliferation and differentiation of embryonic rat pancreas by mesenchymal factor and cAMP. *J. Cell Biol. 63*, 270a

PICTET, R. L., FILOSA, S., PHELPS, P. & RUTTER, W. J. (1975a) Control of DNA synthesis in the embryonic pancreas: Interaction of the mesenchymal factor and cyclic AMP, in *Extracellular Matrix Influences on Gene Expression* (Slavkin, H. C. & Greulich, N. C., eds.), pp. 531–540, Academic Press, New York

PICTET, R. L., RALL, L. B., de GASPARO, M. & RUTTER, W. J. (1975b) Regulation of differentiation of endocrine cells during pancreatic development *in vitro*, in *Early Diabetes in Early Life* (Camerini-Davalos, R. A. & Cole, H. S., eds.), pp. 47–53, Academic Press, New York

PICTET, R. L., RALL, L. B., PHELPS, P. & RUTTER, W. J. (1976) The neural crest and the origin of the insulin-producing and other gastrointestinal hormone-producing cells. *Science (Wash. D.C.) 191*, 191–192

RALL, L. B., PICTET, R. L., WILLIAMS, R. H. & RUTTER, W. J. (1973) Early differentiation of glucagon-producing cells in embryonic pancreas: A possible developmental role for glucagon. *Proc. Natl. Acad. Sci. USA 70*, 3478–3482

RONZIO, R. A. & RUTTER, W. J. (1973) Effects of a partially purified factor from chick embryos on macromolecular synthesis of embryonic pancreatic epithelia. *Dev. Biol. 30*, 307–320

RUTTER, W. J., WESSELLS, N. K. & GROBSTEIN, C. (1964) Control of specific synthesis in the developing pancreas. *Natl. Cancer Inst. Monogr. 13*, 51–65

WOLF, E. (1968) Specific interactions between tissues during organogenesis. *Curr. Top. Dev. Biol. 3*, 65–94

Discussion

Cooke: You apparently want to fuse the concepts of determination and differentiation, Dr Rutter, but I can't quite see how your results enable you to do that, because you are not studying a situation where one group of cells is instructing another one for a developmental choice. The fact that you can put any one of a number of different mesenchymes in contact with the epithelial rudiment, and still obtain pancreas, shows that it is already determined as a pancreas rudiment rather than just as endothelium. I feel sure that this has been caused by its position as a group of cells within the primitive gut, and this, the selective response to position, is the problem of determination. You are studying a situation where one group of cells (mesenchyme) is providing relatively unspecific though necessary environmental conditions that allow another cell group to do something. But that 'something' is already the distinctive developmental programme of the latter cells.

Rutter: Most of our studies on the pancreas are related to the second differentiative transition (cytodifferentiation). Specific products at low levels are already evident. We infer that a primary differentiation occurs before this because we see the transition from nothing to something in the production of those specific molecules. We know that that process also demands mesenchyme. We don't know what regulates the primary or secondary transition but we know that mesenchyme is required. The primary transition may be a model for determination, that is the initiation of cell-specific synthesis. At that point the precursor cell is essentially a gut cell, not a pancreas cell.

Cooke: It is very important to establish experimentally whether, just before your earliest experiments, those cells whose normal fate is subsequently to form pancreas could have been transplanted somewhere else in the embryo, and would then have gone on to form something different. I suspect not.

Rutter: We haven't done those experiments.

Le Douarin: I don't think that you can tell that at this stage the cells of pancreatic rudiment are similar to the other cells of the gut. In the avian embryo, we have performed the experiments mentioned by Dr Cooke, i.e. heterotopic transplantation of the isolated pancreatic endoderm into the mesenchyme of the somatopleure. From the 10-somite stage onwards some cells of the endoderm at the level of the anterior intestinal portal (where the ventral buds of the pancreas arise at a later stage) are already determined to differentiate into pancreatic structures (Le Douarin *et al.* 1968). Do you think that your mesenchymal factor is widespread throughout the mesenchyme of the embryo?

Rutter: Yes.

Le Douarin: In our earlier experiments, we found that the embryonic mesenchyme could be divided into two zones according to its ability to promote the differentiation of endodermal rudiments: a dorsal zone which includes undifferentiated somitic and limb bud mesenchyme, allowing the endoderm to survive but hardly to proliferate and not to differentiate; and the derivatives of the lateral plate mesoderm (including splanchnopleure and somatopleure), which at any level of the embryo are able to stimulate both proliferation and differentiation of the already determined endodermal rudiments.

Rutter: I think that any cell which is determined for pancreas is likely to have a low level of pancreatic specific proteins. That is a hypothesis. When a cell is 'determined', I think there is a change in the chromatin such that low levels of these products are obtained.

Le Douarin: It is also possible that the changes in chromatin which occur at the determination stage are not immediately followed by production of specific products.

Rutter: We only know that we can take mesenchyme from many different small parts of the embryo and it works in this system to a greater or lesser degree. We can't do it from adult; it must be embryonic. These tests are crude in the sense that this system is very sensitive to mesenchyme and only a few mesenchymal cells of the right sort are needed to trigger it off. I would like to try other mesenchymes, such as the mutant-type mesenchymes, rather specifically.

Gluecksohn-Waelsch: Where do you get your MF?

Rutter: One can get it from the same species but we routinely get it from the chick at the time of development when there is plenty of mesenchyme around.

Polani: Is there any evidence on whether MF might perhaps be nerve growth factor?

Rutter: It is a growth factor but not nerve growth factor or any one of a dozen other growth factors that are known. The action is very specific.

Newth: The implication of your thesis seems to be that in the early stages of production of specific protein, one and the same cell may be producing both exocrine and endocrine protein. Have you any direct evidence that this is really so at the early plateau stage?

Rutter: No, but we must ask that kind of a question. We are getting ready to look at gene products by making complementary DNA probes to messages of both exocrine and endocrine products.

Cooke: Could you do that immunologically?

Rutter: No, the levels are too low.

Saxén: Filters do not necessarily prevent cell contacts. I would think that your mesenchymal factor is not transmitting through the filter, but is carried by cytoplasmic processes in the filter.

Rutter: Patricia Coleman and Clifford Grobstein sectioned the filters and found that the cells extended into the fetus but never touched the cells on the other side. Nearly all the cells in the bottom layers started growing and I think it was unlikely that in our experiments many of the cells were touching. I do believe however that the distance has to be a small distance. I think our concepts merge in the sense that in many instances cell contact may be essential. That is, the 'range' of the factor is 0. The most important issue, I think, is that there doesn't have to be cell communication, in the sense of an internal transfusion of material.

Saxén: I think we agree.

Gardner: In suggesting the various types of interaction I think you used metabolic cooperation in a sense that would be unacceptable to many people. You distinguish it from cases of intimate cell contact, and what you refer to as metabolic cooperation most people would call cross-feeding.

The other point I want to make is about the relationship between morphogenesis and differentiation, because it seems that your system and Dr Eguchi's are rather different. As I understand it, in Dr Eguchi's system lens-crystallin is being produced at a time when the cells are still in a flat sheet, before they undergo morphogenesis to form a three-dimensional structure. How good is the evidence that these two processes really are dependent on each other?

Another point is about the specificity, or lack of it, of the mesenchyme: could one exclude the possibility that the endoderm begins by inducing a change in the mesenchyme which then causes the mesenchyme to produce this factor?

Rutter: There is indirect evidence that epithelium induces mesenchyme to produce something, but I don't know whether it is the mesenchymal factor. Such a loop of regulation seems quite feasible.

Škreb: Is this factor really highly specific? Have you ever tried putting another type of epithelium on the Sepharose beads? And have you tried different factors extracted from other tissues?

Rutter: Both those experiments have been done many times. The factor is very specific: no other protein or factor or combination of factors that we have ever been able to use replaces this material.

With respect to the action of factor on other cells, if we make a rather crude preparation from chicken there is a small effect on the pituitary gland. There is a cross-effect like that but we have never been able to get an effect on salivary gland. We believe that there are whole families of compounds which come out of mesenchymal tissues and are more or less specific for a particular kind of receptor. These compounds are either non-specific or specific for each one of the cells, but because the interaction occurs in such a localized way, in a particular area, there will be some instances in which mesenchyme is absolutely specific for epithelium and other instances where cross-reaction is possible.

References

Le Douarin, N., Bussonnet, C. & Chaumont, F. (1968) Etude des capacités de différenciation et du rôle morphogène de l'endoderme pharyngien chez l'embryon d'oiseau. *Ann. Embryol. Morphog. 1*, 29–39

Regulation of mesenchymal cell growth during human limb morphogenesis through glycosaminoglycan-adenylate cyclase interaction at the cell surface

ROBERT O. KELLEY* and GENE C. PALMER†

Departments of Anatomy and Pharmacology†, The University of New Mexico School of Medicine, Albuquerque*

Abstract To determine whether glycosaminoglycan-containing components of the embryonic extracellular matrix–cell surface complex are associated with adenylate cyclase (EC 4.6.1.1), mesenchymal cells were disaggregated from human limb buds (stage 15) and incubated for 30 min at 37 °C in either (*a*) testicular hyaluronidase (hyaluronoglucosidase, EC 3.2.1.35), (*b*) neuraminidase (EC 3.2.1.18), (*c*) Pronase (microbial metalloenzyme, EC 3.4.24.4), (*d*) trypsin (EC 3.4.21.4), or (*e*) control buffered saline, before analysis of enzyme activity (stimulated with 10^{-4}M-noradrenaline (norepinephrine)). Treatment with sodium fluoride revealed an active catalytic component of the adenylate cyclase system. However, little receptor activity was observed after incubation of cells with noradrenaline. Removal of glycosaminoglycan increased enzyme activation by noradrenaline over that of controls, suggesting the presence of a developed but masked receptor component. Untreated cells reaching density-dependent inhibition of growth after incubation in noradrenaline had enzyme activity similar to that of hyaluronidase-treated mesenchymal cells. Patterns of distribution in G_1, S and $G_2 + M$ analysed by flow microfluorometry after enzyme treatment were identical to controls. In addition, cells incubated for 4 h in growth medium containing noradrenaline had normal cell cycle distributions. Cells incubated in medium containing dibutyryl cyclic AMP (db-cyclicAMP: 10^{-5} to 10^{-8}M) had a population doubling time of 40 or more hours (in contrast to an approximate 24 h generation time for untreated cells), and exhibited a consistent perturbation in S. Furthermore, cells incubated in hyaluronidase and cultured for four additional hours in noradrenaline show a pattern of perturbation in S identical to cells cultured in db-cyclic AMP. We conclude that limb mesenchymal cells have developed both receptor and catalytic components of the adenylate cyclase system and that enzyme receptivity to hormonal stimulation is potentiated when cell-surface glycosaminoglycan is reduced.

Growth of vertebrate limbs is predominantly distal (Janners & Searls 1970; Searls & Janners 1971) and interactions between epithelium and mesenchyme through surface-associated extracellular matrix are required for normal morphogenesis and cytodifferentiation (Faber 1971). At least two components of matrices, the collagens and acid mucopolysaccharides (glycosaminoglycans), are known to be important in developmental interactions (Bernfield *et al.* 1973; Meier & Hay 1974), and structural differentiation of collagen and other matrix elements occurs during early development of the vertebrate limb (Kelley & Bluemink 1974). Unfortunately, mechanisms by which cells interact with the microenvironments of developing extracellular matrices are poorly understood (Grobstein 1967).

In recent years, it has become clear that sensory components of cells are located within the complex structure of their external surfaces. Reactions with extracellular factors and with other cells often generate signals which evoke changes in synthesis within the cell interior (Moscona 1974): changes, for example, which may have a role in controlling rates of cell proliferation (Burger 1970). This external cell boundary is organized into a complex fluid-mosaic of protein, lipid and carbohydrate (Singer & Nicolson 1972; Bretscher 1973), the latter contributing to a stainable coat (glycocalyx) associated with the external surface of the subjacent cell membrane (Rambourg & Leblond 1967). These carbohydrates are often complexed with protein, e.g. glycoprotein and glycosaminoglycan (GAG), and with lipid. Numerous lines of evidence suggest that carbohydrate components of the cell coat are involved in cell recognition and adhesion (Roseman 1970), transformation (Inbar & Sachs 1969), and the regulation of cell growth (Mora 1973).

In addition, a growing number of reports indicate that intracellular cyclic purine nucleotides, especially cyclic AMP, are also associated with the control of cell proliferation (Abell & Monahan 1973). Levels of cyclic AMP within a cell are determined by rates of synthesis, catalysed by the plasma-membrane-bound enzyme, adenylate cyclase (EC 4.6.1.1), and by rates of hydrolysis effected by the cyclic AMP phosphodiesterases (EC 3.1.4.1 and 3.1.4.18). The amount of intracellular cAMP fluctuates through the cell cycle (mitotic cells exhibit reduced levels whereas cells in early G_1 possess increased quantities: Sheppard & Prescott 1972) and adenylate cyclase and phosphodiesterase activities are increased and decreased, respectively, as cells develop density-dependent inhibition of growth (Anderson *et al.* 1973).

Since carbohydrate in the glycocalyx (and the investing extracellular matrix) and the activity of adenylate cyclase in the subjacent cell membrane are both implicated in the regulation of cell growth, one may ask whether these components interact with each other or whether they are elements of separate regulatory mechanisms affecting cell proliferation. Stated more concisely, do glycosaminoglycans present in the mesenchymal cell coat have a regulatory association with the plasma-membrane-bound enzyme, adenylate cyclase? Is a reduced amount of surface GAG permissive or repressive for the interaction of adenylate cyclase with biogenic amines known to affect enzyme activity? Furthermore, if GAG is found to interact with adenylate cyclase, is this information transmitted to the cell interior so that behaviour is altered in a consistent pattern?

To probe these questions, we have examined cell-cycle behaviour and RNA synthesis after surface alteration of disaggregated mesenchymal cells from limb buds of human embryos (stage 15) after therapeutic interruption of pregnancy (Kelley *et al.* 1973). In this report we demonstrate the presence of developed receptor and catalytic components of adenylate cyclase in mesenchymal cells; the altered sensitivity of receptors for biogenic amines after removal of GAG; and an associated perturbation of the cell cycle and an increased incorporation of [^{3}H]uridine into RNA after hormone-potentiated activity of adenylate cyclase.

CONDITIONS OF INCUBATION

To remove selected components from the external surface of mesenchymal cells, cultures in exponential and stationary growth were thoroughly rinsed with a glucose-potassium-sodium solution (GKN) and incubated for 30 min at 37 °C in saline containing either (*a*) testicular hyaluronidase (hyaluronoglucosidase, EC 3.2.1.35) (300 i.u./mg; protein-free, chromatographically pure; Nutritional Biochemicals Corp.); (*b*) neuraminidase (EC 3.2.1.18) (*Vibrio cholerae*, 50 i.u./ml; Schwarz Mann); (*c*) Pronase (microbial metalloenzyme, EC 3.4.24.4) (50 µg/ml; K and K laboratories); or (*d*) trypsin (EC 3.4.21.4) (50 µg/ml; K and K Laboratories). Control groups for all experiments were incubated under identical conditions in GKN without enzymes. In previous studies we have reported that these concentrations affect the cell coat but neither disrupt ultrastructure nor remove cells from their substrate (Kelley & Lauer 1975). Although caution must be taken over interpretation, since many commercial preparations of enzymes contain more than one activity, the following properties may be generally assigned to each enzyme. Testicular hyaluronidase digests chondroitin 4- and 6-sulphate in addition to the non-sulphated glycosaminoglycans, hyaluronate and chondroitin. Neuraminidase is specific for neuraminic acid glycosides, liberating sialic acid components of the polymer without affecting the remainder of the molecule. Pronase is a broad-spectrum protease which will digest virtually any protein to free amino acids, whereas trypsin catalyses the hydrolysis of peptide bonds in which the carboxyl group of either lysine or arginine participates. All treated and untreated cultures were incubated further at 37 °C in:

(a) Eagle's minimal essential medium (MEM) containing noradrenaline (norepinephrine) (either 10^{-4}M or 10^{-5}M, dissolved in bovine serum albumin) for 4 h;

(b) MEM containing dibutyryl-cyclic AMP (db-cyclic AMP; 10^{-4}, 10^{-5}, 10^{-6} and 10^{-8}M) for 4 h;

(c) MEM for 4 h (control); and

(d) groups identical to (a), (b) and (c) to which 5 μCi/ml of [5-^{3}H]uridine (New England Nuclear) had been added.

ANALYSIS OF ADENYLATE CYCLASE ACTIVITY

To determine activity of adenylate cyclase in treated and untreated groups, cells were removed from their substrate with a rubber policeman, pelleted and gently homogenized in 2mM-glycylglycine buffer (4°C, pH 7.4, containing 1mM-MgSO$_4$). Part of each homogenate was removed for protein determination (Lowry et al. 1951) and activity of adenylate cyclase was measured on the remainder of each sample by the method of Palmer (1973). An incubation mixture consisting of the following constituents (in final concentrations) was used to assay specific enzyme activity: (a) 0.1 ml of glycylglycine buffer containing 3.3mM-theophylline and 40mM-Hepes buffer at pH 7.4; (b) 0.25 ml of the crude enzyme preparation containing about 0.1 mg protein; (c) 0.1 ml of buffer containing 2mM-ATP and 3mM-MgSO$_4$; and (d) depending upon conditions, 0.05 ml of either control buffer, buffer containing 5mM-NaF, or buffer containing either noradrenaline (10^{-4}M), histamine (10^{-4}M), testosterone (10^{-5}M) or 5-hydroxytryptamine (serotonin) (10^{-4}M). Components were mixed at 4°C, and the reaction was initiated by adding the Mg-ATP mixture (c) and then terminated after 12 min by boiling the samples for 5 min. Samples were cooled and centrifuged at 1000 × g for 10 min, and a sample was assayed for cyclic AMP levels by the protein-binding assay developed by Gilman (1970).

Disaggregated limb mesenchymal cells which attach to substrate and grow as primary cultures have a population doubling time of about 22–24 hours and exhibit a basal level of adenylate cyclase activity which generates 38 ± 10 pmoles of cyclic AMP/mg protein in 12 min. As cells become density-inhibited in their growth patterns (stationary phase), about 71 ± 14 pmol of cyclic AMP/mg protein is produced during a 12-min reaction period. Clearly, the adenylate cyclase system has developed in limb mesenchymal cells and an increase in its activity correlates with a decrease in growth potential of cells in primary culture. Treatment of homogenates with 5mM-NaF generates a relative increase in catalytic activity of about sevenfold (± 3.5-fold) during exponential growth whereas a ninefold (± 3.1-fold) relative increase is observed in cells in stationary growth.

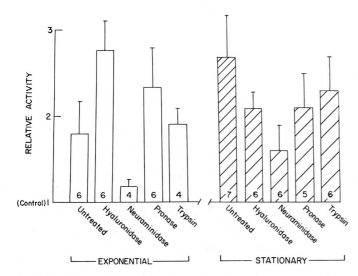

FIG. 1. Relative activity of adenylate cyclase in enzyme-treated and untreated mesenchymal cells after stimulation with noradrenaline (10^{-4} M). The base-line represents control (basal, unstimulated) levels of activity for each experimental group.

Fig. 1 records the relative activity of adenylate cyclase in untreated and treated groups after stimulation with L-noradrenaline, compared to control (unstimulated) levels of enzyme activity. During exponential growth, noradrenaline increased the activity of adenylate cyclase about 1.8-fold over unstimulated levels. Adenylate cyclase activity increased nearly threefold over control levels when cell surfaces were treated with hyaluronidase before stimulation with noradrenaline, suggesting that hyaluronidase-sensitive GAG at the cell surface is associated with receptor components of the adenylate cyclase system. In addition, cells treated in this manner experienced varied population-doubling times, most greater than 40 h. Treatment with neuraminidase, however, removed the sensitivity of adenylate cyclase to stimulation by noradrenaline, suggesting that sialic acid-containing glycoproteins may be part of the receptor complex for this biogenic amine. Treatment with Pronase and trypsin did not evoke a stimulation of enzyme activity significantly different from that in the untreated controls.

When cells achieve density-dependent inhibition of growth, stimulation of adenylate cyclase in untreated cells attains levels similar to hyaluronidase-treated cells in exponential growth. Since Kraemer & Tobey (1972) have demonstrated that cells shed GAG (heparin sulphate) from the cell surface immediately before mitosis, it seems reasonable to suggest that the increased sensitivity of adenylate cyclase to noradrenaline during stationary growth reflects a cell-

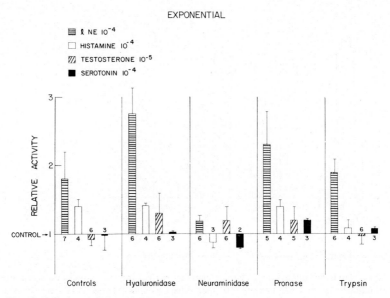

FIG. 2. Relative activity of adenylate cyclase in enzyme-treated and untreated cells in exponential growth after stimulation with noradrenaline (l-NE, 10^{-4} M), histamine (10^{-4} M), testosterone (10^{-5} M) and 5-hydroxytryptamine (serotonin) (10^{-4}M).

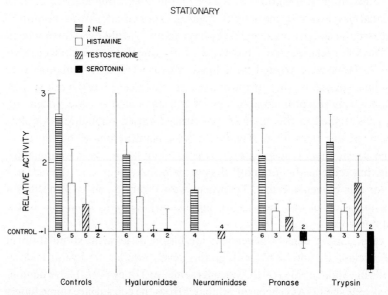

FIG. 3. Relative activities of adenylate cyclase in enzyme-treated and untreated mesenchymal cells in stationary growth after stimulation with noradrenaline (10^{-4} M), histamine (10^{-4} M), testosterone (10^{-5} M) and 5-hydroxytryptamine (10^{-4}M).

initiated removal of surface components which render receptor elements more accessible to stimulating factors. Treatment with hyaluronidase, neuraminidase, Pronase and trypsin facilitates the relative increase of adenylate cyclase activity over control levels in stationary cells, but these levels are lower than those in cells with untreated, presumably unaltered, surfaces.

Histamine, testosterone and 5-hydroxytryptamine have little effect on adenylate cyclase activity in mesenchymal cells in either exponential (Fig. 2) or stationary (Fig. 3) conditions of growth. It is of interest to note that treatment of the cell surface with neuraminidase either reduces or removes the ability of these exogenous factors to bind to receptor components, again suggesting the glycoprotein nature of these elements.

ANALYSIS OF INCORPORATION OF [³H]URIDINE INTO RNA

Fig. 4 records the incorporation of [³H]uridine into RNA (analysed by the method of Ball *et al.* 1973) in treated and untreated cultures incubated with noradrenaline. The base-line of the graph represents control levels of incorporation for each experiment after 15, 30, 60, 90 and 120 min. Incubation of cells in hyaluronidase resulted in an initial increase of incorporation into RNA after

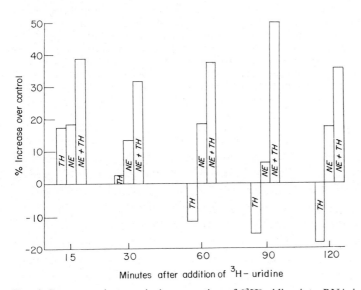

FIG. 4. Percentage increase in incorporation of [³H]uridine into RNA in treated and untreated cell groups, 15, 30, 60, 90 and 120 min after the addition of label. *TH*, mesenchymal cells incubated in testicular hyaluronidase for 30 min before introduction of label; *NE*, cells treated with 10^{-5} M-L-noradrenaline for 30 min before addition of label; *NE+TH*, cells grown in TH for 30 min before addition of L-noradrenaline.

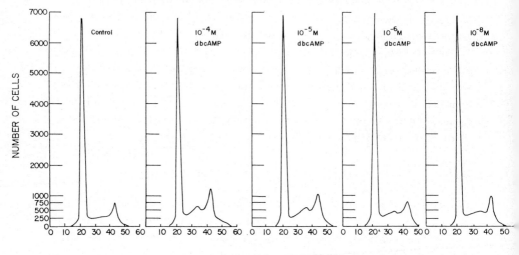

FIG. 5. Distribution profiles of cell cycles in human limb mesenchymal cells grown in serum-supplemented MEM containing db-cyclic AMP (10^{-4} to 10^{-8} M). The prominent peak at channel 20 of each curve reflects the number of G_1 cells in the population; the smaller peaks at channel 40 represent cells in G_2 and M. The portion of each curve between peaks reflects numbers of cells in active DNA synthesis (S). Incubation in db-cyclic AMP effects a perturbation of the S distribution, an increase in the number of cells in either G_2 or M, and a concomitant increase in population-doubling time (from approximately 24 to 40 or more hours).

15 min, followed by a steady decline of synthesis to the termination of the experiment after 2 h. In contrast, noradrenaline stimulated the incorporation of uridine into RNA over the two-hour period, but the percentage of increase fluctuated during that time. Incubation of cells in hyaluronidase for 30 min before the introduction of noradrenaline resulted in a substantial increase in the incorporation of labelled nucleotide into RNA at each point monitored over the two-hour period. Peak incorporation of label into RNA occurred at 90 min in treated cells stimulated with 10^{-5}M-noradrenaline, whereas a similar peak appeared after 60 min in treated cells incubated in 10^{-4}M concentration (not illustrated). Interpretation of the increased incorporation of uridine into RNA after surface alteration awaits determination of which species of RNA is most readily affected. The observation that peak incorporation of label is dependent on concentration of noradrenaline acting at the surface indicates that receptor

components of adenylate cyclase are not altered by treatment with hyaluronidase, however.

CYCLE PROFILES OF CELLS TREATED WITH DB-CYCLIC AMP

To detect perturbation of behaviour during the life cycle of treated and untreated cells, we prepared cultures in exponential and stationary phases of growth for flow microfluorometry (as described by Kelley *et al.* 1973), after Feulgen hydrolysis and subsequent staining with acriflavine. Fluorescent signals (relative DNA content), generated as single cells traverse an argon-ion laser beam, were accumulated in a multichannel pulse-height analyser and displayed as pulse-amplitude frequency-distribution histograms (e.g. Fig. 5). Patterns of cell distribution in G_1,S and $G_2 + M$ for each experimental group were analysed directly from the respective histograms.

The cytofluorometric profile of relative DNA content in disaggregated mesenchymal cells in exponential growth is illustrated in Fig. 5 (control). The pro-

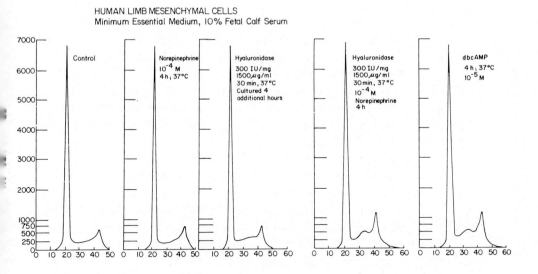

RELATIVE   DNA   CONTENT
(Channel   Number)

Fig. 6. Distribution profiles for cell cycles of mesenchymal cells incubated in noradrenaline (10^{-4} M); hyaluronidase (300 i.u./mg); noradrenaline (norepinephrine) after hyaluronidase treatment; and db-cyclic AMP (10^{-5} M). Profiles of cells treated with noradrenaline and hyaluronidase alone are similar in pattern to controls. Cells incubated in hyaluronidase before treatment with noradrenaline, however, exhibit distribution patterns similar to cultures grown in medium containing db-cyclic AMP.

minent peak at channel 20 reflects the number of G_1 cells in the population, whereas the smaller peak at about channel 40 represents numbers of cells in G_2 and M. The portion of the curve between peaks reflects cells in active DNA synthesis (S). Incubation of cells for 4 h in varying concentrations of db-cyclic AMP (Fig. 5, dbcAMP) produced a prominent perturbation of the S distribution and an apparent increase in the number of cells in $G_2 + M$. Variation of the number of cells in S diminished as concentrations of db-cyclic AMP decreased. In addition, population doubling times of cells cultured in medium containing 10^{-6}M-db-cyclic AMP increased to 40 or more hours. As in other cultured cells (Sheppard & Bannai 1972), increased cellular levels of cyclic AMP are associated with the biological signal for retarded growth of limb mesenchymal cells.

CYCLE PROFILES OF CELLS TREATED WITH HYALURONIDASE AND NORADRENALINE

Fig. 6 records cycle profiles of mesenchymal cells incubated in medium containing either hyaluronidase or noradrenaline. Cells treated with hyaluronidase and prepared for analysis either immediately or after four additional hours of culture had patterns of distribution similar to untreated (control) cells. Similarly, 10^{-4}M-noradrenaline had no demonstrable effect on cycle distributions after 4 h incubation. However, cells treated with hyaluronidase for 30 min and then cultured in noradrenaline for 4 h after removal of enzyme revealed a prominent perturbation in the S distribution of the profile and an apparent increase in the number of cells in the G_2 and M phases of the cell cycle. Distribution of cells after 4 h culture in 10^{-5}M-db-cyclic AMP is included in Fig. 6 for comparison of patterns.

Since stimulation of adenylate cyclase activity after reduction of hyaluronidase-sensitive GAG at the cell surface results in cell behaviour similar to that evoked by addition of exogenous db-cyclic AMP, our suggestion that the effects of surface alteration/stimulation are mediated via the adenylate cyclase–cyclic AMP pathway is strengthened. However, perturbations of the cell cycle are difficult to interpret. Vasiliev et al. (1970) noted that treatment of density-inhibited mouse embryo fibroblasts with hyaluronidase evoked a stimulation of DNA synthesis and mitosis from cells normally blocked in G_1. Their results may be duplicated in our experiments (Fig. 6) in that clearly more cells are in S and either G_2 or M after treatment with db-cyclic AMP or stimulation of adenylate cyclase activity. It is not clear, however, whether the increase in the number of cells in S is the result of more cells leaving G_1 or fewer cells entering G_2 after stimulation.

DISCUSSION

The presence and participation of glycosaminoglycans in various developmental events is well known. For example, Lippman (1968) demonstrated that sulphated GAG inhibits mitosis of mouse L cells in culture. The synthesis and degradation of hyaluronate is associated with proliferation and cytodifferentiation, respectively, of embryonic mesenchymal cells, both *in vitro* and *in vivo* (Toole 1973; Toole & Gross 1971; Toole *et al.* 1972). And Bernfield *et al.* (1973) have documented the role of GAG in the branching morphogenesis of epithelial organs. However, without much additional information on the localization of GAG within and without the mesenchymal cell, the precise nature and composition of GAG at the external cell surface and extracellular matrix, the rates of synthesis and turnover of surface-associated GAG and the activities of glycosyltransferases, etc., it is premature to attempt a prediction of the role in limb development of adenylate-cyclase-associated GAG. Hormone-potentiated enzyme activity after reduction of surface GAG may be an interesting cellular event, but unrelated to the physiological regulation of mesenchymal cell growth which contributes to the forming of limbs (Kelley 1975).

However, it is tempting to speculate that subtle modifications of surface components of mesenchymal cells play a role *in vivo* in permitting extracellular factors (e.g. trophic substances from nerve cells; Singer 1968) to interact with receptor loci of the adenylate cyclase system. From our present observations, an intact complement of GAG would mask receptor sites, resulting in a cell that is dividing at a basal rate. If a cell-initiated reduction in surface GAG begins, or if cells relocate in an environment which is less rich in complex carbohydrate, it seems reasonable to imagine an increased interaction of extracellular factors with adenylate cyclase, an interaction which could alter a cell's proliferative rate and, potentially, permit a shift in cell behaviour from a proliferative mode to one of early differentiation (G_o). It is hoped that such speculation may prove valuable in contributing to our understanding of the spatial patterns which underlie morphogenesis of the human limb.

CONCLUSIONS

These results show that GAG in the mesenchymal cell coat interacts with receptor components of the adenylate cyclase system in the cell membrane. When GAG at the surface is reduced, the relative activity of adenylate cyclase increases after stimulation with the biogenic amine, noradrenaline. As a result, intracellular levels of cyclic AMP increase and exponentially growing cells in turn develop longer generation times, a perturbation in the S phase of the cell cycle, an increased number of cells in either G_2 or M, and an increase in the incorporation of [^{3}H]uridine into RNA. Although the molecular nature of the noradrenaline receptor is not well understood, it is doubtful that GAG is an active component of that receptor. Rather, present results support the conclusion that surface GAG is a cryptic element on the receptor components of adenylate cyclase, masking but not prohibiting the binding of biogenic amine at the surface. The increase in responsiveness of adenylate cyclase to noradrenaline as cells reach stationary conditions suggests that cells may inherently modify the amount of surface GAG as cell density increases. Whether this event contributes to a slowing of growth or is merely an attribute associated with that condition remains to be investigated.

ACKNOWLEDGEMENTS

Grateful acknowledgement is made to Dr Harry Crissman of the Los Alamos Scientific Laboratories for assistance with flow microfluorometry; to Mr John H. Nilson and Ms Rita Laurer for able technical assistance; and to the United States Public Health Service for grant support through HD06177 and MH21584. R.O. Kelley is the recipient of a Research Career Development Award (HD70407).

References

ABELL, C.W. & MONAHAN, T.M. (1973) The role of adenosine 3'5'-cyclic monophosphate in the regulation of mammalian cell division. *J. Cell Biol. 59*, 549–558

ANDERSON, W.B., JOHNSON, G.S. & PASTAN, I. (1973) Transformation of chick embryo fibroblasts by wild-type and temperature-sensitive Rous sarcoma virus alters adenylate cyclase activity. *Proc. Natl. Acad. Sci. USA 70*, 1055–1059

BALL, C. R., VANDENBERG, H. W. & POYNTER, R. W. (1973) in *Methods in Cell Biology* (Prescott, D.M., ed.), Academic Press, New York

BERNFIELD, M.R., COHN, R.H. & BANNERJEE, S.D. (1973) Glycosaminoglycans and epithelial organ formation. *Am. Zool. 13*, 1067–1084

BRETSCHER, M.S. (1973) Membrane structure: Some general principles. *Science (Wash. D.C.) 181*, 622–629

BURGER, M.M. (1970) Proteolytic enzymes initiating cell division and escape from contact inhibition of growth. *Nature (Lond.) 277*, 170–171

FABER, J. (1971) Vertebrate limb ontogeny and limb regeneration: morphogenetic parallels. *Adv. Morphog. 9*, 127–147

GILMAN, A.G. (1970) A protein binding assay for adenosine 3',5'-cyclic monophosphate. *Proc. Natl. Acad. Sci. USA 67*, 305–312

GROBSTEIN, C. (1967) Mechanism of organogenetic tissue interaction. *Natl. Cancer Inst. Monogr. 26*, 279–299

INBAR, M. & SACHS, L. (1969) Structural difference in sites on the surface membrane of normal and transformed cells. *Nature (Lond.) 223*, 710–712

JANNERS, M. & SEARLS, R. L. (1970) Change in rate of cellular proliferation during the differentiation of cartilage and muscle in the mesenchyme of the embryonic chick wing. *Dev. Biol. 23*, 136–168

KELLEY, R. O. (1975) Ultrastructural identification of extracellular matrix and cell surface components during limb morphogenesis in man. *J. Embryol. Exp. Morphol. 34*, 1–18

KELLEY, R. O. & BLUEMINK, J. G. (1974) An ultrastructural analysis of cell and matrix differentiation during early limb development in *Xenopus laevis. Dev. Biol. 37*, 1–17

KELLEY, R. O. & LAUER, R. B. (1975) Nature of external surface of cultured human embryo fibroblasts: ultrastructural and cytochemical analysis utilizing stain and lectin probes. *Differentiation 3*, 91–98

KELLEY, R. O., BAKER, T. I., CRISSMAN, H. A. & HENDERSON, C. A. (1973) Ultrastructure and growth of human limb mesenchyme (HLM15) *in vitro. Anat. Rec. 175*, 657–672

KRAEMER, P. M. & TOBEY, R. A. (1972) Cell-cycle dependent desquamation of heparan sulfate from the cell surface. *J. Cell Biol. 55*, 713–717

LIPPMAN, M. (1968) in *Epithelial-Mesenchymal Interactions* (Fleischmajer, R. & Billingham, R. E., eds.), Williams & Wilkins, Baltimore

LOWRY, O. H., ROSEBROUGH, N. J., FARR, A. L. & RANDALL, R. J. (1951) Protein measurement with the Folin phenol reagent. *J. Biol. Chem. 193*, 265–275

MEIER, S. & HAY, E. D. (1974) Control of corneal differentiation by extracellular materials. Collagen as a promoter and stabilizer of epithelial stroma production. *Dev. Biol. 38*, 249–270

MORA, P. T. (1973) in *Membrane-Mediated Information* (Kent, P. W., ed.), American Elsevier, New York

MOSCONA, A. A. (1974) in *The Cell Surface in Development* (Moscona, A. A., ed.), Wiley, New York

PALMER, G. C. (1973) Adenyl cyclase in neuronal and glial-enriched fractions from rat and rabbit brain. *Res. Commun. Chem. Pathol. Pharmacol. 5*, 603–613

RAMBOURG, A. & LEBLOND, C. P. (1967) Electron microscope observations on the carbohydrate-rich cell coat present at the surface of cells in the rat. *J. Cell Biol. 32*, 27–53

ROSEMAN, S. (1970) The synthesis of complex carbohydrates by multiglycosyltransferase systems and their potential function in intercellular adhesion. *Chem. Phys. Lipids 5*, 270–297

SEARLS, R. L. & JANNERS, M. Y. (1971) The initiation of limb bud outgrowth in the embryonic chick. *Dev. Biol. 24*, 198–213

SHEPPARD, J. R. & BANNAI, S. (1974) *Control of Proliferation in Animal Cells* (Clarkson, B. & Baserga, R., eds.) *(Cold Spring Harbor Conf. Cell Proliferation)*, Cold Spring Harbor, New York

SHEPPARD, J. R. & PRESCOTT, D. M. (1972) Cyclic AMP levels in synchronized mammalian cells. *Exp. Cell Res. 75*, 293–296

SINGER, M. (1968) *Systems Theory and Biology* (Mesarovic, M. D., ed.), Springer, New York

SINGER, S. J. & NICOLSON, G. L. (1972) The fluid mosaic model of the structure of cell membranes. *Science (Wash. D.C.) 175*, 720–731

TOOLE, B. P. (1973) Hyaluronate and hyaluronidase in morphogenesis and differentiation. *Am. Zool. 13*, 1061–1066

TOOLE, B. P. & GROSS, J. (1971) The extracellular matrix of the regenerating newt limb: Synthesis and removal of hyaluronate prior to differentiation. *Dev. Biol. 25*, 57–77

TOOLE, B. P., JACKSON, G. & GROSS, J. (1972) Hyaluronate in morphogenesis: inhibition of chondrogenesis *in vitro. Proc. Natl. Acad. Sci. USA 69*, 1384–1386

VASILIEV, J. M., GELFAND, I. M., GUELSTEIN, V. I. & FETISOVA, E. K. (1970) Stimulation of DNA synthesis of cultures of mouse embryo fibroblast-like cells. *J. Cell Physiol. 75*, 305–314

Discussion

Edidin: It would be nice to think of this extracellular matrix as a general controlling feature for the cell surface, just because of its physical bulk and complex meshwork. The opposite idea is that what you have is a filter with lots of room for things like hormones to permeate. It only looks bulky because you are staining it with ruthenium red. Rather than a filter, this network may be an ion shaft. If this system were saturated with calcium ions, what would that do to adenylate cyclase activity in the cells? When you take away that matrix, you are taking away a lot more than just the stuff that stains.

Kelley: I have no information about calcium ion activity. Recently we have attempted to localize the adenylate cyclase activity in the cells of the disaggregated limb. I was not surprised to find it in the membrane but I was surprised to find it in some of the mitochondria of these cells. Therefore another dimension to this might be that when the filtering aspects of the extracellular matrix are reduced, extracellular amines can get into cells as a consequence of altered membrane permeability. I have no experimental evidence that I am not altering the filtering properties of the cell surface and associated matrix.

Rutter: The problem of using biochemical amines as a probe is not just that a charge can be bound but that these amines are susceptible to oxidation, and the oxidized products exert their own influence in this system.

Kelley: I am not advocating that noradrenaline is in any way physiological under these conditions. It was only an agent which enhanced adenylate cyclase activity. At present, I have no information on the activity of products of oxidation at the cell surface.

Rutter: The point was not that noradrenaline is naturally active but that the effects you get may not be directly from adenylate cyclase but indirectly, through the rest of the stuff. Another probe which didn't have that kind of problem associated with it would be better. Glucagon receptors in those cells might be measured on changes on prostaglandins.

Edidin: Glucagon is degraded by a number of enzyme systems found with most cell preparations.

Rutter: I think you may get rid of glucagon degradation by using various inhibitors. The choice of a probe is important because one doesn't know whether the sort of thing you are getting is artifactual or real.

Kelley: For years we have been thinking in terms of cell interactions —Clifford Grobstein used the term 'matrix interaction'—but we have no grasp of what the matrix is. Recently several investigators have started looking at the collagens and glycosaminoglycans, yet when one examines the matrix structurally the term filter or barrier becomes even more real. Earlier we were talking about contacts and no contacts. At least in this system during the period of inductive interaction there is a substantial structural barrier between the interacting elements. I suspect the same is true in your system, Dr Rutter. One might begin to probe how cells respond after they have conditioned their own immediate microenvironment.

Rutter: Have you never seen cells interacting in any of your studies?

Kelley: Not between the epithelium and the mesenchyme. In this system the mesenchymal cells send processes up to the basal lamina but they never penetrate through it to the epithelium. The basal lamina is always intact, at least in man. Is it the same in your system?

Rutter: One can do the experiment with and without basal lamina. It works with the basal lamina, but I can't say this means that the factor acts through the basal lamina because I don't know whether there are holes through the basal lamina.

There is a contrast between the kinds of effects that we are seeing with the pancreas and the kinds of effects you are studying. In most cultivated cells, if cyclic AMP is increased, cell division is decreased, and that is what you are seeing. In our case it is positive regulation: as we increase cyclic AMP, we increase DNA synthesis.

Kelley: The same is true in chick embryo fibroblasts, to some degree.

Rutter: So one doesn't know whether, in epithelial cells, there is a different sort of regulation in which cyclic AMP is a positive regulator instead of a negative one, or whether there is a signal which is simply tripped by cyclic AMP and then there is a singular pattern? I suspect that most of the cultivated cells may be related to mesenchyme.

McLaren: Dr Kelley, you showed in your earlier work (Kelley 1970) that there are moments in time and space in the morphogenesis of the limb where cell migration may be important. How do you envisage cell migration as fitting in with the extracellular matrix that you have shown us?

Kelley: The matrix may play a directional role, or it may encourage cells to migrate. In early stages of mammalian morphogenesis, unlike avian development, it seems that proliferation is the predominant initiator of limb outgrowth. At about stage 15, it seems that a principal growth mechanism is cell division. At about stages 16–18 a hand plate forms and in sections one can see the cartilaginous primordia of the humerus, radius and ulna, and associated digits. Two things then happen almost simultaneously: focal areas of necrosis develop and what might be interpreted as migration of cells away from these presumptive interdigital areas. John Fallon (unpublished observations) has suggested that the necrotic areas do not grow backwards down into the limb. Rather, mesenchymal cells move away from the presumptive interdigit concomitant with digital outgrowth in a distal direction. The matrix at this point becomes electron-lucent. The cell-poor areas do not have as much detectable matrix as at earlier stages when cells were still proliferating in that area. In addition, there are striking differences in this extracellular matrix structure which make one wonder whether cells are 'trapped'. As the matrix slowly changes, other genomically controlled behaviour develops; cells begin to divide and others move away.

Reference

KELLEY, R.O. (1970) An electron microscopic study of mesenchyme during development of interdigital spaces in Man. *Anat. Rec. 168*, 43–54

Final discussion

McLaren: Our meeting began with a session on differentiation and determination in the mammalian embryo, and the fate of the various cell populations. We discussed what we meant by 'determination' and we seemed to be in fair agreement on definitions but it became clear later that we were by no means in agreement about what determination actually involves. We dealt with both preimplantation and postimplantation development but much of the discussion centred on the development of the blastocyst, both the differentiation into trophectoderm and inner cell mass, and the rather mysterious phenomenon of vacuolization and its relevance to blastocoele formation. It became clear that we are in a good position now to formulate hypotheses which can be tested, and a number of new experimental approaches were suggested. Apart from the urgent need for investigation of a bigger range of species, my strongest impression was of the need for a more rigorous assessment of cell types, for example the use of electron microscopy to detect tight junctions and thus identify trophectoderm cells.

Further discussion of terminology for the various cell layers in the early period, and further clarification of the fate of the primitive endoderm, seemed to be needed. In this final session we might deal briefly with these points; also Dr Gardner has agreed to tell us more about his experiments on injecting teratocarcinoma cells into blastocysts.

We then considered the role of cell proliferation and cell movement. It became clear that there is not yet enough information for these quantitative aspects of development to be linked with determinative events, at least in mammals, but obviously this is the goal towards which one must work.

Next we moved on to genetic and chromosomal influences on development. One strong emphasis was on how early the embryonic genome starts functioning, both at the biochemical level as Dr Chapman showed us, and at the morphological level described by Dr Pedersen. At the chromosomal level Dr Gropp told us about the late effects of trisomy, going right up to birth, but it became clear there too, I think, that the primary effects of the various chromosome imbalances may well be exerted substantially earlier, maybe as early as gastrulation. We moved on to the antigenic maturation of the embryo, with particular reference to antigens at the *H-2* locus, and the role of the cell surface, both in antigenic differentiation and in ultrastructural differentiation in *T* locus mutants. The circumstantial evidence is certainly very strong that cell surface defects are primary in these mutants, and direct immunological evidence on this point may be forthcoming before long.

We had a useful discussion on possible ways of improving *in vitro* culture systems and we also considered the types of gene action that can affect early development.

We considered differentiation in the context of the vertebrate eye, pancreas and limb. We saw the possible link-up between biochemistry and morphogenesis, though again the direct link-up must await future work. At the end we came back to the cell surface and the possible role of the extracellular matrix, or surface-associated matrix. It seemed as though cell contact (like human contact) was a relative rather than an absolute concept.

One point that surprised me was how little reference has been made this week to the role of the mother in development. In the Ciba Foundation Symposium 10 years ago on *Preimplantation Stages of Pregnancy*, there was considerable emphasis on the environment in which development was happening, the reproductive tract, yet in fact at that stage of development the maternal environment seems relatively unimportant. Once the embryo has implanted, it is in much more intimate contact with the mother, and one would think that maternal influences would play a larger part in development.

On terminology, I think the term trophectoderm is a great improvement on trophoblast, and inner cell mass I suppose is all right until somebody starts working on species where it is not inner. Descriptively, trophectoderm is polar or mural. The chief problem comes at the next point of decision, when the inner cell mass differentiates into two tissues that traditionally in mammals have been referred to as ectoderm and endoderm. They tend nowadays to be called primary or primitive ectoderm and endoderm. I have also heard the possible alternatives epiblast and hypoblast suggested. The choice between 'endoderm' and 'hypoblast' is not entirely linguistic, because it involves knowledge of the subsequent fate of the tissue.

TERMINOLOGY FOR GERM LAYERS

Gluecksohn-Waelsch: It is bad enough having had to get used to the inverted germ layer situation where the ectoderm is inside and the endoderm outside. 'Epi' and 'hypo' really mean above and below. That may be appropriate in species where the ectoderm is above and the endoderm is below, but it may confuse the issue in other species.

Cooke: The use of 'epi' and 'hypo' does bring out the probable homology with the comparable layers in the chick, once one has got used to turning it upside down mentally. I prefer this usage because it doesn't beg questions about what the cells are going to form, in terms of future structures.

McLaren: As far as possible, terminology should not beg questions.

Gluecksohn-Waelsch: Would the primary ectoderm then differentiate into intra-embryonic and extra-embryonic derivatives?

McLaren: No. If Richard Gardner's experiments are confirmed it looks as though the extra-embryonic ectoderm comes from the trophoblast (p. 13; Fig. 1, p. 48). The primary ectoderm or epiblast would differentiate into the embryonic part of the egg cylinder and would form the primitive streak, subsequently giving rise perhaps to all three germ layers, ectoderm, mesoderm and endoderm. Did you have some reservations about the fate of the primitive endoderm or hypoblast, Dr Rutter?

Rutter: I was less concerned about that aspect than about the experiments in which the various layers were separated and their fates were determined. The question is really one of plasticity. In large measure that is what happens but I don't know whether that is what must happen.

McLaren: Presumably the terminology should as far as possible reflect what actually happens in normal development.

Rutter: Yes.

Morriss: Dr Gardner, at what stage do you envisage the outer layer (endoderm or hypoblast) as changing over to intra-embryonic endoderm which has not come from the primary endoderm?

Gardner: We don't know whether the attenuated endoderm over the embryonic part of the egg cylinder just degenerates or whether it can be pushed up into the yolk sac region. It is premature to comment. We are now putting rat cells in and analysing various stages by immunofluorescence and we hope that will make it clear.

Morriss: If you used Hsu's (1973) technique and cultured to the stage at which postimplantation embryo culture can take over, wouldn't you be able to see whether the same cells were sitting there being endoderm all the time, or whether they were invaded and taken over by cells which had come from what we are calling primitive ectoderm?

Gardner: If one could get that system working so that morphogenesis was really normal then perhaps vitally dyed cells could afford a solution.

Morriss: I was thinking of cell markers as well.

Gardner: The problem with this sort of analysis with intra-species chimeric combinations in the mouse is the lack of a suitable marker that will identify all the progeny of injected cells *in situ*. With chromosome markers, one has to mash up the tissues. With glucosephosphate isomerase (EC 5.3.1.9) isozymes, again one has to mash up tissues. In the latter case I think we would be confident that we could detect a 3 % component but not much less than that. When we injected primitive endoderm cells into host embryos of a different strain, 50 % of the conceptuses analysed at about day 15 or day 17 were chimeras. The level of yolk sac chimerism was very high in some cases. So I think it is most unlikely that the cells failed to contribute to the embryonic endoderm for trivial reasons such as chance partitioning. There are enough of them to give a reasonable probability that they would contribute to the latter unless, as we believe, they are restricted in developmental potential from doing so.

Morriss: Even though your evidence is so good I am unable to understand it in relation to the ultrastructural evidence. Perhaps the early gut structures —foregut, midgut, hindgut, and the liver diverticulum—are all from this early so-called primitive endoderm, and the epithelium is colonized by these other cells at a much later stage when the gut is becoming more sophisticated.

Gardner: A certain amount of tissue is needed before the glucosephosphate isomerase analysis can be done. The idea of the late analysis at days 15–17 is that one can sample a whole lot of organs that are largely composed of endoderm.

Morriss: So you still don't know when primitive endoderm stops being part of the embryo—that is, if it ever was part of it?

Gardner: We just can't say whether it ever was. Even in morphology post-implantation stages are very confusing in the mouse. If normal morphogenesis beyond the blastocyst stage can be obtained *in vitro*, and I do not think it has yet, fate-mapping by use of vital dyes may help to resolve this and other problems. In addition, rat–mouse chimeras provide us with static pictures of the distribution of all mitotic descendants of injected cells at any stage after injection into blastocysts of the other species.

Gluecksohn-Waelsch: Where do you think the distal or parietal endoderm comes from?

Gardner: We can't say anything about that. It breaks down, together with the giant cells, by day 14 or so, so it has completely gone when we are doing our analysis. Again the injected rat cells will resolve that question. I should imagine that it is an extension of the proximal extra-embryonic endoderm.

Hensleigh: At what stage do you collect the rat cells that are injected?

Gardner: We are trying to do a series of injections of rat cells isolated from successive 24-hour stages to follow this endoderm problem through.

Kelley: Dr Škreb has suggested that the primary endoderm is a quiescent or latent tissue in culture. And Dr Rutter pointed out that there is plasticity in the endodermal derivatives. What do you mean by plasticity?

Rutter: Two aspects of plasticity are obviously important. One is where a cell is pluripotential and can clearly give rise to several other components. Another is where a group of cells can give rise in varying proportions to other derivatives. The analysis that I talked about was made for groups of cells, not for individual cells, so I don't know which of those is involved. There are several reasons for believing that plasticity really reflects a pluripotential cell but that is not a point that I wish to advocate strongly. And since everything we were looking at then was to some extent differentiated I wouldn't argue that it was not an aspect of differentiation. I would say that if that kind of plasticity is evident at a relatively late stage, conceivably one step before terminal differentiation, it could obviously be present earlier as well. I have been using the term to connote changes in function but I have no specific knowledge about the mechanism.

Newth: It is interesting that in a discussion of precision in terminology people are already using primary and primitive as if they were interchangeable. Mammalian embryologists will have to make up their minds. For different kinds of endoderm or ectoderm I would rather talk about primary than primitive, because primitive has connotations which I don't think mammalian embryologists are really interested in. On the evidence we have had, I think it would be premature to say much that is anything but topographical about the embryonic cell populations up to the end of gastrulation. If the cell populations can be divided by their position in such a way that one can say with some confidence that a particular cell belongs to this population or that, then it may be convenient to name the populations. But on the endoderm problem all the discussions have been loaded with a philosophy about endoderm which can be traced back for about 150 years and which I think has been deserted everywhere else. The same problem arose with birds and insects. People no longer worry about it—the words are always topographical and nothing else. If you make that decision in principle, you can start coining words if it is worth it and if it is convenient.

McLaren: Purely descriptive terms for these layers of cells are certainly needed and what you have said influences me in favour of the epiblast–hypoblast terminology.

Newth: Other terms that have been used worried me a little. 'Blastulation' was used but a young blastocyst is nothing like a blastula in any other animal so 'blastocyst formation' would seem better. Most developmental biologists would not talk about mammalian blastulae but about blastocysts.

McLaren: It is one useful function of a gathering like this to bring out these points and perhaps to initiate terminology that will be somewhat less random.

TERATOCARCINOMA CELLS: A MODEL FOR DIFFERENTIATION

Gardner: Studies on the early mammalian embryo are hampered by several problems. One is that, as mentioned in our presentation (Gardner & Rossant, this volume), critical events take place in very small populations of cells. Another arises from the fact that major processes of differentiation take place in early postimplantation stages that are still largely inaccessible to experimental manipulation in culture. A possible way round some of these difficulties is to use teratocarcinoma cells as a model system for looking at certain aspects of differentiation *in vitro*. Teratocarcinoma stem cells form a variety of differentiated cell types both *in vivo* and *in vitro*, and can be produced in several ways. However, their validity as a model depends on the extent to which they resemble normal embryonic cells. This can only be established by finding out whether they can participate in normal embryogenesis. Brinster (1974) was the first to obtain evidence that cells isolated from *in vivo* tumours could yield viable mouse chimeras after injection into blastocysts. Drs V. E. Papaioannou, M. McBurney, M. J. Evans and I (unpublished work) have recently confirmed and extended Brinster's work, by injecting cultured teratocarcinoma cells into blastocysts.

The principal genetic markers used to distinguish cells of the host embryos from those of teratocarcinoma origin were differences at the glucosephosphate isomerase (Gp^i-1) locus, albino versus pigmentation, and agouti (A) versus non-agouti (a^e) coat colour. Clumps of between 20 and 40 cultured embryonal carcinoma cells derived from two C3H teratocarcinomas (C17 and C86) and one 129/J teratocarcinoma (SIKR) were injected into three series of host blastocysts. The rate of development to term of the injected blastocysts was high (67%).

One normal overt chimera was obtained among four offspring that developed from blastocysts injected with SIKR cells. It exhibited extensive internal chimerism when killed at six weeks of age. No evidence of tumours was found in this animal.

Cells of one of the C3H teratocarcinomas (C17) yielded four overt chimeras, three of which grew into healthy adult mice. The fourth developed two subcutaneous tumours shortly after birth and died at 7 days of age. GPI analysis established that embryonal carcinoma-derived cells were present in several macroscopically normal organs and tissues, in addition to both tumours.

None of the mice obtained from blastocysts injected with C86 cells exhibited ocular or coat chimerism. However, six developed one or more tumours which were evident at birth, or shortly thereafter. Histological examination of the tumours indicated that they were poorly differentiated teratocarcinomas, and GPI analysis revealed that they all contained teratocarcinoma-derived cells. The C86 teratocarcinoma cells differ from C17 and SIKR in containing 41 chromosomes (trisomy of chromosome 11), and having a limited capacity for differentiation in adult hosts. The results with the SIKR and C17 cells suggest that teratocarcinoma cells can differentiate normally after being introduced into early embryos. The three living chimeras obtained by injection of C17 cells are being test-bred. If functional germ-line chimerism can be demonstrated, it would open up the possibility of inducing and selecting mutant cells in culture, and then converting them into mice.

McLaren: You said you were looking at differentiated cell products in the liver. Doesn't the very appearance of pigment in the chimera show that the donor cells have formed differentiated cell product?

Gardner: Yes, but we want to establish whether cells contributing to other macroscopically normal organs and tissues are also producing the appropriate luxury molecules. This can be done for tissues whose specific differentiated products exhibit genetically determined polymorphisms.

Gropp: Did the chromosomal abnormality that you mentioned arise during *in vitro* culture?

Gardner: No. Dr Susan Iles produced the tumour by transplanting the embryonic region of an 8-day conceptus under the testis capsule of an adult animal in March 1973. The changes in potency and chromosome number occurred in an early transplant generation. Cells of all three tumours have now been cloned *in vitro.* We are currently injecting smaller numbers of cloned cells directly into the inner cell masses of host blastocysts. It is possible that injection of larger clumps of cells may not be the best way to obtain chimerism. For example, if we inject one inner cell mass cell into a host blastocyst, its mitotic descendant can form about half a mouse. This is similar to the level of chimerism obtained when an entire inner cell mass composed of roughly 15 cells is transplanted. This difference may be attributable to the intervention of the as yet obscure process of size regulation when the number of cells of the early embryo is substantially increased.

Gropp: In the mouse derived from a blastocyst injected with C86 cells, were those tumours malignant even though they showed controlled growth during fetal development?

Gardner: We did not transplant any of the tumours because we wished to analyse them histologically and biochemically. We have photographed the overt chimeras at regular intervals to see whether the pigmented areas spread—i.e. whether the teratocarcinoma-derived melanocytes behave like melanoma cells. So far the patches have remained as stable as those of conventional chimeras.

Gropp: I am hesitant about the interchangeable use of the words 'teratoma' and 'teratocarcinoma'. There are difficulties in pointing out the criteria for malignant versus benign tumours. At least, pathologists would like the usual criteria of malignancy to be considered if a tumour is classified as a teratocarcinoma.

Gardner: I agree that terminology is inconsistent and confusing. I have followed the tradition of using the term teratoma for differentiated tumours that lack embryonal carcinoma cells and cannot be perpetuated by transplantation, and teratocarcinoma for transplantable tumours in which embryonal carcinoma cells persist. Whether the latter exhibit metastasis could only be determined if they were surgically excised from hosts and tumours arose later in other sites. So far as I am aware this has not been done.

Bennett: That is the standard usage.

Saxén: I agree with Dr Gropp. Teratocarcinoma is a well-defined type of tumour and human pathologists have been using it for decades. Now many people seem to use the term teratocarcinoma for almost any kind of benign embryonic tumour, but it is probably too late to do anything about it.

Škreb: What would you call a tumour which can kill the host in two or three months? Teratocarcinomas in C3H/H mice kill the host simply by growing, without metastasis. Is that not enough evidence for malignancy?

Gropp: I think Dr Saxén is right. It is too late to change the terminology.

Rutter: With teratocarcinomas and normal tissue one could also try doing reconstitutions with molecules or molecular mixtures. Although growth may be aberrant, the molecules which relate to interaction between the various cells may be the same. It might be possible to pile up sufficient quantities for teratocarcinomas to be used as a source for looking at the molecules which affect the various cells. I believe it is nearly time to look at those interactions again. People have thought for a long time that just because a variety of components give non-specific induction, any kind of isolation which attempts to discern the mechanism of those early inductions is bound to yield some equivocal result and hence be a failure. I don't think that is the case. There are many other ways of explaining those non-specific inductions than by assuming that any one of a number of molecules will really do the induction itself. It would be a good time now to begin fractionating and try to decipher these things.

Gardner: I hesitate to call this a classical inductive interaction between polar trophectoderm and inner cell mass because it apparently doesn't show a very precise temporal specificity. The inner cell mass seems to be required for some time; nevertheless the effect seems to be one of stimulating proliferation rather than any specific differentiation.

Rutter: The factors involved early in development may not stimulate cell proliferation. At the early times many cells may have this competence but it is near the determination of differentiation where one needs to be concerned about relative growth rates and where precise regulation of cell growth becomes crucial.

Gardner: If Dr Tarkowski is right it would seem that unless cells become enclosed they are going to form trophectoderm, and that some change in the conditions of cells is needed for them to go to inner cell mass. You indicated that in the pancreas, left to their own devices, these cells would become endocrine cells, Dr Rutter. So it may be that cells that follow a linear pathway need special signals or inducers to push them away to a different state. I wonder whether this has any general validity.

Rutter: I have a strong prejudice that there are lineages of cells where development may be perturbed, in one way or another. We have attempted to find out whether these early 'pertodifferentiated' cells are pluripotent by cloning them in culture. We had no trouble getting endocrine A and B cells but we never got exocrine cells unless the tissue had tight junctions. A factor might act to form or maintain tight junctions which would secondarily influence further development. There is one instance of 'defective mesenchyme'. The *Acomys* mouse pancreas contains 30–40% endocrine cells. We took early embryos from these animals and did a cross mesenchyme–regular mouse epithelium experiment, getting a large number of endocrine cells. With regular epithelium and mesenchyme we got a small number of endocrine cells. Whatever is happening is a deficiency in the mesenchyme. That notion may turn out to be the correct one.

Pedersen: Cultured mouse blastocysts can readily develop extra-embryonic structures; up to 50% of embryos give rise to yolk-sac vesicles in about a week of culture if the serum is raised to 15–20% after attachment and trophoblast outgrowth. This occurs even with calf serum. The problem is that the portion of the embryo that gives rise to the fetus does not generally develop. This may be a situation where additional factors, not present in the culture medium, are needed to stimulate the primary ectoderm into the waves of proliferation Dr Snow has described. We have no evidence yet for a specific complex factor derived from the mother, but one may be needed in this case.

McLaren: Perhaps one should try adding a few drops of Dr Rutter's mesenchymal factor!

Pedersen: We have tested several purified factors isolated from serum for their growth-promoting properties. As yet none of them significantly alleviates the serum requirement for inner cell mass growth.

Hensleigh: In cultures with some batches of human cord serum, a high percentage of embryos develop to the egg-cylinder stage. In these egg cylinders the number of cells undergoing mitosis is remarkable: a high rate of cell division seems to be important for successful embryonic development *in vitro*.

Snow: Their growth profile is similar to the growth profile of the *in vivo* egg cylinder, where there is slow proliferation up to a point and then enormous acceleration. They seem to behave perfectly normally.

McLaren: It is fascinating to reread the discussion in *Preimplantation Stages of Pregnancy*. Some points raised there have lain fallow ever since. Some have come up again at this symposium. But a lot of the points raised in those earlier discussions have been the subject of vigorous experimental investigations during the intervening 10 years. As the earlier symposium became almost required reading for anybody entering the field, it may well have exerted a significant influence on the direction of research. I have a feeling that our discussions here this week may prove equally fruitful.

References

BRINSTER, R. L. (1974) The effect of cells transferred into the mouse blastocyst on subsequent development. *J. Exp. Med. 120*, 1049–1056

CIBA FOUNDATION SYMPOSIUM (1965) *Preimplantation Stages of Pregnancy*, Churchill, London

GARDNER, R.L. & ROSSANT, J. (1976) Determination during embryogenesis, in this volume, pp. 5–18

HSU, Y.-C. (1973) Differentiation *in vitro* of mouse embryos to the stage of early somite. *Dev. Biol. 33*, 403–411

Index of contributors

*Entries in **bold** type indicate papers; other entries refer to discussion contributions*

Adler, D. **115**
Bennett, Dorothea 24, 43, 69, 105, 107, 109, 111, 112, 113, 130, 174, 220, 223, 224, 225, 231, 234, 298
Chapman, V. M. 24, **115**, 124, 125, 126, 127, 128, 129, 130, 173
Cooke, J. 41, 42, 43, 67, 98, 108, 112, 225, 226, 270, 271, 272, 293
Edidin, M. 23, 41, **177**, 194, 195, 196, 197, 225, 288
Eguchi, G. 106, 236, **241**, 253, 254, 255, 256, 257
Gardner, R. L. **5**, 19, 20, 21, 22, 24, 42, 44, 67, 68, 69, 99, 106, 108, 109, 111, 112, 126, 150, 151, 172, 196, 224, 229, 230, 231, 232, 233, 235, 236, 237, 256, 257, 272, 293, 294, 296, 297, 298, 299
Gluecksohn-Waelsch, Salome 23, 42, 43, 66, 69, 70, 98, 104, 107, 110, 112, 127, 149, 151, 172, 173, 174, 195, 196, 221, 222, 224, 226, 229, 231, 233, 235, 236, 238, 254, 255, 257, 272, 292, 293, 294
Graham, C. F. 21, 23, 113, 126, 128, 129, 130, 153, 194, 195, 228, 233, 234
Gropp, A. 43, 100, 127, 129, **155**, 171, 172, 173, 174, 194, 223, 255, 257, 297, 298
Gurdon, J. B. 66, 67, 107, 124, 222, 230, 231, 233, 234, 235, 254, 255
Hensleigh, H. C. 23, 152, 153, 227, 228, 229, 294, 300
Hogan, Brigid L. M. 23, 45, 109
Kelley, R. O. 41, 45, 68, 100, 125, 197, 225, 256, **275**, 288, 289, 294
Labarca, C. **115**
Le Douarin, Nicole **71**, 98, 99, 100, 271

Levak-Švajger, B. **27**
McLaren, Anne **1**, 19, 21, 23, 24, 39, 42, **47**, 67, 100, 103, 104, 105, 106, 107, 109, 111, 126, 127, 129, 150, 152, 173, 195, 221, 224, 228, 229, 230, 231, 234, 235, 236, 237, 289, 291, 293, 294, 296, 297, 299, 300
Morriss, Gillian M. 42, 44, 173, 174, 256, 293, 294
Newth, D. R. 67, 98, 104, 108, 111, 194, 196, 236, 253, 254, 256, 272, 294
Palmer, G. C. **275**
Pedersen, R. A. 107, 108, 112, 125, **133**, 150, 151, 152, 153, 174, 223, 228, 232, 235, 299, 300
Pictet, R. L. **259**
Polani, P. E. 112, 113, 129, 172, 256, 272
Rossant, Janet **5**
Rutter, W. J. 22, 23, 42, 67, 70, 105, 106, 110, 129, 130, 151, 152, 230, 254, 256, **259**, 270, 271, 272, 273, 288, 289, 293, 294, 298, 299
Saxén, L. 39, 43, 97, 107, 108, 171, 194, 221, 272
Škreb, N. **27**, 39, 41, 42, 43, 44, 45, 99, 100, 106, 107, 108, 109, 110, 150, 171, 220, 228, 273, 298
Snow, M. H. L. 19, 20, 21, 41, **53**, 66, 67, 68, 69, 70, 106, 172, 222, 223, 224, 229, 233, 235, 236, 238, 300
Spiegelman, Martha 69, **199**, 220, 221, 222, 223, 224, 225, 226,
Spindle, A. J. **133**
Švajger, Z. **27**
Tarkowski, A. K. 18, 19, 24, 39, 110, 111, 150, 172, 234, 235, 236, 237
Wolpert, L. 21, 39, 98, 105, 108, 109, 110, 125, 130, 196, 255, 257
Wudl, Linda **115**

Indexes compiled by William Hill

301

Subject index

Abercrombie's formula
60, 63

adenylate cyclase activity
278, 284, 288

adrenomedullary cells, origin of
86

antigens, teratoma defined
186

antigenic immaturity
179

Ascaris, **chromatin diminution in**
14

asymmetry, development of
235

Auerbach's plexus
90, 99

autonomic neuroblasts, migration and differentiation
88, 99

autonomic neurons, origin of
86

axial organization
201

basement membrane
11

bilateral symmetry
235

binary decisions
107, 108

blastocoele formation
23

blastocysts
binding sites   195
cell numbers   152
cell surface antigens   188
culture systems   227
development   299
formation   18, 19, 24
orientation   236
process of hatching   135
reaction with H2 sera
   180, 181
terminology   291
treatment with bromo-
   deoxyuridine   134

blastoderm, gastrulation
32

blastomeres
becoming trophoblast cells
   20
cell number   121
cleavage in   151, 152
determination   8
development   22
ICM cell number   9
microenvironmental dif-
   ferences   8

blastulation, terminology
295

blood cell chimeras
42

bromodeoxyuridine
134
effect on DNA and RNA
   synthesis   145, 153
effect on differentiation
   144

effect on ICM   143, 152
effect on postimplantation
   development   141

brown adipose tissue
35, 37, 42

bursa of Fabricius
91

calcium ion activity
288

carbohydrate on cell surface
276

carotid bodies
83, 98

catecholamine synthesis
90

cells
allocation of   104
binary decisions   107, 108
blistering   223
definition of state   105
development of   111
markers   73, 100, 230, 294
'pertodifferentiated'   299
profiles treated with
   hyaluronidase   284
pseudopodia   223
treated with dibutyryl
   cyclic AMP   283

cell associations in T-locus mutants
199–226

cell–cell interaction
22, 200, 260, 272, 288
mechanism of   268

303

cell–cell recognition
199, 201
cell cycles
63
timing of   67
cell division
106
cyclic AMP and   289
speed of   66
synchrony   69
cell junctions in t⁹ mutant
207
cell locomotion
194, 196, 205, 224, 291
cell migration
early stage of   100
in interspecific chimeras
71–101
limb growth and   289
cell numbers
61
estimation of   63
cell organization
223
cell proliferation
64, 291
mesenchymal factor acting
on   262
rates of   276
cell shape changes
205, 217
cell surface
glycosaminoglycan-
adenylate cyclase inter-
action at   275–290
organization of   276
protuberances   223, 224
t⁹ mutant   208
cell-surface antigens
177–197
cell-surface differentiation
177–197
antigens   201
in early mouse embryos
181
cell surface lipids in mutants
224
cell surface membrane
lipid bilayers   187
metabolism   225
structural changes   191
cell surface proteins
195

cell types, differentiation of
260
cephalic crest cells
79
chimeras
13, 233, 296
aggregation   66
blood cell   42
cell migration in   71–101
chimeras, mouse–quail
98
chimeras, quail–chick
75
chordamesoderm
215
differentiation of   210
chromatin
271
chromosomal abnormalities
2, 222, 297
incidence of   155
survival rates   156
chromosomal influences
291
cleavage
62, 152
culture conditions and   19
delay and arrest   138,
140, 152
homozygous yellow
embryos   138, 140
rate of   125, 126, 134
cleft palate
162
collagen
276
concanavalin A receptors
195
contamination in cultures
42, 43
Coturnix coturnix japonica
245
craniofacial hypoplasia
163
cryptic preformation
20
culture systems
227
requirements for post-
implantation growth
136
cyclic AMP
cell division and   289

controlling cell proliferation   276
cyclic AMP derivatives
265
cyclopia
166, 167
Cynops pyrrhogaster
246

DNA
67, 126
assay   130
mesenchymal cells, 283
staining   74
DNA replication
106
avian pigment cells   244
transdifferentiation and
252
DNA synthesis
265
effect of bromo-
deoxyuridine   145, 153
mesenchymal factor
stimulating   267, 269
DNA transfer
260
depigmentation
256
desmosomes
207
determination
5–25
cell population and   14
definitions   103, 109, 270,
291
inside–outside hypothesis
8, 9, 10, 19, 20, 21
labile   105
trophectoderm versus
ICM cells   6
dibutyryl cyclic AMP
23, 266
cycle profiles of cells
treated with   283
differentiation
at cellular level   106
bromodeoxyuridine
affecting   144
definitions   103, 104, 109,
270, 291
morphogenesis and   272

states of 107
diploids
172
Down's syndrome
156, 168
Drosophila
5, 104, 230, 257
duodenal innervation
88

ectoderm
20, 41, 60
anomalies of 232
cell number 61
cell population 107
cell synchrony 69
cycle time in 55
definition of 44
developmental potential of
31, 37, 40
differentiation 137, 153
formation 55
mitotic index 57
necrosis 229
primitive 29
skin formation by 42
tissue volume 61
ectoderm–mesoderm balance
in mutants
221
ectoderm–mesoderm layer
42, 43
ectopic transfer
56
Edward's syndrome
156
egg cylinder
293, 300
cell numbers 57
cell volumes 59
double 237
embryo part of 234
growth and gastrulation
55
H-2 antigens on 181
in T-locus mutants 234
embryonic shield
culture of 41
experiments with 28
germ layers of 29
movement of cells across
56
teratomas from 28

endoderm
14, 20, 60
cell number 61
developmental potential
30, 36
differentiation 30, 40, 44,
137, 153
origin of 37
tissue volume 61
endoderm, primitive
29, 33, 39, 293, 294
determination of 10
enzyme activity
in preimplantation period
116, 124
in single cells 130
epiblast and hypoblast combination
100
epidermis formation
33
epithelial cell membranes
262
exencephaly
164, 166, 171, 173
exophthalmia
165
eye, development of
237
eye tissue, regeneration of
241

face
development of 81, 163
malformations of 173
α-fetoproteins
288
foregut formation
31, 37, 294

gametes, H-2 complex
expression in
179
gastrulation
30
cell movement during 66
in rodents 55
genes
affecting cell surface component 222
haemoglobin chain 173
H-2 complex 177
regulatory 128

T-locus 201, 217, 225
t⁹ 217
gene expression in mouse
116
gene mutations
230
genetic effects on development
133–154
genetic markers
296
genetic variation of
glucuronidase
115
germ cells
development of 112
in birds 72
origin of 110
primordial 110, 111
germ layers
developmental potential
of 27–45, 110
formation of 27, 71
inversion of 236
of embryonic shields 29
primary 107
terminology 292
germ line
continuity of 111
origin of 13
germ-line chimeras
13
germ plasm
112
glucagon
259
glucosephosphate isomerase
124, 294
glycosaminoglycan-
adenylate cyclase inter-
action
275–290
glucose-6-phosphate
dehydrogenase
116, 124
glucuronidase
activation of 122
activity in sperm 126
activity per cell 124
difference in activity 129
genetic variation of
115–131
in blastomeres 125
rate of synthesis 119

glucuronidase, *continued*
 regulatory gene for 127
 sex differences 128
 synthesis 119, 122, 125
growth impairment, trisomy
 and
 168

β-haemoglobin chain genes
 173
haemopoietic stem cells
 113
 origin of 91
haploidy
 127, 174
head
 development of 31
 malformations of 171
Hensen's node
 34, 213
histamine
 280, 281
histocompatibility 2 complex
 antisera 189
 expression in gametes and
  embryos 179
 genes and products of 177
homozygous c^{6H} embryos
 149
homozygous yellow embryos
 134, 232
 anomalies in 150
 development of 137
 transplants 151
hormone-like factors in
 mesenchymal epithelial
 interaction
 259
hyaluronidase
 277, 284
5-hydroxytryptamine
 280, 281
hypoxanthine phosphoribosyltransferase
 116

inner cell mass (ICM)
 109, 153, 299
 and trophectoderm dif-
  ferentiation 12
 cell numbers 9
 determination of 6, 11,
  14, 19, 20

effect of bromode-
 oxyuridine on 143, 152
differentiation 109
formation 105
in mouse 49
measurements of 62, 67
relation with trophecto-
 derm 229, 233
sensitivity of 139
teratoma antigen on 186
terminology 292
inside–outside hypothesis
 8, 9, 10, 19, 20, 21
insulin
 259
intestinal muscles
 88
iris epithelial cells
 246

labile determination
 105
lactate dehydrogenase
 116, 124
lens, differentiation
 241, 246
 in amphibian pigment cells
  246
 in avian retinal pigment
  cells 242
lens regeneration
 273
lentoid bodies
 243, 245, 248, 254, 255,
  256
limb growth, cell migration
 and
 289
limb morphogenesis
 275–290
limb regenerating cells
 255
lipid metabolism in mutants
 224
lungs
 269
lymphocytes
 187
lymphoid cells
 93
lysosomes
 125

malformation syndromes
 from excess vitamin A
  164, 171, 173, 174
 in trisomy 162
maternal effect mutant
 231
maternal role in development
 292
Meissner's plexus
 90, 99
melanin
 254
mesenchymal cell growth in
 limb morphogenesis
 275–290
mesenchymal-epithelial cell
 interaction
 260, 273, 289
 factors in 259–273
 mechanism 268
mesenchymal factor (MF)
 259–273
 acting on epithelial cell
  membranes 262
 biological effects of 261
 detection of 260
 effect on cell proliferation
  262
 effects on other cells 273
 nature of 261, 272
 regulating morphogenesis
  268
 types of activity 265
mesenchyme
 45
 defective 299
 in mutants 221, 222
 migration 173
 zones of 271
mesenchyme cell
 t^9 mutant 208, 221
mesoderm
 developmental potential
  35, 36
 formation 28, 201
 mitotic index 57
 tissue volume 61
mesoderm cells
 69
 cycle time 55
 division 67
 number 61
 surface appendages 207

t^9 mutant   203, 205, 207
  migration of   220
metacentrics
  157, 158
metaplasia, transdifferentiation and
  257
microphthalmia
  164
mitotic activity
  68
mitotic drive
  112
morphogenesis
  differentiation and   272
  regulation by MF   268
morula determination
  14
mouse, early development of
  7
  growth in   47–51, 53, 54
  T-locus mutant   200
mouse–quail chimeras
  98
mutants, use of
  149
mutant anucleolate
  72
mutant Gus^h
  230
mutant, hairpintail
  231
mutant, homozygous yellow
  134, 150, 232
  development of   137
  transplants from   151
mutant, kinky
  238
mutant, maternal effect
  231
mutant T
  antisera in   220
  characterization of   208
  embryo of   208
mutant t^9
  203
  antisera   220
  mesenchymal cells of   221
mutant T locus
  231, 233
  cell associations   199–226
  morphological observa-
    tions   201

neural tube in   210, 217
notochord in   213

nerve growth factor
  272
neural crest, derivatives
  77, 86, 98
  evolution of   75
  migration of   71
neural tissue, formation of
  33
neural tube
  defects   166
  T-locus mutant   210, 217
neuraminidase
  277
neuroblasts, differentiation
  98
neuroepithelium
  association with
    notochord   213
  in T-locus mutant   213,
    215
newt, pigment cells of
  257
  transdifferentiation in   246
nitrosoguanidine
  106
noradrenaline
  cells treated with   284,
    288
  stimulating mesenchymal
    cells   279
notochord
  in T-locus mutant   210,
    213
  stabilizing factors   214

oesophagus
  83
ovarian transplants
  151

pancreas, development of
  259
pancreatic cells
  271
Patau's syndrome
  156
'pertodifferentiated' cells
  299
phaeomelanin
  140

pharyngeal region, development of
  81, 90
phenylalanine
  169
pigment epithelial cells
  241, 252
placenta
  retarded growth   171
  trisomic   169
plasticity
  295
polypeptides, surface antigens
  and
  190
polyribosomes in t^9 mutants
  225
postimplantation growth
  culture requirements   136
  effect of bromode-
    oxyuridine development
    141
  in vitro   153
postimplantation period,
  immediate
  53–70
  cell numbers in   48
  death   128
  embryos   1
primitive streak
  99, 201
  formation   68
  in t^9 mutant   203
  position of   237
progesterone synthesis
  230
prostaglandins
  288
proteins
  on surface layer   191, 195
protein synthesis
  127
protodifferentiation
  106

quail, retinal pigment cells
  245
quail–chick chimeras
  75

radiation, effects of
  174
  on inner cell mass, 139

retinal pigment cells
  stability in differentiation
    244
  transdifferentiation from
    248
RNA, incorporation of
[³H]uridine into
    281
RNA synthesis
    74, 116
  effect of bromo-
    deoxyuridine 145, 153
  on mesenchymal cell sur-
    face 277
RNA transfer
    260
mRNA
    118, 122
  inherited 126

salivary glands
    269
skin formation
    42, 82
social factors
    2
sperm cells, cell components
on
    220
spina bifida
    165
steroid hormones in culture
media
    229

T-locus mutants
  see under mutants, T-locus
teratocarcinoma
    298
  ectopic transfer and 56
  sex incidence of 112
teratocarcinoma cells
    296

aggregation with cleavage
    stage embryos 22
  culture of 21
teratogenic stimuli
    2
teratoma
    298
  from embryonic shields
    28
terminology
    291, 292, 295
testicular teratocarcinomas
    111, 112
testicular teratomas
    181
  antisera 182
  cell surface antigens and
    182
testicular tumours
    113
tetraploidy
    172
thymus, stem cell origin in
    91
tissue transplantation
    177
trachea
    83
transdifferentiation
  factors affecting 252
  metaplasia and, 257
  of vertebrate cells 241–
    256
trisomic placenta
    169
trisomy
  comparative develop-
    mental aspects 166
  developmental charac-
    teristics 160
  exogenous teratogens and
    164
  growth impairment and
    168

  in mouse 157
  morphological conse-
    quences of 155–174
trophectoderm
  antigenicity of 179
  cell numbers in 49
  cells, 185
  determination 6, 14
  development 142
  differentiation 12, 19, 23,
    109
  formation 105, 299
  H-2 complex antigens on
    196
  in mouse 47
  outgrowth 135
  relation with ICM 229,
    233
  terminology 292
  vacuolization and 21
trophoblast
  see trophectoderm

ultimobranchial bodies
    83
uridine kinase
    116, 124

vertebrate cell, trans-
differentiation of
    241–256
vertebrate limb growth
    275
visceral skeleton
    82, 98
vitamin A excess
    164, 171, 173, 174

Wolffian lens regeneration
    254

Xenopus
    13